Collins Photo Guide

Ferns Mosses and Lichens
of Britain and North and Central Europe

COLLINS
PHOTO GUIDE

FERNS, MOSSES & LICHENS
OF BRITAIN
NORTHERN & CENTRAL EUROPE
HANS MARTIN JAHNS

TEXT BY HANS MARTIN JAHNS
ASSISTED BY A.K. MASSELINK

TRANSLATED AND REVISED BY:
EDMUND LAUNERT, ALAN EDDY,
JACK R. LAUNDON & RITA J. LAUNDON

HarperCollins*Publishers*

HarperCollins*Publishers*

Farne, Moose, Flechten Mittel-, Nord- und Westeuropas was first published in Germany in 1980 by BLV Verlagsgesellschaft mbH. München.

© BLV Verlagsgesellschaft mbH, München 1980
© in the English translation and additional material William Collins Sons & Co Ltd 1983

00 99 98 97 96
10 9 8 7 6 5 4 3 2

ISBN Hardback edition 0 00 219254 3

Filmset by Servis Filmsetting Ltd, Manchester

Colour reproduction in Germany by Eurocrom 4, Treviso
Printed by Appl, Wemding, Germany
Bound by Auer, Donauwörth, Germany

Contents

Preface to the English edition

Their size and habit have won ferns a place in some floras and guides to flowering plants, but liverworts, mosses and lichens present a widely neglected field. Most literature on these groups is geared towards the needs of the specialist, difficult to use for the amateur and usually not of much help to the beginner. The authors of this book have approached this problem in an entirely novel way by supplementing keys and descriptions for these small plants with photographic portraits. They recognize, however, that this method cannot satisfy the specialist and that it would be impossible at any rate to cover all the species by this method, since many can be identified only with the aid of a microscope. Their aim is to make it possible for the layman to acquaint himself with a representative selection of species or genera which are likely to be encountered in the field. The area covered by the book is northern Europe from the British Isles and France to Germany and Scandinavia, and the Alps.

The simplest way of naming a plant would be to go through the illustrations in this book attempting to match it with one of the photographs. However, it is usually much quicker to make an identification by using the dichotomous key provided for each group of plants (pp. 31–54). This is the classical method for naming plants. At the same time it induces the user to observe characters carefully and allows the beginner to learn the characteristics of the plants. The keys offer always one alternative (a and b) to follow until one has arrived at the name of the genus or species. Then one can confirm the result by looking at the relevant illustration (or, in a few instances a choice of key-entries). For a successful use of the keys the reader should familiarize himself with the information in the introductory chapters and the necessary terminology, which is explained in the glossary (pp. 55–60).

Almost all the fern species which may be found in Europe and in the British Isles are mentioned in this book and most of them are illustrated – very rare species which are known from a very restricted area, such as the Hebridean horsetail (*Equisetum × dycei* Page) and a few rare hybrids are omitted. In the case of liverworts, mosses and lichens there are so many species that only a relatively small proportion of the total number can be included. They have been selected from those most likely to be encountered or those most interesting to discover which can be identified without recourse to a microscope. The keys to these groups will lead to the most important genera and in the case of mosses and liverworts to a large number of typical species. A number of species of liverworts, mosses and lichens which were not in the original German edition have been added by the translators and 23 species of liverworts and mosses have been depicted in additional line drawings. For the lichens chemical methods which are essential for the naming of a number of species, but which were not in the original text, have been added by the translators. Additional information on the habitat and distribution of species in the British Isles have been given where they differ from the European. Added species which are not illustrated are placed close to the illustrated one to which they are related and the principal differences between them have been described.

English names are given only when they have been long-established for the species, but this applies only to larger plants such as ferns and more conspicuous or frequently found species of the other groups. The translators have endeavoured to use only English names which are either found in the major Floras or are recommended by the Botanical Society of the British Isles.

Names following the scientific names of plants are those of the scientists who first described and named them. Enlargement of photographs is indicated by × and a numeral indicating the number of times magnified placed in square brackets. Figures in bold type in the text refer to photograph or figure numbers.

Ferns (Pteridophyta)

The higher plants, making up the major part of land vegetation, have elaborate vascular systems, leafy shoots and roots, which anchor them to the soil. Such plants are known collectively as Cormophytes. Plants of simple structure, lacking leaves, stems or roots, are called Thallophytes. Ferns and their allies, the Pteridophytes, may be considered the most primitive of the Cormophytes for, although they possess vascular systems and produce roots (two characteristics which are lacking in the other two groups of plants treated in this book, the mosses and liverworts and the lichens), they do not produce flowers and fruits: they are spore-producing vascular plants (vascular cryptogams).

General characteristics

All ferns have alternating heteromorphic and heterophasic generations; this means that the life-cycle of a fern goes through two alternating phases of generations. The first is the sporophyte which is apparent as the actual fern-plant as encountered on the pages of this book; it produces the spores. The second phase starts with a spore which develops to culminate in the prothallus. Besides the contrast in both structure and size, the fundamental difference between the two phases is that they contain differing numbers of chromosomes. The nucleus of each cell of both the spore and the prothallus contains a fixed number of chromosomes (n). This number varies greatly from species to species. When the sexual organs are formed on the prothallus a cell-division takes place in the course of which each individual chromosome is split lengthwise; a process termed mitosis. Both the male sperm (produced in the male organ, the antheridium) and the female egg (produced in the female organ, the archegonium) contain the same number of chromosomes as their mother-cells, namely n. When fertilization, the fusion of the sperm with the egg, takes place the fused cell consequently contains a double set of chromosomes ($2n$). This fertilized cell, which finally culminates in the sporophyte, immediately undergoes cell-division (mitosis) and this process is continued until the sporophyte reaches maturity, each cell-nucleus having $2n$ chromosomes. When the spores are formed within the sporangia, on the underside of the leaves, the spore-mother-cell divides into four spores, each containing half the number of chromosomes of the mother-cell, namely n. This complex process, which takes place in two stages, is termed meiosis. Fern spores are almost always free of chlorophyll but can be coloured brown or yellow by carotenoids.

In most ferns, in the strictest sense, with the exception of *Ophioglossum* (**33**) and its allies, the prothallus is soft, very small and not long persistent. It may look like a liverwort and is fixed to the substratum by hair-like unicellular rhizoids. Its sexual organs, the archegonium and the antheridium are formed on its lower surface (**I F**). They are composed of fewer cells than those of the mosses (**III B, D**) but are principally of the same structure. The archegonium (female organ), usually formed by a single cell-layer, is bottle-shaped and consists of a venter and neck (**I J**). The venter contains the egg cell which is fertilized in this position by a motile spermatozoid (**I H**), formed in the antheridium (male organ, **I G**), which will swim through a film of water covering the plant to reach the archegonium, entering it through the neck. The actual fern, termed the sporophyte, develops from the egg cell after fertilization (**I K**) as explained above.

In *Equisetum* (horsetail species) the prothallus is divided into four lobes and is very short-lived. In contrast it takes the spores of clubmosses several years to germinate, and the resulting prothallus reaches sexual maturity only after 12–15 years.

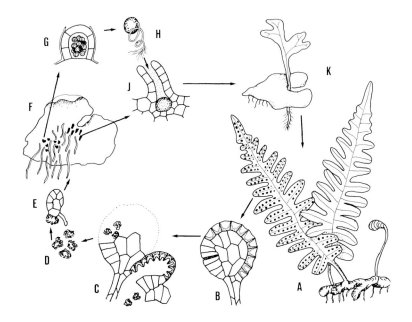

I Alteration of generation in ferns: A sporophyte, B sporangium C dissemination of spores, D spores, E development of prothallus, F production of archegonia and antheridia on prothallus, G antheridium, H male sperm, J female egg in archegonium, K developing sporophyte.

Symbiotic fungi (*Mycorrhiza*) most probably play a role in sustaining the prothalli for such a long period. From an evolutionary point of view such a slow mode of propagation must be disadvantageous to these plants but this handicap is counteracted by the fact that clubmosses propagate very effectively by means of creeping stems (stolons) – vegetative propagation. In many localities clubmosses are threatened with extinction; in some countries they are protected by law.

A very interesting reduction is reflected in the alternation of generations in *Selaginella* which is characterized by extraordinarily small and reduced prothalli and by heterospory, that is the formation of micro- and megaspores; the former are borne in microsporangia in the upper part of the cone and the latter in megasporangia in the lower part (**15**). The microspores produce male and the megaspores female prothalli. Both are, however, reduced to an extent that they – with their sexual organs – remain within the spores. Similar extreme reductions can be observed in the Hydropterides (**97**, **98**) and in Isoetes (**31**). Such a reduction has played an important rôle in the evolution of the Spermatophyta (seed plants) which now dominate the vegetation of the earth. A direct descendency of the Spermatophyta from the above groups is not presumed.

Stem and roots

Pteridophyta are a highly diversified group of plants and the sporophyte, the visible part of the plant, displays a multitude of structures which differ from family to family. Ferns have stem, roots and leaves. The stem contains a complex system of conducting tissues: the xylem, which carries water and the phloem, for the transport of metabolites (nutritive substances resulting from the process of photosynthesis). The arrangement of vascular bundles in the stem differs markedly from those of the seed plants; its various patterns offer the scientist clues to phylogenetic relationships.

Fossil ferns formed massive trees; their stems increased in thickness by means of a peripheral layer of cells, the cambium, which remains active for the lifetime of the plant. This secondary thickening of stems is characteristic for the majority of flowering plants but restricted to only a few groups of recent ferns, e.g. *Isoetes* (**31**) and *Botrychium* (**32**). Some tropical ferns still develop into large trees with erect stems but in all our native ferns the stem grows mostly horizontally and in the majority of species underground. Subterraneous stems are termed rhizomes; only their leaves appear above ground or, in the case of *Equisetum* (**17–30**), their lateral branches. These visible branches of *Equisetum* are characterized by nodes and more or less regular internodes. Since the leaves of *Equisetum* are greatly reduced the green and often much divided branches have taken over the function of photosynthesis.

Leaves

The leaves of pteridophyta display great variety in both shape and arrangement. Species of *Selaginella*, *Lycopodium* and its allies, and *Equisetum* possess very small, mostly undivided leaves, the microphylls. In most 'true ferns' the leaves are large and frequently divided to a varying degree: they are known as macrophylls. In all European 'true ferns' these macrophylls are the only visible part of the plant. In scientific literature fern leaves are also referred to as fronds in order to distinguish them from the leaves of seed plants. A striking example of a fern leaf is seen in *Pteridium* (**1** and **42**) the mighty fronds of which are a single large pinnately divided leaf which grows from an underground rhizome. The anatomy of most fern leaves is already complex and in certain species a differentiation into specialized tissues, as known from seed plants, is discernible. Stomata, similar in structure to those found in Bryophyta, are also present. The leaves of ferns of aquatic habitats are rather different in both shape and structure. The floating leaves of *Salvinia* (**98**) are equipped with air-filled chambers to increase their buoyancy, moreover individual leaves of this species have been transformed into root-like structures (**94**). The filiform or subulate leaves of *Isoetes* (**31**) can be mistaken by the uninitiated for those of sedges or rushes.

Another peculiarity is to be found in *Selaginella*, the leaves of which have, on the upper surface at their base, a scale-like appendage, termed the ligula. It is thinly membranous, tongue-shaped and usually colourless and may be instrumental in the water-intake of the plant. Such an organ is also present in *Isoetes*.

The small leaves of *Selaginella* and the Lycopodiaceae (clubmoss family) are either arranged spirally or in ranks along the stem. In some instances the leaves of one or two ranks are different in shape and size from those of others as can be seen in *Selaginella helvetica* (**13**). In species of the genus *Equisetum* the leaves are greatly reduced; they are arranged in whorls just above the stem-nodes and fused into a sheath (clearly seen in **22**). The leaves of the 'true ferns' appear either singly or in rosettes (often forming dense crowns) on a rhizome (**40**, **83**) which may grow below or above ground. The development of an underground leaf-bud may take years. In the case of *Dryopteris filix-mas* (**69**) all the cells of the leaf as it appears in spring are already present in the

11

underground bud; all that is needed is a stretching of the cells when the conditions are right, and this explains the rapid growth of many fern-leaves. With the exception of *Ophioglossum* and some related species all young fern leaves are upwardly inrolled on account of the fact that initially the lower surface of the leaf grows faster than the upper (see **55** and **43**).

Spores, sporangia and sporophylls

In all members of the Pteridophytes the spores are formed in small chambers, the sporangia, which are situated on the leaves. In Lycopodaceae the sporangia are usually reniform in outline and placed on the upper surface of leaves near the base (**7**). In the simplest case, as elucidated by *Huperzia* they are positioned in the axils of normal leaves (**7**); in most instances, however, sporangia develop on small special leaves, the so-called sporophylls which are different from ordinary leaves in both shape and size and mostly arranged in terminal cones or spikes (**9** and **10**). The same kind of arrangement occurs in *Selaginella*, but here in the upper part of the spikes microspores are produced and in the lower, megaspores (**13**). Micro- and megaspores are also found in the Isoetaceae (**31**) where they are produced in sporangia situated at the base of the subulate leaves which are typical for this family. The *Equisetaceae* have spores of one kind only. They are formed in sac-like sporangia which are suspended, several together, on the lower surface of peltate sporangiophores; these are born in alternating whorls forming a more or less dense terminal cone. The sporangiophores are reminiscent of minute one-legged tables (**19**). The cones appear either at the apex of ordinary green plants (**30**) or terminate separate brownish stems (**19**). Spores of *Equisetum* differ from those of other pteridophytes by a very peculiar structure: the spore is surrounded by a perispore the outer layer of which consists of small parallel bands (haptera) coiled around the spore as long as it is moist (**II D**). When the spore dries these bands gradually unwind and become extended; however, they remain connected with both the spore and each other. When moistened they curl up again. These hygroscopic movements are instrumental in spore-dispersal, and at the same time the linkage of spores by these haptera may have the effect of keeping the resulting dioecious prothalli close together in order to facilitate fertilization.

In 'true Ferns' which represent the vast majority of Pteridophyta the sporangia offer important characters for classification. There are two major divisions: the Eusporangiatae (e.g. *Ophioglossum* and *Botrychium* (**32**, **33**)), in members of which the wall of the mature sporangium consists of several cell-layers, and the Leptosporangiatae in which this wall is formed by a single cell-layer. The Leptosporangiatae constitute the largest group within the Pteridophyta. The sporangia are situated either on the surface of normal leaves (**96, I A**) or on special fertile leaves (**40**, **45**) or even on a different part of a leaf (**32**, **33**). In some instances a clear transition from normal leaves to fertile ones is discernible (**34**).

In most ferns the sporangia are gathered in small groups, the sori; and these are often protected by a membranous structure known as the indusium. The shape of the indusium and its attachment to the sorus can be important for recognizing species and genera: it may be reniform (**70**), peltate (**94**), circular (**49** – here inflated as well), linear or oblong (**52**, **87**). The sporangia of many ferns possess a special and often complicated opening mechanism. In *Polypodium* (**96**) a prominent dark coloured ridge, consisting of one row of cells, can be seen along the upper edge of the helmet-shaped sporangium (**I B, C, II A**); this is the annulus. Whereas the outer walls of its constituent cells are thin the dividing walls as well as the inner walls are considerably thickened. As the sporangium becomes mature the cells lose water by evaporation and because the volume of water in the cell is reduced the consequent reduction in the cohesive power of

II A *Polystichum aculeatum* [×300] sporangium at moment of opening and ejecting spores; C *P. aculeatum* [×200] sporangium fully opened before returning to initial position (compare **93**, see p. 103). B *Osmunda regalis* [×75] opening sporangium showing spores before dispersal; E *O. regalis* [×40] empty halves of sporangium. D *Equisetum arvense* [×400] spore surrounded by coiled haptera (compare **18**, see p. 73).

the water causes the outer (thinner) wall of the cell to be dented inwardly (**II A**). This creates a tangential force which prizes apart two special cells of the annulus (the stomium indicated dark in **I B** left) and makes the annulus snap backwards. Immediately afterwards the cohesive pull within the cell ceases and the annulus, which is elastic in construction, returns into its initial position. In the course of these two rapid movements the spores are catapulted away from the sorus. Many ferns, especially the Polypodiaceae, have this type of cohesion mechanism for ejecting their spores. In others spore dispersal is effected by different means: in *Osmunda regalis* (**34, 35**) for example the sporangia are not arranged in sori and do not possess an annulus;

opening is effected by a series of apical cells which dry out and split the sporangium into halves (**II B**, **E**) and thus release the spores. The Hydropterides are very specialized (**100**, **101**). Their sori, with micro- and megasporangia, are contained in hardened sporocarps which open valve-like through internal pressure caused by the swelling of a mucilaginous substance.

Distribution and ecology

The majority of Pteridophytes prefer humid shaded habitats. Only a relatively small number is adapted to dry and sunny conditions by having either reduced surfaces or a covering of hairs or scales to prevent the loss of moisture. The greatest number of fern species are found in the tropics of both hemispheres.

Mosses and Liverworts (Bryophytes)

Bryophytes are in many ways intermediate between thallophytes and cormophytes, but they present certain difficulties in classification. Mosses have leafy stems (**113**) but the fine, hair-like structures anchoring them to the soil are not true roots, as microscopic study shows. Some liverworts have a simple, ribbon-like form, without stems or leaves and are clearly thallophytic in character (**288**). At one time, the thallose forms were called 'liverworts' and the leafy forms 'mosses'. However, the situation was shown to be more complicated when improved methods of study revealed that some of the leafy forms were clearly more akin to liverworts than to mosses in their anatomy and mode of reproduction and these were therefore classified as 'leafy liverworts' (e.g. **319**). In very broad terms, bryophytes are divided into the large groups, mosses (Musci) and liverworts (Hepaticae), with the latter group including both thallose and leafy forms. Most modern authorities recognise a third group, the thallose 'hornworts' (Anthocerotae) as being distinct from the true liverworts.

An earlier, but now outmoded view was that thallose liverworts, of relatively simple structure, are primitive and resemble forms from which other bryophytes are descended. The thallose *Anthoceros* (**285**) with its peculiar chloroplasts, capsules and stomata, seems to demonstrate distant links with both algae and ferns. Whatever their origin, the bryophytes are an exceedingly old group and its main divisions are now held to be the separate products of different lines of evolution from an erstwhile unknown but very ancient ancestor, probably of the Devonian Period, about 350–400 million years ago. Electron-microscopic and biochemical studies of moss chloroplasts show them to be identical in structure and chlorophyll complement to those of ferns and flowering plants.

The structure of liverworts

Among the thallose liverworts, some have simple form (e.g. *Riccardia pinguis*, **295**) but others (e.g. *Marchantia polymorpha*, **292**) are more complex with tissues organised into several distinct layers. *Marchantia* thalli have a lower, epidermal layer bearing scales and attached to the soil by rhizoids. Above this is a thick layer of colourless tissue composed mainly of colourless cells containing granular storage products and with scattered oil cells (sometimes also with fungal hyphae = mycorrhiza). The green, assimilatory tissue is arranged in columns within special cavities below the upper, transparent epidermis which is itself supported by a regular, hexagonal arrangement of partitions (areolae). The centre of each areole is perforated by a complex pore to allow passage of air and carbon dioxide, analogous to the stomata of higher plants but without the ability to open and close to regulate water loss.

Marchantia and its relatives grow from clusters of meristematic apical cells but *Metzgeria* (**300**–**302**) and its relatives grow from a single, wedge-shaped apical cell. There is considerable variation in the form of thalli: in *Metzgeria* the thallus has a sharply defined midrib and thin wings, while *Fossombronia* (**307**) has lateral wings divided into distinctly leafy appendages.

Growth of the true foliose liverworts, the large group Jungermanniales, proceeds from a single, tetrahedral apical cell which produces, in regular sequence, three rows of leaves. In some genera one row is completely suppressed, so that only two ranks of leaves are evident, but the majority have two rows of fully developed, larger leaves with a third, smaller row on the underside of the shoot, the reduced leaves being called amphigastria. The leaves of most foliose liverworts develop from two initial cells and are normally basically two-lobed (**IV G**). The lobes may be more or less equal, or one

15

may be reduced and variously modified as in *Frullania*, for example (**V B 354**) in which it forms a minute water-sac. Sometimes leaves may divide into more than two lobes (*Lepidozia*, **316**) which, in extreme examples, may be reduced to mere hair-like processes (*Blepharostoma*, **314**). The leaves are thin textured (one cell thick) and never have mid-ribs. Stems are anatomically simple without internal conducting strands. On the whole, leafy liverworts are poorly adapted to resist desiccation.

The structure of mosses

Stems and leaves of mosses are anatomically more complex than those of foliose liverworts, most having conducting strands and midribs and a greater diversity of cell form. Although the shoots develop from tetrahedral apical cells like those of the leafy liverworts, torsion normally prevents a three-ranked leaf arrangement. Rarely, leaves may be in three ranks (*Fontinalis*, **224**), two ranks (*Fissidens*, **154**) or five ranks, but in the majority of mosses leaves are not arranged in regular rows. Except for the midribs, leaves are normally one cell thick with most or all of the cells containing chloroplasts, although groups of specialized cells at the basal angles of leaves (alar cells) may lack them. In the highly organised *Polytrichum* (**109**–**117**) the assimilatory cells are in longitudinal lamellae on the upper surface of the leaf (**IV F**). Some moss leaves have narrow borders of cells that differ in form from those of the lamina (*Mnium*, **194**–**200**). Peat mosses (*Sphagnum*, **123**–**133**) and *Leucobryum* (**150**) have their assimilatory cells interspersed with large, empty, hyaline cells capable of holding large amounts of water. Carpets of *Sphagnum* can hold great quantities of water and play an important role in the regulation of water loss on moorlands and some acid woodlands. Many mosses can absorb water over their whole surface (ectohydric) while others take in water through their rhizoids in a way analogous to vascular plants (endohydric). Among ectohydric mosses, many species are able to survive in a state of desiccation for long periods (even several years) and can grow on exposed rocks (*Grimmia* **170**). In addition, such plants often have hair-pointed leaves which reflect much of the sun's heat (*Grimmia*, **170**, *Tortula*, **159**).

The sexual reproduction of bryophytes

The sexual reproductive organs of bryophytes are very characteristic in form, rather similar to those of ferns but with little resemblance to those of flowering plants. The female organ is the archegonium, a long-necked, flask-shaped structure containing an egg cell in its base (**III D**). The male organ is a stalked, ovoid to spherical antheridium which, at maturity, releases a large number of very small, biflagellate antherozoids. The motile antherozoids require a film of water in which they can swim to an archegonium. Fertilization occurs when an antherozoid penetrates the neck of the archegonium to fuse with the egg cell. Male and female organs may be on separate plants (dioecious) or on the same plant (monoecious); in the latter they may occur together (synoecious), separately on the same shoot (paroecious) or on different shoots (autoecious). In mosses the sex organs are usually interspersed with sterile hairs (paraphyses), and are frequently enclosed in modified, enveloping leaves (perichaetia). In foliose liverworts the archegonia are usually contained in a sheath (perianth) derived from three fused leaves. In many thallose liverworts the sex organs are enclosed in cavities in the thallus. *Marchantia* and its relatives are more complicated in that the archegonia, and sometimes also the antheridia, are borne on specialized outgrowths of the thallus (**292**).

The egg cells and antherozoids are known as gametes, hence the plants that produce them are called gametophytes. The gametophyte generation has a single chromosome

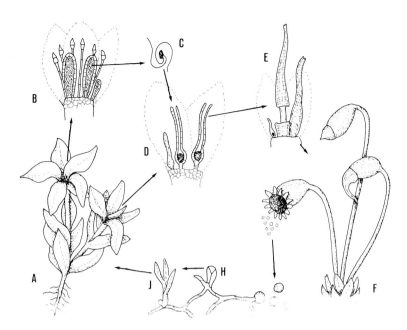

III The life cycle of mosses (explained in the text): **A** monoecius moss, **B** antheridia, **C** bi-flagellate antheroid, **D** archegonium containing egg, **E** fertilized cell (zygote), **F** sporophyte (still attached to gametophyte), **G** spore, **H** protonema with bud, **J** bud developing into gametophyte.

set per cell and is therefore haploid. A fertilized egg cell (zygote) has a double chromosome set per cell and is diploid. In bryophytes the zygote develops into a spore-producing generation, the sporophyte, which remains attached to the gametophyte and is largely parasitic upon it. At maturity the sporophyte consists basically of a penetrating foot, a stalk (seta) and a spore-producing capsule. It is the reduction-division (meiosis) in the sporogenous tissue in the capsule that produces haploid spores and these will germinate to give rise again to haploid gametophytes. On germination, moss spores first grow into green, branched filaments (rarely small thalli) called protonema which develop buds that grow into new plants. In mosses the protonema is extensive, resembling green algae, and may persist for many months but in liverworts it is very transient, consisting of only a few cells.

The sporophyte

In liverworts the capsule is relatively simple in form, spherical to ovoid. The seta is delicate and elongates suddenly only after the capsule has matured. Spores are interspersed with linear, spirally thickened, hygroscopic elaters (**V A**) which may be loose or attached at one end to the capsule wall. When ripe, the capsule usually splits longitudinally into four valves and movements of the elaters help to regulate spore dispersal. In *Marchantia* the capsules are borne on the underside of stalked, umbrella-

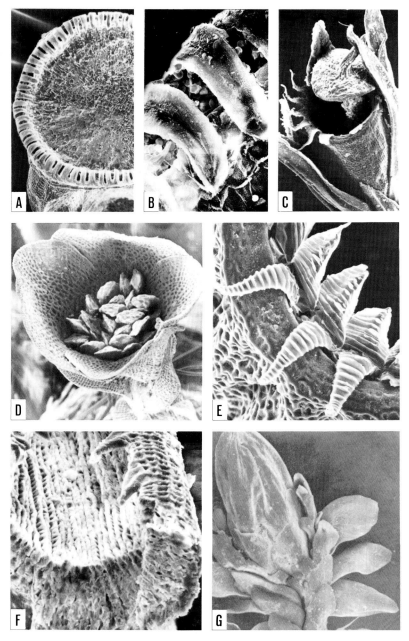

18

IV **A** *Polytrichum strictum* [×20]: peristome and epiphragm of spore capsule after lid has fallen. **B** *P. strictum* [×200]: peristome teeth. **C** *Schistidium apocarpum* [×15]: capsule with falling lid still attached to the columnella and single row of peristome teeth. **D** *Tetraphis pellucida* [×100]: gemmae in a cup formed from enlarged leaves. **E** *Bartramia pomiformis* [×150]: mouth of capsule with double row of peristome teeth. **F** *Polytrichum formosum* [×100]: part of leaf showing the lamellae on the upperside. **G** *Diplephyllum taxifolium* [×25]: leaves with smaller upper lobe folded over the larger lower lobes as seen from above, also the large perianth containing the archegonia.

---

shaped outgrowths of the thallus and the setae remain short, while in *Riccia* (**297**) the capsules are immersed in the thalli and simply disintegrate as the thalli decay. *Anthoceros* has a very different sporophyte. It is long-lived, growing continuously from the base while splitting into two valves above. Unlike true liverworts, the capsule of *Anthoceros* has stomata.

The moss sporophyte is usually complex. At first it is enveloped in the expanded remains of the archegonium which later remains adherent to the capsule as a small hood or cap (calyptra). The seta develops gradually and is usually more or less stiff, with an internal conducting strand that conducts nutrients from the gametophyte to the developing capsule. Young capsules are green and are usually furnished with stomata and assimilatory tissue. Mature capsules vary in shape but typically are composed of a basal portion (apophysis), consisting mainly of assimilatory tissue, a median portion, containing spores, and an upper portion forming a lid. When ripe, a ring of specialized cells (annulus) below the lid ruptures and the lid falls to reveal, usually, a single or double ring of peristome teeth. There are no elaters mixed with the spores but the moss peristome is hygroscopic and can control the release of spores.

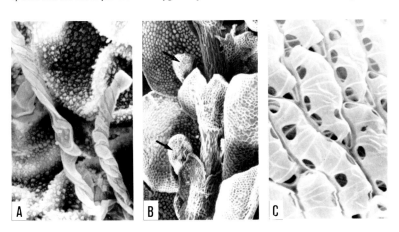

V **A** *Pellia epiphylla* [×800]: spores and elaters. **B** *Frullania tamarisci* [×40]: underside of shoot showing bilobed leaves, in which the underlobe is modified into a small water-sac (arrowed), and bilobed amphigastria. **C** *Sphagnum palustre* [×350]: part of leaf composed of large, inflated hyaline cells with pores and fibrils, between which are the long, narrow photosynthetic cells (arrowed).

Moss peristomes vary greatly according to species and families and are very important in relation to classification.

In *Polytrichum* and its allies, the top of the capsule, after fall of the lid, remains closed across the top by a plate of cells (the epiphragm). In windy conditions, spores are shaken out through the gaps between the rigid teeth (**IV A & B**). *Andreaea* capsules open by four slits, rather like liverworts. *Sphagnum* capsules lack peristomes, the spores being released by the explosive casting off of their lids and expulsion of the spores.

Vegetative reproduction

Most bryophytes can grow from small pieces of shoot or even leaves. In addition, specialized methods of reproduction are commonly developed. For example, young leaf-tips of foliose liverworts often bear small gemmae (**336**, **345**) which can be scattered and grow into new plants. *Marchantia* has striking gemma-cups on the dorsal side of the thallus (**294**). The moss *Aulacomnium androgynum* (**205**) produces a pinhead-like cluster of gemmae on stalks while *Tetraphis* (**122**) produces gemmae at the stem ends, surrounded by enlarged leaves. Some mosses produce bulbils or other propagules in the leaf axils or small underground tubers on their rhizoids. Sometimes, in *Schistostega* (**121**), gemmae may be formed on the protonema.

Occurrence and biology

Although water is essential for their sexual reproduction, bryophytes are basically land plants and only a few species are secondarily adapted to aquatic environments, (e.g. *Fontinalis*, **224**). Only rarely is a thin cuticle developed (e.g. *Mnium*, **195**) and most species dry out readily. Therefore, the majority of bryophytes are characteristic of moist or shady habitats. Nevertheless, many mosses survive long periods of desiccation, even several years in some cases, and can endure high temperatures in the dry, dormant state (temperatures of *c.* 70°C have been recorded). On the whole, bryophytes thrive in lower light-intensities than lichens and most higher plants, and become the dominant plant form in forests and caves. In forest habitats, especially in tropical rainforests, many occur as epiphytes on trunks and twigs and even on evergreen leaves. A large proportion of species prefer acid habitats (particularly the leafy liverworts), notable among these being *Sphagnum* which often grows in bogs with a pH as low as 3.5. Other species (particularly ectohydric, acrocarpous mosses) may be markedly calcicolous.

Lichens

Symbiosis of algae and fungi

Lichens are unique in being composed of two organisms, algae and fungi, which form a close symbiotic association. Symbiosis is a prolonged permanent contact between dissimilar organisms. Lichens are popularly confused with mosses. In herbals produced before their different characters became recognised they were often included with mosses but they are quite different and not related. The cup-shaped fruiting body of many lichens (VI A; 412) at once places them apart. However, it was not until the late 19th century that the true nature of lichens was known. In 1866 de Bary established that the 'gonidia' in lichens were, in fact, algal cells. This conclusion that lichens were a living biological community was actively disputed by many leading lichenologists of the time, who still considered them to be autonomous. However, it is now universally accepted that lichens are a symbiosis between two partners. One partner is always a fungus (the mycobiont) and the second partner an alga (the phycobiont). Most mycobionts belong to the Ascomycetes (with fruiting bodies containing asci), but a few are Basidiomycetes (with fruiting bodies containing basidia; mushrooms and toad-stools belong here, **654**), whilst there is one phycomycete (lower fungi, **655**). A few lichens (*Lepraria*, *Thamnolia*, **653**) never fruit and are therefore placed in the fungi imperfecti (imperfect fungi). The phycobionts belong to the large group of green algae (Chlorophyceae) and the smaller group of blue-green algae (Cyanophyceae), as well as quite rarely the yellow-green algae (Xanthophyceae).

In a lichen thallus the fungus is the dominant partner, and usually forms most of the lichen plant. It is not, apparently, free-living, and can only survive when in contact with the appropriate alga. The fungus produces the fruiting bodies or sexual organs of the lichen plant. On the other hand, the alga usually forms a layer within the lichen thallus completely surrounded by fungal tissue; only in exceptional cases does it form the greater part of the lichen thallus. Moreover, many (probably not all) lichen algae are free-living as well as occurring within lichens. In lichen plants the algae multiply both vegetatively (by cell division) and asexually (by producing aplanospores), but have no sexual reproduction. It is because of the dominant nature of the mycobiont that the lichens are now classified amongst the Fungi. They are no longer regarded as a separate group for the purposes of classification, but are instead regarded as a 'biological nutrition group'.

Why do the fungus and algae live together?

A symbiosis is more common than is generally realised. However, the old view of a symbiosis is that it must be of mutual benefit to all the partners involved. In a lichen plant the symbiosis is clearly of great benefit to the fungus. The alga produces the green pigment chlorophyll, which builds up carbohydrates from carbon dioxide and water by means of photosynthesis, in which energy is absorbed from sunlight. The carbohyd-rates are then absorbed by adjoining fungal hyphae by diffusion and utilised for growth. It was formerly thought that haustoria – specialised branches which penetrate the living algal cells – were involved in nutrient transfer, but these are now regarded as vestigial structures of parasitic fungi that developed lichenised associations with algae. The algal cells are not overtly harmed by the transfer of nutrients to the fungus partner, a balanced relationship having been evolved between the symbionts.

The advantages for the algae are more difficult to define. In most lichens the algal

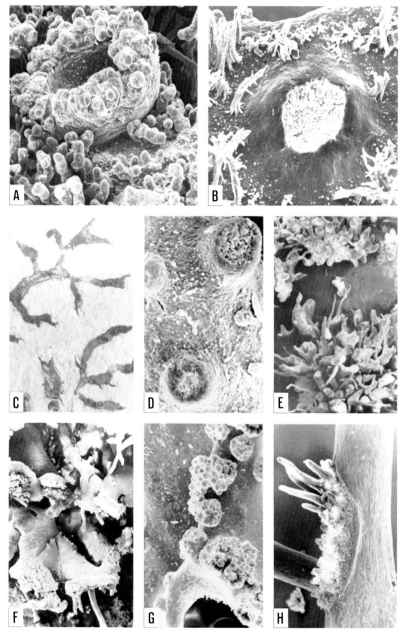

22

layer is surrounded by fungal tissue and therefore protected from intense light, drought, and heat. Thus the alga is sheltered and can live in extreme conditions (such as rock surfaces on high mountains) where it would otherwise be destroyed by the harsh environment. The fungus also could not live alone under such conditions as it would have no carbohydrates. Together the alga and the fungus can colonise habitats otherwise unoccupied, which gives lichens a decisive advantage in competition for space.

The fungus and the alga have to reach a position of equilibrium with each other in order to survive. The fungus must not deprive the algae entirely of nutrients or it would be killed. Thus the symbiosis in lichens is one of controlled parasitism.

Anatomical adaptation in the symbiosis

The adaptation of the fungus and the alga in living together, often in extreme environments, has led them to adopt forms and structures not found in fungi and algae when living alone. Every fungus forms branched filaments, the hyphae, which are interwoven. In the lichen plant the fungus and the alga form different strata, seen in a cross-section under the microscope. The algal layer (**VIII A–C**) is distinguished by its green colour. Above the algal layer there is usually a protective layer of fungal hyphae, the cortex (**VIII A**). This consists of short, thick-walled cells which coalesce to form a compact layer. Below the algal layer is a strata of lax fungal hyphae called the medulla, often with a compact layer of cells below forming the lower-cortex (**VIII A**).

Most shrubby lichens are concentrically layered. Beneath the cortex is the algal layer, but the centre of the thalline strands are often hollow. Many beard-lichens which hang from trees become quite heavy. One group of these (*Usnea*, **386–394**) has developed a tough central strand to support this weight, which can be easily seen when a branch is carefully broken (**VII A**).

Both the upper- and the undersurfaces of lichens are sometimes covered with hairs (**VI B, VIII F**), a coating of salt crystals or dead cells forming a pruina (**610**), or thin outgrowths (cilia, fibrillae). The underside often has rhizinae (**VI F, VII B, VIII G–K**), which resemble roots. In many lichens a growth of fungal hyphae occurs at the margin of the thallus to form a black border called a prothallus (**459**). Fungal hyphae can also form a felty mat called a tomentum on either the upper or lower surface of the thallus.

The durable thallus – advantages and drawbacks

The stratified cartilaginous thallus makes a lichen very hardy and long-lived in comparison with free-living fungi and algae. Shrubby lichens (**472**) become at least 10 years old, whilst crustaceous lichens can take up to 100 years to become old. Many lichens grow about 1 mm a year, although some fast-growing foliose lichens – *Peltigera*, **567** – can grow between 2–3 cm a year.

The protective cortex provides the lichen with a problem. It hinders the essential gas exchange of photosynthesis. In order to overcome this problem many lichens develop

---

VI A *Parmelia saxatilis* [×15]: cup-shaped apothecium; thallus and apothecium with cylindrical isidia (See **423**). **B** *Sticta sylvatica* [×50]: cyphella between hairs (See **586**). **C** *Phaeographis dendritica* [×13]: branched lirellae. **D** *Parmelia exasperata* [×200]: breathing pore at apex of papilla (See **432**). **E** *Parmelia crinita* [×15]: scaly isidia with cilia (See **410**). **F** *Physcia tenella* [×10]: farinose soredia in labriform soralia; thallus with light rhizinae. **G** *Lobaria pulmonaria* [×15]: granular soredia on ridge of thallus (See **581**). **H** *Bryoria furcellata* [×25]: soredial isidium.

breaks in their cortex, so that breathing pores are formed. Regular holes occur on the underside in *Sticta* (**586**), called cyphellae (**VI B, VIII E**). These have a cellular structure. Other lichens develop simple breathing pores called pseudocyphellae (**VIII D**; **399**) on their upper or lower surfaces, which sometimes even take the form of small pointed warts (**VI D**; **432**).

Nitrogen supply through blue-green algae

Certain lichens contain blue-green algae. These form heterocysts which are able to fix atmospheric nitrogen, thus providing compounds for the fungus partner. The nitrogen so produced contributes significantly to various ecosystems. Some lichens containing green algae also have blue-green algae enclosed in a thallus proliferation, called a cephalodium (**VIII L**; **566, 583**). Cephalodia can also lie hidden in the thallus. In a few lichens there is a continuous layer of blue-green algae superimposed on a layer of green algae; *Solorina crocea* (**565**) is an example. In a few lichens the same fungus forms morphologically different chimeroid associations with both green and blue-green algae; an example is *Sticta canariensis* (**585**) (green algal morphotype) and *S. dufourii* (blue-green algal morphotype).

Reproduction of the lichen – the sexual process

Reproduction brings special problems for lichens. The mycobiont only is involved in sexual reproduction and it forms a fruiting body. Most Basidiomycete lichens form small cap fungi or 'toadstools'. Sexual reproduction is also common in the lichenised Ascomycetes. The spores are formed in a sac called an ascus. The asci are situated between sterile filaments, the paraphyses, in a fruiting layer (the hymenium) (**VIII B**). The hymenium is often situated in a cup-shaped fruiting body, called an apothecium (**VI A, VIII B**; **440**), on the surface of the thallus. In other lichens asci are formed in a

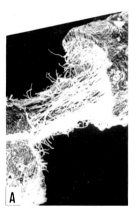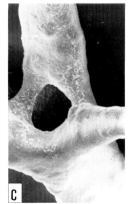

VII A *Usnea* sp. [×25]: broken thallus with extending central strand. B *Peltigera membranacea* [×15]: felted underside with veins and squarrose rhizinae (See **567**). C *Cladonia uncialis* [×15]: perforated axil between the branches of the thallus (See **471**).

pear-shaped fruiting body with an opening only at the end; this is known as a perithecium (**VIII A**; **650**). Less common are linear fruiting bodies called lirellae (**VI C**; **635**) which are modified apothecia, and also asci which disintegrate at maturity to liberate free spores in the hymenium (a mazaedium; **363**, **366**, **370**). These remarks do not take account of some special developments that are of much importance to the systematics of fungi and lichens.

Many lichens produce small pear-shaped bodies in the thallus called pycnidia (**VIII C**). In these tiny asexual spores (conidia) are liberated. The function of conidia is not established; they appear to be organs of vegetative reproduction, but, although never proved, their function has long been considered to be as agents of fertilisation.

Vegetative reproduction

The sexual process is often not favourable for dispersal. Fungal spores must germinate and find a suitable algal partner in order for a new lichen to be formed. In one or two species there is apparently a common dispersal for both partners. The fungus spores are ejected with adhering algal cells from the fruiting body. Nevertheless, this method

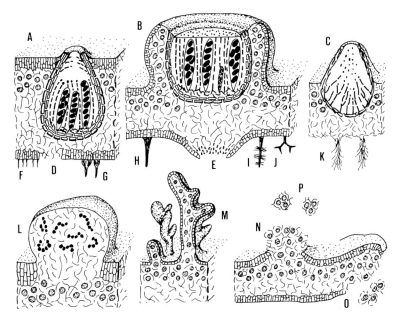

VIII Lichen structures: **A** corticate thallus with perithecium; **B** apothecium with double margin (the thallus forms an algal layer and the fruiting body a second, inner layer); **C** non-corticate thallus with projecting pycnidia; **D** pseudocyphella; **E** cyphella; **F** hair; **G** bulbous rhizinae; **H** simple rhizinae; **I** whorled rhizinae, **J** forked rhizinae; **K** fibrous rhizinae; **L** cephalodium with chains of blue-green algae on a thallus with green algae; **M** branched isidia, the bases with non-corticate breaking-off points; **N** soralium on the surface of the thallus; **O** labriform soralium; **P** soredia.

is extremely rare. In several species sexual reproduction has become redundant; the fruiting bodies remain sterile or are seldom formed. For many lichens a successful method of vegetative reproduction has been developed.

A primitive dispersal method is thallus fragmentation. When dry many lichens are very brittle, and trampling over a lichen heath (**358**) produces hundreds of fragments, both partners being present in the new lichen plants produced from the accidental damage to the old thalli. Many lichens, however, are not of a fragmentary nature; a large number of these produce outgrowths of tissue, containing both an algal layer and a cortex, which break off at the base and are able to form a new lichen plant. These are called isidia (**VIII M**), and they take different forms, chiefly warty (**432**), cylindrical (**VI A**; **423**), claviform (**428**), scaly (**VI E**; **573**), and coralloid (**537**).

Even more common than isidia as agents of vegetative reproduction are soredia. These differ from isidia in the lack of a cortex. They are formed by cracks appearing in the cortex and the emergence of tissue from the algal layer. Small granules are formed of both algal cells and fungal hyphae (**VIII P**); the granules are then dispersed to develop into new lichen plants. Aggregations of soredia are called soralia (**VIII N**). These are shaped in different ways, their form playing an important rôle in systematics. Soralia can be divided into two types: diffuse soralia (**479**) and delimited soralia. The latter are confined to certain parts of the thallus, and occur either on the surface or at the tips. On the surface may be distinguished punctiform soralia (**437**), maculiform soralia (**VI G**; **426**), rimiform soralia (**425**), maniciform soralia (**442**), and marginal soralia (**406**). Terminal soralia comprise capitiform soralia (**439**), labriform soralia (**VI F**, **VIII O**; **438**), and helmet-shaped soralia (**613**).

In a few cases (e.g. *Parmelia subaurifera*, **433**) both soralia and isidia occur simultaneously on the thallus, or more frequently one originates from the other. In the latter case are soredial isidia (**VI H**; **618**), where the isidia originate by forming outgrowths from soredia, or isidial soralia (**436**), in which the soredia originate by the breaking off of the tips of the isidia.

Many lichens have evolved into 'species pairs' in which one lichen (the primary species) is always fertile and without vegetative propagules, whilst the other (the secondary species) is sorediate or isidiate and rarely fruits; otherwise they have the same morphology and chemistry. Examples are *Ochrolechia tartarea* (**627**) and *O. androgyna*, *Parmeliella plumbea* (**551**) and *P. atlantica* (**552**), and *Usnea florida* (**390**) and a chemotype of *U. subfloridana*.

Physiological adaptation

Lichens live for a very long time. They grow in extreme environments. In the Antarctic and in the alpine zone on high mountains they grow on snow-free rocks where no other plants can survive. In deserts and even under water at the seacoast lichens grow and flourish. They are able to survive in these extreme conditions because they are able to lose their water quickly and thus reduce photosynthesis so that the thallus becomes dormant. In this dormant state they can survive cold temperatures of $-196\,°C$ (liquid nitrogen) and high temperatures of $+100\,°C$. Most lichens survive best in temperatures ranging from $-20\,°C$ to $+70\,°C$; different temperatures apply to aquatic and tropical lichens. When the thallus is moist the metabolism is active and the lichen more easily damaged. Therefore rapid drying out to the dormant state is essential for survival in hot and cold conditions. Drying out in itself does not lead to damage.

Desert lichens receive water from dew or from the air in the early morning. After sunrise there is a burst of photosynthesis as the thallus dries out before it becomes dormant. Thus in about three hours at dawn the desert lichens obtain all essential nutrients for the day.

Despite their adaptations, water relations remain for lichens a difficult problem. Most lichens prefer to dry out slowly. Thus they favour districts with high humidity. That is why the richest lichen vegetation occurs on high mountains and where there is an oceanic climate. Here lichens dominate the vegetation (**358**). The lower temperatures of high mountains also benefit photosynthesis, which functions best between $+10°C$ and $+15°C$.

Lichen substances

Lichens produce a remarkable number – about 200 – of secondary substances. These are phenolic acids (depsides, depsidones, etc.) and pigments. They occur in quantity within the thallus and are deposited on the outer surface of the hyphae. These substances are seldom produced in non-lichenised fungi, and about 60 are restricted to lichens. Most are formed only in the symbiotic state, and not by the mycobiont in separate culture. They have significant ecological rôles, acting as light-screening compounds, chemical weathering compounds, allelopathic compounds, and anti-herbivore defence compounds. They are most important for the systematics of lichens. All specimens of a single species have either the same secondary substances or are composed of two, rarely more, chemical strains of differing compounds. Related species have a related chemistry. Lichen substances are identified by the use of thin-layer chromatography or, less commonly, by microcrystal tests. Colour tests are also useful for identification purposes.

Chemical colour tests on lichens

Simple chemical tests aid lichen identification. Different lichens often have a different chemistry, their substances producing distinctive colours with certain chemicals when a minute drop of a solution is placed on either the cortex or medulla. To expose the white medulla for this purpose remove a small piece of cortex with a razor-blade or scalpel. Apply the appropriate chemical to the lichen with the tip of a glass rod, a capillary pipette, or the wooden end of a match, then use a hand lens or binocular to observe the colour change. Use only a minute drop of chemical because a large drop will discolour the specimen and make it useless for future study. The reaction should be noted on a label for the benefit of others and to prevent harmful repetition.

The following chemical reagents are used for colour tests and referred to in the text by the code given:

C: calcium hypochlorite solution. Parozone and other bleaches are the most suitable form of this chemical. Store in a refrigerator and renew at least at yearly intervals.

K: potassium hydroxide solution (about 20 per cent strength).

KC: potassium hydroxide solution followed by bleach.

P: *p*-phenylenediamine freshly dissolved in either alcohol or water.

P should be used with caution and not permitted to contaminate the skin or get into the air since it can produce rashes, blindness, brain damage, etc. It discolours paper, making books and labels unsightly. Following a P test, the part of the lichen used should be discarded, and the solution carefully washed away with running water, before watch-glass, rod, hands, etc. are given a thorough wash. The suppliers recommend that rubber gloves should be worn.

When no colour change is observed a negative sign is recorded, e.g. C−. Positive reactions are as follows:

C+ orange This means that the part of the lichen to which the chemical is applied turns orange. Several lichen substances produce this colour, especially gyrophoric acid.

C+ red Denotes lecanoric acid.

C+ deep green Denotes strepsilin.

K+ yellow Several lichen substances produce this colour, especially atranorin.

K+ brilliant yellow Denotes thamnolic acid.

K+ yellow changing to red Denotes norstictic acid.

K+ violet-red Denotes an anthraquinone, commonly parietin.

KC+ orange Several lichen substances produce this colour, especially barbatic acid and physodic acid.

KC+ violet Denotes picrolichenic acid.

P+ orange Usually denotes thamnolic acid.

P+ red Usually denotes fumarprotocetraric acid.

Lichens and environmental pollution

Although lichens can withstand extreme environmental conditions, most are susceptible to environmental contamination. This is because of their efficient absorption systems, by which harmful substances can be accumulated. Air pollution, especially sulphur dioxide (SO_2), has the greatest effect on lichens. High sulphur dioxide levels are found throughout most towns and cities and industrial areas, and here the lichen flora is often reduced to only a few resistant species. The pollution is usually emitted

Table 1. Scale for the estimation of mean winter sulphur dioxide levels in England and Wales using lichens on tree bark. Adapted from Hawksworth & Rose (1976).

Zone	Mean winter SO_2 ($\mu g/m^3$)	Moderately acid bark
0	?	Epiphytes absent
1	over 170	Green algae at base; lichens absent
2	about 150	Green algae up trunk; *Lecanora conizaeoides* (**444**) at base
3	about 125	*Lecanora conizaeoides* up trunk; *Lepraria incana* at base
4	about 70	*Hypogymnia physodes* (**438**), or *Parmelia saxatilis* (**423**), or *P. sulcata* (**425**) at base
5	about 60	*Hypogymnia physodes* or *Parmelia saxatilis* or *P. sulcata* up trunk
6	about 50	*Parmelia caperata* (**409**) at base; *Pertusaria* (**628–629**) present
7	about 40	*Parmelia caperata* up trunk; *Usnea subfloridana* present
8	about 35	*Usnea ceratina* (**391**) or *Parmelia perlata* (**414**) present
9	under 30	*Lobaria pulmonaria* (**581**) or *Usnea florida* (**390**) present
10	'pure'	*Lobaria scrobiculata* (**582**) or *Teloschistes flavicans* (**591**) or *Usnea articulata* (**393**) present

28

from high chimneys, so that it drifts over quite large areas giving rise to 'background air pollution'. The present poverty of the epiphytic lichen flora over rural parts of eastern England, the Netherlands, and northern Germany is due to the background air pollution from industrial centres.

Different lichens are susceptible to differing levels of sulphur dioxide pollution. Whilst high levels kill most lichens, moderate levels kill off certain sensitive lichens but allow others to survive and multiply. Therefore the lichen vegetation (see Table 1) can be used to estimate the severity of air pollution at any given locality and to prepare maps showing pollution zones.

Although most lichens are harmed by pollution, a few species are found only where environmental pollution is present. The best example is *Lecanora conizaeoides* (**444**), which has become abundant over the North European Plain during the past hundred years due to the spread of air pollution.

Lichens are also affected by other forms of pollution. The effects of heavy metals can be seen by the absence of lichens from water run-offs from metal, especially lead, surfaces. Agricultural sprays affect lichen vegetation adversely. Radioactive fallout does not harm lichens, but they absorb the radionuclides and thereby pass the harmful caesium and strontium on to unsuspecting animals which feed upon them. Thus Lapps have been affected by an increase in body burdens of these substances resulting from the *Cladonia* – reindeer – Lapps food chain.

Exploitation

Today lichens are of great practical importance as biological indicators of environmental pollution. Their industrial exploitation has, however, suffered a marked decline. Formerly they were used in quantity for the commercial dyeing of wool, but today they are only used for this purpose in cottage industries. However, large quantities of *Roccella* (**644–645**) are still used for making the world's supply of litmus paper, and two species, oak moss *Evernia prunastri* (**395**) and tree moss *Pseudevernia furfuracea* (**396**), are harvested in vast amounts in the forests of France, Yugoslavia, and Morocco for the perfume industry. The most exploited of all lichens is *Cladonia stellaris* (**472**) which is collected in abundance in Scandinavia for use as winter forage for reindeer, floral decoration (especially wreaths), and for making model trees. In Japan Iwatake *Umbilicaria esculenta* is used in the food industry as a delicacy.

Lichens have been used as medicines for a considerable period. In medieval times they were used chiefly according to the relationship between their appearance and the disease or affected organ. Thus *Xanthoria parietina* (**602**) was used as a remedy for jaundice and tree lungwort *Lobaria pulmonaria* (**581**) against lung diseases, whilst dog lichen *Peltigera canina* was considered effective as a cure of rabies. The antibiotic properties of lichen acids have given lichens some effect in controlling diseases, so that today Iceland moss *Cetraria islandica* (**399**) is still exploited as a mucous purgative cough inhibitor, and usnic acid is produced from species of *Cladonia* and marketed as an effective antibiotic against skin infections.

Growth forms

The systematic classification of lichens is based on the structure and development of the fruiting body and its contents. However, the external form of lichens is also of some importance.

The form of some small lichens is largely determined by the algae. The small hair lichens (e.g. *Racodium*) have algae forming their central strand. Algae form chains of cells throughout the thalli of the jelly lichens (**371**–**377**) and determine their general shape.

In most lichens the fungus forms the greater part of the thallus and is responsible for its form. In these lichens belonging to the Ascomycetes the following growth forms are recognised:

1. Crustaceous lichens. The thallus forms a crust over the substrate (**454**, **634**). In many species the thallus is areolate (i.e. forming a mosaic divided by cracks) (**623**, **624**), whilst in a few lichens the thallus is completely immersed and scarcely visible. Sometimes lobes are developed at the margin (**598**, **622**), such lichens differing from foliose species by the lack of a lower cortex; these are called placoid or squamulose species.

2. Foliose lichens. The thallus forms a leafy growth over the substrate, and has a distinct upper and lower side (**438**, **571**). Some foliose lichens (e.g. *Umbilicaria*, **523**–**36**, **538**) are more or less orbicular and only attached at a central point called an umbilicus.

3. Fruticose lichens. The thallus forms a shrubby outgrowth from the substrate and has a radial structure so that the upper and lower surfaces are identical (**381**, **540**). Some species (*Cladonia*, **479**–**504**) have a dimorphous thallus, that is a crustaceous or squamulose primary thallus from which arise vertical hollow fruticose structures (podetia) which are part of the apothecia. In some cases the primary thallus disappears with age leaving a pure fruticose lichen to survive (e.g. *Cladonia* subgen. *Cladina*, **472**–**476**, **478**).

Key to genera and species of ferns

1a Stem jointed, with distinct nodes, usually hollow, grooved, simple or branched; leaves not green, forming a sheath just above the nodes. Sporangia arranged in whorls and forming a terminal cone (**17–30**) **61**

1b Stems not distinctly joined; leaves almost always green **2**

2a Free-floating aquatic plants.. **10**

2b Terrestrial or aquatic plants but always rooting in soil **3**

3a Terrestrial plants **4**

3b Aquatic plants, growing at the bottom of lakes or on land inundated by water most of the time **7**

4a Leaves not differentiated into lamina and petiole, shorter than 1 cm, undivided, often scaly-appressed or somewhat spreading **5**

4b Leaves always differentiated into lamina and petiole, longer than 1 cm (usually much longer), entire or divided (usually the entire plant above ground consisting of leaves) **11**

5a Leaves of two sizes and arranged in 4 ranks along the stem; the lateral ones larger, spreading; the upper ones smaller, more or less appressed and pointing forward (**13**) .... *Selaginella helvetica* (p. 102)

5b Leaves all alike, arranged spirally or in ranks, usually more or less appressed, more rarely spreading **6**

6a Leaves sharply toothed along the margins and at the apex, arranged spirally .... *Selaginella selaginoides* (p. 72)

6b Leaves with the margins entire, apex not toothed but sometimes ending in a bristle-like point **55**

7a Leaves clearly differentiated into a slender petiole and 4 almost crosswise (clover-like) arranged leaflets (**99**) .... *Marsilea quadrifolia* (p. 104)

7b Leaves not differentiated into petiole and lamina, subulate or filiform ... **8**

8a Plant growing at the bottom of lakes and always totally submerged, growing from an underground corm-like stem (**31**) **9**

8b Plants growing in aquatic situations but never completely submerged and almost always appearing above the water surface. Leaves arranged along a creeping, slender rhizome, at the base often with hard globular sporocarps (**101**) .... *Pilularia globulifera* (p. 104)

9a Leaves 8–25 (50) cm long, upruptly narrowed at the apex, dark green, rather stiff. Megaspore surface covered with short, rounded tubercles (**31**)
Isoetes lacustris (p. 78)

9b Leaves usually shorter, 4–12 (20) cm long, light green or grass-green, tapering evenly from the base to a fine apex, flexible. Megaspore-surface covered with short spines .... *Isoetes echinospora* (p. 78)

10a Leaves densely imbricate, in 2 ranks, 2-lobed, with the upper lobe up to 2.5 mm long (**97**) .... *Azolla filiculoides* (p. 102)

10b Leaves separate, arranged in whorls of 3: 2 of each whorl entire and floating, 10–14 mm long; one finely divided and root-like (**98**)
Salvinia natans (p. 102)

11a Plants very small (superficially moss-like). Leaves very thin (consisting of only one cell-layer) and translucent **12**

11b Plants small to large, not moss-like in appearance. Leaves thick or thin but never filmy and translucent **14**

12a Rhizome 2–4 mm in diam. Leaves mostly over 10 cm long (7–35 cm); pinnae 1–2-pinnatisect with the ultimate lobe short. Indusium tubular or campanulate; receptacle exserted as a long bristle
Trichomanes speciosum (p. 80)

12b Rhizome filiform, usually less than 1 mm in diam. Leaves at the most 10 cm long; pinnae irregularly dichotomously divided. Indusium 2-valved; receptacle not exserted **13**

13a Indusium-valves circular, toothed. Leaves flat, 2–8 (12) cm long, bluish-green (**36, 37**) .... *Hymenophyllum tunbrigense* (p. 80)

13b Indusium-valves ovate, entire. Leaves with the pinnae bent back from the rhachis, olive-green (**38**) .... *Hymenophyllum wilsonii* (p. 80)

14a Fertile leaves or fertile parts of leaves clearly different from sterile leaves or sterile parts of leaves **15**

14b Fertile leaves not or not markedly different from sterile leaves or sterile parts of leaves **19**

15a Stem forked into an entire or simply pinnate leaf and a fertile spike or panicle (**32, 33**). Plant lower than 30 cm **75**

15b Plant without apparent stem: leaves usually in tufts or crowded at the apex of a stout stock **16**

16a Leaves 1-pinnate; pinnae entire (**2, 45**) .... *Blechnum spicant* (p. 82)

16b Leaves 2–4-pinnate or 1-pinnate and then with pinnatifid pinnae............ **17**

17a Sterile leaves 30–150 cm long, forming a funnel, 1-pinnate with pinnatifid pinnae; fertile leaves arranged in the centre of the funnel, in appearance like ostrich-feathers (**40**) .... *Matteucia struthiopteris* (p. 80)

17b Sterile leaves not arranged as above, 2–4-pinnate **18**

18a Leaves 30–300 cm long, 2-pinnate; outer leaves sterile; inner leaves of crown fertile, with 2–3 pairs of sterile pinnae at the base and 5–14 fertile pairs above; plants of damp and peaty localities (**34, 35**) ...... *Osmunda regalis* (p. 78)

18b Leaves up to 20 (30) cm long; outer sterile leaves 3-pinnatisect; fertile leaves without sterile pinnae at the base, 3–4-pinnate. Sori concealed by the reflexed leaf-margin; plants growing on rocks, screes or stone walls (**41**)
Cryptogramma crispa (p. 80)

19a Leaves 2–3-pinnate, usually shorter than 30 cm; petiole almost capillary, glossy black, somewhat zig-zag-shaped; pinnules wedge-shaped bright green (**39**) .... *Adiantum capillus-veneris* (p. 80)

19b Leaves, even when 2–3 pinnate, different; petiole always straight and not capillary **20**

20a Leaves undivided or slightly lobed, strap-shaped, 15–50 cm long. Sori in opposing pairs and appearing like a single oblong or linear sorus (**51**)
Phyllitis scolopendrium (p. 86)

20b Leaves pinnate, pinnatifid, palmate or forked **21**

21a Leaves distinctly pinnate, palmate or forked **23**

21b Leaves only pinnatifid (pinnae joined at the base to a varying degree as seen in **96**) **22**

22a Lower leaf-surface covered with pale overlapping scales; pinnae ovate or ovate-oblong. Sori linear (**64, 65**) .... *Ceterach officinarum* (p. 88)

22b Lower leaf-surface without scales; pinnae oblong. Sori large, circular or elliptic (**3, 95, 96**) .... *Polypodium sp.* (p. 102)

23a Leaves singly, borne on very long yellowish petiole, 60 – (over) 400 cm long, 3-pinnate; primary pinnae spread sideways, thus the entire plant appearing like a stem with leaves (**1, 42–44**) .... *Pteridium aquilinum* (p. 82)

41a Large plant, forming one or only a few crowns. Leaves soft, 50–150 cm long, without glands beneath; each pinnule with 3 or more sori; indusium 1.5 mm in diam. (**69, 70**) .... *Dryopteris filix-mas* (p. 90)

41b Smaller plant, forming several crowns. Leaves 30–50 cm long, stiff, beneath with tiny glands; each pinnule with 1–2 (rarely more) sori; indusium not over 1 mm in diam. .... *Dryopteris oreades* (p. 90)

42a Leaves 2-pinnate with more or less deeply pinnatifid pinnules; basal pair of pinnules of the lowermost pair of pinnae almost equal (**73, 74**)
Dryopteris submontana (p. 90)

42b Leaves 3- or 4-pinnate; basal pair of pinnules of the lowermost pair of pinnae distinctly unequal **43**

43a Scales of the petiole usually dark brown or blackish in the middle and pale brown at the edges. Indusium beset with stalked or sessile glands (rarely without glands) **44**

43b Scales of the petiole of uniform colour. Glands on the indusium absent or sessile **45**

44a Lowermost basal pinnule of the basal pinna less than half as long as the pinna. Spores dark brown (**75, 76**)............... *Dryopteris dilatata* (p. 99)

44b Lowermost basal pinnule of the basal pinna longer than half the pinna. Spores pale brown .... *Dryopteris expansa* (p. 94)

45a Leaf-lamina triangular-ovate to triangular-lanceolate, on the lower surface or both surfaces sprinkled with tiny glands, fragrant when rubbed; pinnules more or less concave. Indusium with sessile glands and irregularly toothed (**68**) .... *Dryopteris aemula* (p. 90)

45b Leaf-lamina lanceolate or ovate-lanceolate, without glands and not fragrant; pinnules flat. Indusium without glands or rarely with a few stalked glands, not toothed (**77**) .... *Dryopteris carthusiana* (p. 94)

46a Sori oblong to ovate; indusium slightly bent (as seen in **87**). Rhizome-scales without network of dark cell-walls............ *Athyrium filix-femina* (p. 98)

46b Sori linear to elliptic; indusium not bent, resembling the sorus in both shape and size. Rhizome-scales with a network of dark cell-walls (use lens!) ... **47**

47a Leaves densely and completely covered beneath with overlapping scales, deeply pinnatisect (**64, 65**) .... *Ceterach officinarum* (p. 88)

47b Leaves glabrous or sparsely scaly beneath, irregularly forked, pinnate or pinnately lobed **48**

48a Leaves irregularly dichotomously forked, with narrow linear segments (**60, 61**) .... *Asplenium septentrionale* (p. 88)

48b Leaves 1–3-pinnate; segments not narrowly linear **49**

49a Leaves 1-pinnate or rarely 2-pinnate in the lower part **50**

49b Leaves 2–3 (4)-pinnate **53**

50a Leaves 1-pinnate above and 2-pinnate below; pinnae narrowly cuneate, irregularly forked above (**62**) .... *Asplenium × alternifolium* (p. 88)

50b Leaves 1-pinnate throughout; pinnae not cuneate **51**

51a Rhachis green-winged; pinnae longer than 10 mm (**63**)
Asplenium marinum (p. 88)

51b Rhachis not winged; pinnae shorter than 10 mm **52**

52a Rhachis reddish-black to brown-black (**58, 59**)
Asplenium trichomanes (p. 88)

52b Rhachis green (**53, 54**) .... *Asplenium viride* (p. 86)

53a Lowest pair of pinnae a little shorter than those of the middle of the 2-pinnate lamina; leaves lanceolate, stiff; pinnules with a cuneate base
Asplenium billotii (p. 88)

34

53b Lowest pair of pinnae the longest; leaves mostly triangular **54**

54a Petiole green (only darkish near the ground) base not widened; pinnae 3–5 on either side (**57**) .... *Asplenium ruta-muraria* (p. 88)

54b Petiole blackish throughout, base widened; pinnae always more than 5 on either side (**55, 56**)........................ *Asplenium adiantum-nigrum* (p. 86)

55a Sporophylls leaf-like, not arranged in terminal cones (yellow sporangia in the axils of leaf-like sporophylls). Stems of erect or suberect plant only rooting near the base. Leaves usually in 8 rows (**6**) ...... *Huperzia selago* (p. 68)

55b Sporophylls different from leaves, arranged in terminal cones. Stems creeping and rooting almost over their entire length. Leaves usually in 4 rows or spirally arranged **56**

56a Leaves spirally arranged **57**

56b Leaves arranged in 4 rows **59**

57a Stem short, 2–10 cm long, terminated by an erect branch bearing the cone (**8**, young)... *Lycopodiella inundata* (p. 68)

57b Stem up to several meters long, creeping, with numerous upright lateral branches **58**

58a Apex of leaf with a whitish hair-like bristle. Cones usually paired (**9**)
Lycopodium clavatum (p. 68)

58b Apex of leaf without bristle-like hair. Cones solitary (**10**)
Lycopodium annotinum (p. 68)

59a Stem creeping above ground; branches glaucous (**12**)
Diphasiastrum alpinum (p. 68)

59b Stem creeping below ground **60**

60a All leaves of the 4 rows of equal size (**11**) *Diphasiastrum tristachyum* (p. 68)

60b Leaves of 2 rows smaller than the ones of the other 2
Diphasiastrum complanatum (p. 68)

61a Plant without green stems **62**

61b Plants with green stems or at least with green branches........................ **63**

62a Leaf-sheath with 6–12 teeth. Cone 0.8–3.5 (4) cm long (**17, 18, 19**)
Equisetum arvense (p. 72)

62b Leaf-sheath with 20–30 teeth. Cone longer than 4 cm
Equisetum telmateia (p. 74)

63a Stem unbranched or if branched then branches not arranged in whorls ... **64**

63b Stem branched, with the branches arranged in whorls **69**

64a Cone blunt. Stems not persistent. Stomata (use strong lens!) on the surface **67**

64b Cone pointed or drawn-out to a fine point. Stems persistent. Stomata sunk into the surface **65**

65a Teeth soon falling off; sheath with a blackish ring above and below (**25, 26**)
Equisetum hyemale (p. 74)

65b Teeth persistent **66**

66a Stem much-branched, hollow about $\frac{1}{2}$ of diam. of stem. Teeth of sheath 8–20
Equisetum ramosissimum (p. 74)

66b Stem simple or branched only at the base, hollow only $\frac{1}{4}$ the diam. of the stem. Teeth of sheath 6–8 (**30**) .... *Equisetum variegatum* (p. 74)

67a Stem smooth to the touch. Teeth of sheath without ribbs. Hollow of stem wide ($\frac{4}{5}$ its diam.) .... *Equisetum fluviatile* (p. 74)

67b Stem not smooth to the touch. Teeth of sheath ribbed. Hollow of the stem smaller (at most $\frac{2}{3}$ its diam.) **68**

68a Teeth of leaf-sheath with a distinct yellow margin. Branches hollow and with their lowermost internode shorter than the sheaths on the stem (**27**)
Equisetum palustre (p. 74)

68b Teeth of leaf-sheath not with a yellow margin. Branches solid and with their lowermost internode longer than the sheath on the stem (**17**, **18**, **19**)

Equisetum arvense (p. 72)

69a Stem branched up to the apex, 10–13 mm in diam., almost smooth to the touch, whitish, with 20–40 grooves (**21**, **22**)   *Equisetum telmateia* (p. 74)

69b Stem usually unbranched in the apical region; usually only up to 7 mm in diam., green, grooves pronounced **70**

70a Teeth of leaf-sheath on stem fewer in number than stem-grooves (**23**, **24**)

Equisetum sylvaticum (p. 74)

70b Teeth of leaf-sheath on stem as many as grooves, awl-shaped **71**

71a Teeth of leaf-sheath on stem ribbed. Hollow of the stem wide (at least $\frac{4}{5}$ its diam.) (**28**, **29**) .... *Equisetum fluviatile* (p. 74)

71b Teeth of leaf-sheaths on stem not ribbed. Hollow of stem narrower (at most $\frac{2}{3}$ its diam.) **72**

72a Branches solid, their lowermost internode longer than the relevant sheath on the stem **73**

72b Branches hollow, their lowermost internode markedly shorter than the relevant sheath on the stem **74**

73a Branches more or less triangular, spreading horizontally or recurved. Hollow of stem about $\frac{1}{2}$ its diam. (**20**) .... *Equisetum pratense* (p. 74)

73b Branches more or less quadrangular, pointing upwards (sometimes erect). Hollow of the stem about $\frac{1}{4}$ its diam. (**17**, **18**, **19**)

Equisetum arvense (p. 72)

74a Cone sharply and shortly pointed. Stem with 8–10 grooves, its hollow more than $\frac{1}{2}$ its diam. .... *Equisetum ramosissimum* (p. 74)

74b Cone blunt. Stem with 6–8 grooves, its hollow less than $\frac{1}{2}$ its diam. (**27**)

Equisetum palustre (p. 74)

75a Sterile leaf-lamina 1-pinnate; fertile part a panicle (**32**)

Botrychium lunaria (p. 78)

75b Sterile leaf-lamina undivided; fertile part a spike **76**

76a Leaves single (very rarely 2); lamina longer than 30 mm and wider than 20 mm (**33**) .... *Ophioglossum vulgatum* (p. 78)

76b Leaves 2–3 together; lamina shorter than 30 mm and narrower than 20 mm **77**

77a Leaf-lamina lanceolate to ovate, apex pointed, with free nerve-endings within the network of veins .... *Ophioglossum azoricum* (p. 78)

77b Leaf-lamina lanceolate to linear-lanceolate, apex obtuse, without free nerve-endings within the network of veins ... *Ophioglossum lusitanicum* (p. 78)

Key to genera and selected species of mosses and liverworts

This key includes all the mosses and liverworts described and illustrated in the main part of the book and some additional species, for which no further description is given. The plants not appearing elsewhere in the text are marked with an asterisk (*).

1a Plants apparently composed entirely of seta and large, asymmetrical capsule. Rare plant on acid humus or rotting wood
Buxbaumia (p. 110)

1b Plants either thallose or distinctly leafy.. **2**

2a Plants obviously differentiated into stems and leaves **17**

2b Plants thallose, with or without scales or irregular lobes **3**

3a Plants free-floating on water (uncommon) **4**

3b Plants on solid substrates: soil, rocks, trees etc. **5**

4a Plants narrow, elongate, without conspicuous ventral scales
Riccia fluitans (p. 168)

4b Plants short and wide, with conspicuous, elongated ventral scales. Rare; ponds in S. Britain .... **Ricciocarpus natans*

5a Thalli broad, with a regular hexagonal network on the dorsal surface, each mesh (areole) with a pore in the centre **6**

5b Thalli various; if broad, never with areolae on the upper surface......... **10**

6a Special lunate or cup-shaped structures, containing green, discoid gemmae, on upper side of thallus. Mainly in man-made habitats......... **7**

6b Without gemmiferous structures. Mainly in 'natural' habitats **8**

7a Gemmae in cup-shaped structures. Plants commonly fertile
Marchantia (p. 160)

7b Gemmae in crescent-shaped structures. Rarely fertile
Lunularia (p. 160)

8a Thalli 3–4 mm wide, the margins rolling back when dry to expose the dark, blackish-purple underside. Fruit enclosed in a black, bivalved involucre under the apex of the thallus. On rock ledges in the south and west; uncommon .... **Targionia*

8b Thalli wider, 5 mm or more, not rolling back to cover upperside when dry **9**

9a Areolae rather indistinct in mid-thallus. Margins and scales purple
Reboulia (p. 158)

9b Areolae distinct, thalli brown or purple at margins... *Preissia* (p. 158)

9c Areolae distinct, pores very conspicuous, thallus bright green or yellowish
Conocephalum (p. 158)

10a Plants in green, irregular rosettes. Capsules very long, thread-like, splitting above into two ribbon-like valves
Anthoceros (p. 158); *Phaeoceros* (p. 158)

10b Plants elongate or, if in rosettes, then capsules immersed in thallus...... **11**

11a Plants small, furcate, in rosettes closely attached to mineral soils. Capsules spherical, immersed in the thallus .... *Riccia* (p. 160)

11b Plants elongate, tufted or in extensive, irregular mats........................ **12**

12a Thalli narrow, ribbon-like, under 3 mm wide, with very thin wings and narrow, sharply defined midrib; margins usually ciliate
Metzgeria (p. 162)

12b	Thalli over 3 mm wide or, if narrow, then without sharply defined midrib and margins not ciliate..	**13**
13a	Thalli very narrow, either in small, bright green tufts or regularly pinnately or bipinnately branched and forming small fronds ***Riccardia*** (p. 160)	
13b	Thalli creeping, irregularly branched or furcate	**14**
14a	Branches arising from the underside of the sharply defined midrib. Rare species... ***Pallavicinia*** (p. 162)	
14b	Thallus furcate or branches arising laterally....................................	**15**
15a	Thalli simple, without flask-shaped gemmaphores or dark dots, usually less than 4 mm wide and bright green. Fruits, if present, lateral	
	Riccardia (p. 160)	
15b	Thalli either with dark dots and flask-shaped structures or more than 5 mm wide. Deep green to dull, slate green or purplish.............................	**16**
16a	Thalli translucent, with dark dots (colonies of blue-green algae) and flask-shaped structures, containing gemmae, on the dorsal side	
	Blasia (p. 162)	
16b	Thalli more or less opaque, smooth, without dark dots or gemmae	
	Pellia (p. 162)	

LEAFY PLANTS

17a	Leaves strictly in 2 or 3 rows along the stem	**18**
17b	Leaves not in strict rows, rarely in 5 rows or shoots sometimes flat ...	**56**
18a	Leaves in 3 equal rows or in 2 rows with a third row of smaller underleaves (amphigastria)	**43**
18b	Leaves in 2 rows or underleaves vestigial and inconstant	**19**
19a	Leaves with erect, sheathing, white bases and thread-like, very narrow 'blades' .... ***Distichium*** (p. 120)	
19b	Leaves more or less flat, lanceolate to orbicular or lobed	**20**
20a	Leaves with distinct midribs	**21**
20b	Leaves without midribs	**23**
21a	Leaves conduplicate-bilobed, with a smaller, dorsal lobe bent over a longer, ventral lobe .... ***Diplophyllum*** (p. 172)	
21b	Leaves not divided into lobes (lower lamina sometimes split to form a sheath)	**22**
22a	Shoots pectinate with closely set leaves; leaves lanceolate with part of lower lamina apparently split to form a sheath ...... ***Fissidens*** (p. 120)	
22b	Leaves rather distant, rotund or broadly oval, simple	
	Plagiomnium (p. 000)	
23a	Leafy shoots scattered, flat, arising from a conspicuous, glistening, persistent protonema .... ***Schistostega*** (p. 110)	
23b	Leafy shoots usually in tufts or mats. Protonema lacking	**24**
24a	Plants very small, leaves densely packed and shoots cylindrical or club-shaped, pale and bleached-looking or tinged blackish	
	Gymnomitrium (p. 172)	
24b	Plants elongate or at least leaves separable; plants rarely silvery	**25**
25a	Leaves simple, not divided into lobes or deeply notched	**26**
25b	Leaves variously divided into 2 or more lobes or deeply notched.........	**33**
26a	Leafy shoots ascending, stiff, without rhizoids, arising from creeping, leafless bases .... ***Plagiochila*** (p. 170)	
26b	Leafy shoots prostrate, usually with abundant rhizoids, or erect and densely tufted but without leafless, creeping bases	**27**
27a	Shoots erect, forming medium-sized to rather large cushions	**28**
27b	Shoots prostrate, forming mats or creeping among mosses	**29**

28a Plants blackish green, by alpine streams and springs
Jungermannia cordifolis (p. 170)

28b Plants greenish, tinged brown and red. On acid, dry humus
Mylia taylori (p. 170)

29a Gemmae abundant on young leaves and/or shoot tips **30**

29b Gemmae absent.. **31**

30a Plants small, reddish-brown, on dry peat and rotting wood.
Odontoschisma denudatum (p. 176)

30b Plants greenish, upper leaves elongate; on wet peat among mosses and Sphagnum .... *Mylia anomala* (p. 170)

31a Plants elongated, brown; on wet, acid peat
Odontoschisma sphagni (p. 176)

31b Plants various, green; on mineral soils, rocks or wood **32**

32a Leaves convex and deflexed, rather large plants
Pedinophyllum (p. 170)

32b Leaves concave, erect to erect spreading. Mainly small plants
Jungermannia (p. 170)

33a Leaves 2-lobed, sometimes conduplicate **34**

33b Leaves mainly 3–4-lobed, not conduplicate **42**

34a Leaves conduplicate, i.e. one lobe folded over, and usually lying against the other... **35**

34b Leaves not folded **37**

35a Smaller lobe folded under the larger lobe, hidden from above
Radula (p. 174)

35b Smaller lobe folded over the larger, visible from above **36**

36a At least the larger lobe elongate and much longer than wide
Diplophyllum (p. 172) (also *Douinia and *Tritomaria*, p. 168)

36b Both lobes more or less orbicular to quadrate
Scapania (p. 174) (also *Sphenolobus*, p. 168, and *Tritomaria*, p. 168, in part)

37a Ends of leaf lobes blunt or rounded **38**

37b Ends of lobes acute, sometimes drawn out into filiform points............ **40**

38a Shoots ascending; leaves closely set and more or less squarrose; plants usually dark, purple-black or brownish............... *Marsupella* (p. 268)

38b Shoots various, green or prostrate or leaves distant and not squarrose **39**

39a On acid soils. Often blackish, with balloon-like perianths
Gymnocolea (p. 172)

39b On acid soils. Usually dull green, often in pools. With flagellae but without inflated perianths .... *Cladopodiella* (p. 172)

39c On calcareous soil or rocks. Usually pale   *Leiocolea turbinata* (p. 168)

40a Stems rather short and fleshy with closely set leaves. Gemmae common. On acid, peaty soils
*Lophozia but see also *Leiocolea* (p. 168 mainly basic soils)

40b Stems elongated, thin; leaves often minute and distant **41**

41a Exceedingly small plants. Leaves not much wider than stems, often toothed. Gemmae sometimes present............... *Cephaloziella* (p. 174)

41b Reddish plants, on wood; lobes inflated and concave *Nowellia* (p. 172)

41c Green plants, usually on soil or peat. Lobes slightly concave but not saccate .... *Cephalozia* (p. 172)

42a Stems short, fleshy. Rhizoids usually bright purple-red
Fossombronia (p. 164)

42b Stems elongate. Leaves with 3–4 equal lobes ... *Barbilophozia* (p. 168)

42c Stems elongate or small. Leaves with 3 very unequal lobes (sometimes almost conduplicate)...... *Tritomaria* (p. 168, also *Sphenolobus*, p. 168)

43a Leaf lobes hair-like or lobes fringed with long cilia **44**

43b Leaf lobes more or less flat, sometimes toothed but never ciliate **48**

44a Plants very pale, bipinnately branched, with a woolly consistency; leaves formed almost entirely of pale, hair-like cilia ...... *Trichocolea* (p. 164)

44b Plants, if pale, small and attenuated, not woolly; if robust and bipinnate, then reddish or brownish and with obvious lamina as well as cilia **45**

45a Thin, pale whitish or brownish plants. Leaves entirely composed of 2–4 hair-like cilia **46**

45b Plants small to medium sized; leaves with distinct laminate portion ... **47**

46a Pale, whitish or yellowish plants on basic or neutral soils
Blepharostoma (p. 166)

46b Brownish plants, on acid humus and peat *Kurzia* (syn. *Lepidozia* (p. 166)

47a Plants reddish-brown, leaves profusely ciliate .... *Ptilidium* (p. 164)

47b Plants green, leaves with 3–4 filiform segments ... *Lepidozia* (p. 166)

48a Large, aquatic moss; Leaves undivided, keeled or concave, in 3 equal rows
Fontinalis (p. 140)

48b Small to medium-sized, mainly terrestrial or epiphytic liverworts with variously divided leaves **49**

49a Leaves and amphigastria similar in size and shape **50**

49b Amphigastria smaller than leaves, usually differing in form **51**

50a Small, dull or blackish plants; leaves small, straight, erect
Anthelia (p. 164)

50b Medium to large, reddish plants; leaves long, usually curved. On cliffs and ravines in the west .... **Herberta*

51a Viewed from above, upper leaves overlapped by the lower (incubous) **52**

51b Viewed from above, upper leaves overlapping the lower (succubous) ... **55**

52a Leaves 2-lobed, the underlobe folded under the larger, rounded upper lobe **53**

52b Leaves lobed or not but lobes similar in form and size, not conduplicate **54**

53a Lower lobe more or less flat. Plants usually green, robust
Porella (p. 176)

53b Lower lobe formid into a minutely stalked, helmet-shaped water-sac. Plants usually dark purple to brownish.................. *Frullania* (p. 176)

53c Lower lobe minute, inflated into a water-sac but not stalked. Plants small, to very small, green or yellowish .... *Lejeunea* (p. 176)

54a Plants robust, ascending. Leaves deflexed, with usually 3 broad teeth at apices. Never gemmiferous .... *Bazzania* (p. 164)

54b Plants small, usually more or less prostrate, pinnately branched, green. Leaves with 3–4 narrow, finger-like lobes. Not gemmiferous
Lepidozia (p. 166)

54c Plants pale, translucent, prostrate; leaves entire or minutely 2-lobed. Often very gemmiferous .... *Calypogeia* (p. 174)

55a Leaves rotund, concave. Amphigastria small and entire *Nardia* (p. 267)

55b Leaves rotund to oval, convex and deflexed. Amphigastria vestigial.
Plagiochila; *Pedinophyllum* (p. 170)

55c Leaves oblong-rotund, entire or very shallowly notched. Amphigastria deeply bifid and toothed .... *Chiloscyphus* (p. 166)

55d At least the older leaves 2-lobed, the lobes often finely tapered to acute tips. Amphigastria bifid and toothed .... *Lophocolea* (p. 166)

56a Plants large to very large, 5–30 cms or more, usually erect and in cushions. Branches arranged in bunches (fascicles) at more or less regular intervals,

67b Plants various, if blackish, then with distinct midribs and/or hair points   **68**

68a Shoots small, cylindrical, shining and silvery, with concave, closely overlapping leaves...   **69**

68b Shoots various, either not silvery or shoots of different form **70**

69a Very common, lowland plants on paths, walls etc. even in towns
Bryum argenteum (p. 130)

69b Frequent mountain plants on wet rocks by streams, etc. **Anomobryum*

69c Uncommon mountain plants on ledges and in crevices of basic rocks, sometimes pink-tinged .... **Plagiobryum*

70a Leaves long and narrow, more than 6 times as long as wide, tapering to fine points formed largely of the midrib **71**

70b Leaves rotund, ovate, lingulate or lanceolate, less than 5 times as long as wide..   **84**

71a Midrib, above leaf base, very broad, more than $\frac{1}{2}$ width of leaf. Leaves with setaceous points and sometimes hair-tipped. Base of leaf usually with reddish auricles or leaves markedly deciduous. Stems usually tomentose
Campylopus (p. 114, common); *Dicranodontium* (p. 116, uncommon);
Paraleucobryum (p. 116, rare)

71b Midrib less than $\frac{1}{3}$ width of leaf or, if broader, then plants small and leaves lacking auricles and not deciduous; never hair-pointed **72**

72a Plants large and robust. Leaves more than 7 mm long, usually curved and turned to one side. Stems tomentose. Leaf bases with brown auricles
Dicranum (p. 118)

72b Plants small to medium sized. Leaves various but, if falcate and secund, then stems not tomentose and leaves lacking auricles.......................   **73**

73a Leaves stiff, grey-green or blue-green, widely spreading. Capsules spherical ....*Bartramia* (p. 136)

73b Leaves curved and falcate or soft-textured, often flexuous. Plants rarely glaucous. Capsules usually more or less cylindrical...........................   **74**

74a Leaves very narrow, strongly curved and turned to one side..............   **75**

74b Leaves spreading, not falcate and secund **76**

75a Leaves deep green to blackish. Plants either on alpine rocks or on dry, calcareous rocks and soil in the lowlands .... **Ditrichum*

75b In green tufts or patches, mainly on lime-free soil in woodlands
Dicranella (p. 116)

76a Plants in compact, green or yellow-green cushions on trees, rarely on lime-free, sandstone rocks **77**

76b Plants various; if in compact tufts, then on soil or calcareous rocks and walls **78**

77a Leaves entire. Capsules common, erect, cylindrical and smooth, pale when dry and empty .... *Dicranoweisia* (p. 116)

77b Leaves entire. Capsules erect, club-shaped, ribbed or leaves with terminal clusters of reddish-brown gemmae .... *Ulota* (p. 138)

77c Leaves toothed above. Capsules very rare
Dicranum montanum (p. 118)

77d Leaves toothed or not. Capsules nearly always present, club-shaped and horizontal .... *Orthodontium* (p. 128)

78a Plants very small, less than 5 mm tall, few-leaved, in scattered colonies on bare rocks or pebbles .... *Seligeria* (p. 262); **Brachydontium*

78b Plants usually more than 5 mm high, more or less densely leafy **79**

79a Plants green or yellow, in compact cushions, 3–10 cm deep, in crevices of mountain rocks. Leaves entire .... *Tortella* (p. 122); **Amphidium*

42

79b Plants smaller or in lowland habitats or leaves toothed **80**

80a Leaves toothed, plants in cushions, usually abundantly fertile. Mainly in the mountains **81**

80b Leaves entire, plants tufted or not; often barren **82**

81a Yellowish green plants. Capsules cylindrical, asymmetrical and inclined. Leaves erect-spreading to slightly secund.......... ***Cynodontium*** (p. 116)

81b Green to yellowish plants, as above but leaves spreading-recurved
*Oncophorus

81c Dull green, blackish below. On siliceous rocks and walls. Often polysetous; capsules erect, symmetrical ... ***Ptychomitrium*** (p. 264); ****Glyphomitrium***

82a Leaves markedly squarrose. On calcareous, sandy soils. Lowland
Pleurochaete (p. 122)

82b Leaves spreading but not strongly bent back (squarrose) **83**

83a Green, rather delicate plants on burnt ground, flower pots, etc.
*Leptobryum

83b Brown plants. Leaves erect, with reddish auricles. Mainly by mountain streams .... ****Blindia***

83c Leaves opaque, flexuose. On rocks, walls and soil
Barbula (p. 106); ****Weisia***

84a At least the upper leaves ending in a whitish hair-point, or the midrib extended beyond the leaf tip in a long bristle **85**

84b Leaves rounded, blunt or acute but nerve, if excurrent, only forming a short mucro **87**

85a Leaf apex broad, obtuse, rounded or retuse; midrib excurrent in a hair-point or awn **86**

85b Uppermost leaves with several long marginal cilia in addition to hair-point. Fruit sessile, large and conspicuous .... ***Diphyscium*** (p. 110)

85c Leaf apex narrowed to an acute apex; hair-point long or short:
Grimmia (p. 124); ***Rhacomitrium*** (p. 126); ***Schistidium*** (p. 124)

86a Leaf apex broadly pointed. Plants densely tufted, on rocks. Capsules ovoid, usually on strongly curved setae.................. ***Grimmia*** (p. 124)

86b Leaf apices rounded, obtuse, truncated or retuse. Capsules erect and cylindrical. On rocks, walls and sand .... ***Tortula*** (p. 122)

86c Leaves deep green, concave. Capsules on long setae, club-shaped and pendulous .... ***Bryum capillare*** (p. 122)

86d Capsules erect, on very short setae and partly immersed among the leaves
Orthotrichum diaphanum (p. 138)

86e Leaves nerveless, whole plant hoary, often prostrate ***Hedwigia*** (p. 140)

87a Leaves broad but with narrow bases, rotund to broadly ovate, usually with distinct borders of narrow cells, toothed or not. Leaf apices very broad, rounded, minutely mucronate or retuse
Plagiomnium (p. 133); ***Rhizomnium*** (p. 132)

87b Leaves various; if obtuse to rounded above, then lingulate from broader insertion **88**

88a Plants small to very small (2–10 mm tall) on bare soil. Capsules ovoid, sessile or almost so, lacking lids and peristomes
Pleuridium (p. 262); ***Phascum*** (p. 262); ****Ephemerum***; ****Pseudephemerum***;
*Archidium; ****Acaulon***

88b Plants larger or, if small, then capsules stalked and/or with peristomes and deciduous lids **89**

89a Leaves with margins distinctly bordered, toothed or not **90**

89b Leaf margins entire or toothed, but not differing from lamina in texture **91**

90a Border strong, distinctly and often doubly serrate

Mnium (pp. 106, 132, 134)

90b Border entire. Leaves ovate or lanceolate, acute .... *Bryum* (p. 130)

90c Border entire. Leaves lingulate, bluntly pointed ... *Cinclidotus* (p. 124)

91a Lower parts of stems coated with a dense, brownish tomentum **92**

91b Rhizoids often numerous but not forming felt-like tomentum **93**

92a Leaves lanceolate, rather bluntly pointed. Plants laxly tufted or scattered among Sphagnum, etc. Capsules rare, oval-cylindric

Aulacomnium (p. 134)

92b Leaves triangular, abruptly tapered to very acute apices. Capsules common, spherical. Plants grey-green to yellow-green, erect, tufted

Philonotis (p. 136)

92c Leaves elongate triangular, very widely spreading, plicate. Plants golden brown. Capsules very rare. Plants more or less prostrate

Breutelia (p. 136)

93a Leaf tips blunt or rounded; midrib ceasing in or below leaf tip **94**

93b Leaf tips narrow, acute or midrib projecting beyond apex in a mucro **95**

94a On wet, acid rocks, mainly in hilly districts ...... *Rhacomitrium* (p. 126)

94b On calcareous soil and rocks. Capsules, if present, at first hidden under conspicuous, white, conical calyptras................. *Encalypta* (p. 122)

94c On basic rocks and walls. Capsules elongate-cylindric. Calyptra small

*Tortula subulata

94d On tree-roots, etc., usually near water

*Tortula latifolia; **Orthotrichum obtusifolium*

94e Leaves flat at margins, distinctly toothed near apex

Dichodontium (p. 116), **Leptodontium*

94f Leaves pale, conspicuously squarrose-recurved. Wet mires and springs

Dicranella palustris (p. 263)

95a Leaves ovate to ovate-lanceolate, widest at about the middle; usually rather translucent and glossy **96**

95b Leaves narrowly lanceolate to narrowly lingulate, usually broadest at the base; usually matt or opaque **97**

96a Plants on old animal droppings on moors. Fruit erect and symmetrical, with conspicuous apophyses much larger and wider than urns

Splachnum (p. 126); *Tetraplodon* (p. 126); **Haplodon*

96b Plants on peat, rocks or wood. Capsules pendulous, symmetrical, smooth

Bryum (p. 130); *Pohlia* (p. 130); **Mniobryum*

96c Plants of bare soil, burnt ground and gardens. Capsules inclined, asymmetrical, deeply grooved when old and dry *Funaria* (p. 106, 128)

96d Small, gregarious plants, on soil or humus. Capsules erect, without peristomes ...... *Physcomitrium* (p. 128); *Funaria* (*Entosthodon*, p. 128)

97a Capsules normally present, on short setae, usually grooved. Calyptra conical, often pleated and with scattered setae. Commonly epiphytic ... **98**

97b Capsules, if present, usually on long setae; rarely grooved. Calyptra asymmetrical and soon lost. Rarely epiphytic **99**

98a Leaves more or less erect and hardly altered when dry

Orthotrichum (p. 138)

98b Leaves long and narrow, strongly curled when dry...... *Ulota* (p. 138)

98c Leaves small, spirally twisted when dry................. *Zygodon* (p. 265)

99a Plants in very compact, deep cushions on mountain rock ledges, usually where constantly wet

*Anoectangium; **Gymnostomum*; **Hymenostylium*

99b On wet, calcareous rocks, often encrusted with calcium carbonate
Eucladium; *Barbula tophacea*

99c On dry soil. Capsules oval; peristome absent or short .... *Weisia*

99d On soil, rocks, walls, etc. Capsule cylindrical. Peristome long, twisted
Barbula (p. 106); *Trichostomum*; *Oxystegus*

99e On soil; capsules wide-mouthed. Peristome absent or vestigial
Pottia (p. 263)

99f On burnt ground, peat, lime-free soil, roofs walls and rocks. Usually profusely fertile in spring with massed, purple setae. Capsule slightly curved and inclined .... *Ceratodon* (p. 130)

100a Plants dendroid, i.e. with secondary, ascending stems arising from creeping, leafless primary stems. Shoots leafless at base, much branched above, resembling miniature trees **101**

100b Plants various, sometimes stiff and frondose but not with erect 'trunks' **102**

101a Branches mainly simple, radiating. Leaves pleated, yellowish
Climacium (p. 140)

101b Branches often again branched, forming flat, spreading heads. Dark green
Thamnium (p. 142)

101c Rather indistinctly dendroid. Shoots under 5 cm tall; mat-forming
Isothecium (p. 142)

101d Shoot systems strongly rolled up when dry. Leaves blunt or rounded at apices. Mainly on trees; rare .... *Leptodon* (p. 142)

102a Leaves with white hair-points; plants conspicuously hoary when dry ... **103**

102b Leaves sometimes with filiform tips, but not with white hairs **104**

103a Leaves with midribs; narrowly lanceolate .... *Rhacomitrium* (p. 126)

103b Leaves without midribs, ovate .... *Hedwigia* (p. 140)

104a Leaves narrowly lanceolate, opaque in texture. Shoots with clusters of very short branches. On lime-free rocks.................. *Rhacomitrium* (p. 126)

104b Leaves various, if narrow and opaque, then branches elongate, not clustered or abbreviated **105**

105a Shoots more or less frondose, bipinnately or tripinnately branched **106**

105b Shoots simple, irregularly or pinnately branched............................. **107**

106a Stems reddish, leaves translucent; midribs short or absent
Hylocomium (p. 156)

106b Stems blackish, leaves opaque; branch leaves minute. Midrib reaching almost to leaf tip .... *Thuidium* (p. 142)

106c Stems green to light brown. Stem leaves cordate, squarrose. Branch leaves lanceolate. Midribs distinct .... *Eurhynchium praelongum* (p. 150)

106d Shoot systems strongly rolled up when dry. Leaves blunt or rounded at apices. Mainly on trees; rare .... *Leptodon* (p. 142)

107a Leaves of branches distinctly to very strongly curved and turned, to one side (usually downwards).. **108**

107b Leaves spreading in all directions; suberect to spreading or recurved ... **111**

108a Leaves with distinct midribs that reach beyond mid-leaf **109**

108b Leaves without midribs, or midribs extremely short and double **110**

109a Midribs very strong, running into the leaf tips. On wet rocks and base-rich mires. Green or usually orange-brown plants
Cratoneuron (pp. 106, 146)

109b Midribs narrow, often ceasing well below leaf tips. In mires, pools and bogs. Green, brown, orange-brown or red ... *Drepanocladus* (p. 146)

109c Leaves short-pointed or blunt. Midrib usually thin. On rocks in streams
Hygrohypnum

109d Leaves rugose. Midrib shortish. On dry, basic soils

Rhytidium (p. 154)

109e Leaves ovate, acute. Plants in silky mats on smooth rocks by streams

*Brachythecium plumosum

110a Densely pinnate, feathery plants on acid soil and humus in mountainous districts. Uncommon .... *Ptilium* (p. 154)

110b Golden, densely pinnate, feathery plants on calcareous or base-rich rocks and soil. Lowland to alpine. Common .... *Ctenidium* (p. 152)

110c Pinnately branched or more or less simple plants, green to brownish, more or less glossy but not feathery. On acid, basic and neutral soils, rocks, walls, trees etc. Common (in part) ...... *Hypnum* (p. 154); *Pylaisia* (p. 154)

110d Robust, dark, turgid, little-branched plants in boggy ground

Scorpidium (p. 144)

110e Robust, irregularly branched, brownish plants on dry, basic soils in hilly districts. Leaves rugose. Uncommon .... *Rhytidium* (p. 154)

110f Stiff, robust, brownish plants on acid humus. Pinnate

Rhytidiadelphus loreus (p. 156)

111a Stem leaves strongly recurved-squarrose, the tips directed backwards. Very common in grasslands and lawns

Rhytidiadelphus squarrosus (p. 156)

111b Leaves often widely spreading but not recurved **112**

112a Stems simple or pinnately branched, often lacking rhizoids. Leaves with blunt, rounded or abruptly mucronate apices. Ground-dwelling **113**

112b Stems various: closely attached to substrate by rhizoids, or leaves acute **116**

113a Leaves with distinct midribs reaching to mid-leaf or beyond.............. **114**

113b Leaves lacking midribs, or midribs short and double **115**

114a Shoot tips pale. Leaves very concave, abruptly contracted to long, hair-like, filiform points. Terrestrial in basic woodland

Cirriphyllum (p. 148)

114b Yellowish plants, regularly pinnate with tumid shoots. Leaves very concave, abruptly contracted to short filiform tips. Grasslands and open woodlands .... *Pseudoscleropodium* (p. 146)

114c Leaf tips blunt or rounded, without filiform tips. In mires

Calliergon (p. 144)

115a Leaves blunt, translucent, yellowish. Stems bright reddish brown. Terrestrial in acid woodlands and heathlands ... *Pleurozium* (p. 106, 150)

115b Shoot tips conspicuously acute with tightly overlapping leaves. Stems green to yellow-brown. In damp grasslands and marshes

Calliergon cuspidatum (p. 144)

115c Shoots cylindrical but not conspicuously pointed at tips. Stems not reddish. Yellow-green to brownish plants in dry calcareous grasslands

*Entodon

116a Leaves very small, mostly under 1 mm long or, if longer, then very narrow and plants silky **117**

116b Leaves larger, many more than 1.5 mm long **118**

117a Deep green to brownish, thin mats on damp, shaded rocks; leaves lanceolate. Common lowland plants with reddish setae and conspicuous pale calyptras... *Amblystegium* (p. 144)

117b Brownish plants on exposed, calcareous mountain rocks

*Psedoleskeella

117c Silvery plants with tumid shoots and very concave leaves. Rare alpine plant .... *Myurella* (p. 142)

46

117d Leaves concave but plants not silvery. Trees and rocks in the mountains; rare .... *****Pterigynandrum*****

117e Dark green, matted plants on damp woodland banks, etc. Leaves ovate
*****Heterocladium*****

117f Small, silky plants with very narrow, linear leaves. Frequent on rocks and trees in lowland districts .... *****Rhynchostegiella***** (p. 266)

117g On tree roots by water. Dull plants with strong leaf-midribs
*****Leskea***** (p. 140)

117h On tree roots by water rare. Dark green, midrib absent...... *****Myrinia*****

118a Epiphytic moss with narrow, ascending, branched shoots. Capsules immersed in perichaetia along one side of branches
*****Cryphaea***** (p. 264)

118b Plants matted or not on trees. Capsules on long setae **119**

119a Coarse, robust, erect-growing terrestrial plants with stiff, acute, pale, spreading leaves. In basic scrub and woodland
*****Rhytidiadelphus triquetris***** (p. 156)

119b Plants smaller; if robust, then not rigid and erect **120**

120a Leaves conspicuously longitudinally pleated (plicate), hence appearing striate **121**

120b Leaves smooth or inconspicuously plicate only when dry **122**

121a Leaves broadly triangular, rather short-pointed. Stiff, straggling, dark green or yellowish plants of basic woodlands. Common
*****Eurhynchium striatum***** (p. 150)

121b Leaves long-tapering, silky, with thin midribs. Rocks, walls and calcareous turf. Common .... *****Homalothecium***** (= *****Camptothecium*****, p. 150)

121c Leaves long-tapered. Plants pale, whitish. Uncommon
*****Brachythecium glareosum*****

121d Leaves without midribs. Plants not silky. Dry rocks and tree trunks, uncommon .... *****Leucodon***** (p. 138)

121e Leaves without midribs, golden, brown to pink or red. Rare mountain plant on wet, calcareous rock ledges .... *****Orthothecium***** (p. 150)

121f Little-branched, robust, golden-brown plants with stems matted in brown tomentum .... *****Breutelia***** (p. 136)

122a Leaves without midribs or midribs short, faint and double **123**

122b Leaves with distinct midribs reaching to mid-leaf or beyond.............. **124**

123a Plants golden yellow or golden brown, in mires or dry calcareous grasslands .... *****Campylium***** (p. 265)

123b Slender, inconspicuous, greenish plants in shaded rock clefts, etc.
*****Isopterygium*****

123c Green, matted plants on tree-bases and stumps *****Dolichotheca***** (p. 150)

124a Plants coarse, matt, straggling. Leaf margins coarsely toothed with many teeth directed more or less backwards. Mainly on trees
*****Antitrichia***** (p. 138)

124b Plants coarse, leaves elongate and blunt at tips. Mainly on rocks and old walls; matt green or yellowish.................................... *****Anomodon*****

124c Plants slender or, if coarse, then rather glossy and leaf margins entire or finely denticulate; leaves acute **125**

125a Pinnately branched shoot systems strongly rolled up when dry. Leaves small, rounded-obtuse. Rather rare, mainly on trees *****Leptodon***** (p. 142)

125b Shoot systems almost unaltered when dry. Leaves acutely pointed **126**

126a Shoots mostly sub-dendroid, i.e. with ascending shoot systems rather densely branched above with branches directed in one direction **127**

126b Shoots basically creeping, or with only branches ascending **128**

127a Leaves strongly appressed to branches when dry; shoots conspicuously curved. On calcareous rocks and skeletal calcareous soils **Scorpiurium*

127b Leaves laxly appressed or unaltered when dry. On trees and rocks
Isothecium (p. 142)

128a Branch leaves small, not glossy, opaque. Pinnately branched plants in calcareous grasslands .... *Abietinella* (p. 142)

128b Branch leaves small or large, more or less glossy or translucent **129**

129a Plants of permanently wet habitats; by streams, ditches and waterfalls **130**

129b Plants of various habitats, often humid but not permanently wet **131**

130a Branch leaves broadly oval, concave, shortly acute
Rhynochostegium riparioides (p. 148)

130b Branch leaves flat, lanceolate, untoothed, often more or less complanate
*Amblystegium riparium

130c Leaves concave, finely acute or very pale, usually denticulate
Brachythecium (p. 148)

131a Plants usually slender. Lids of capsules long-beaked
Eurhynchium (p. 150)
sens. lat. *Eurhynchium* (p. 150); *Rhynchostegium* (p. 266); *Cirriphyllum* (p. 148); *Rhynchostegiella* (p. 266)

131b Plants usually robust. Lids of capsules short, conical
Brachythecium (p. 148); **Scleropodium*

Key to genera of lichens

This key includes all lichen genera dealt with in the book. It should be noted that it has not been possible to include all common lichen genera (e.g. *Lepraria*, *Verrucaria*) in the text and therefore these are also absent from this key.

1a	Fruiting bodies stalked. Thallus crustaceous or of small squamules......	**2**
1b	Fruiting bodies sessile, immersed, or absent. Thallus crustaceous, foliose, or fruticose...	**10**
2a	Fruiting bodies minute, pin-shaped, with mazaedia	**3**
2b	Fruiting bodies moderate, with hymenial discs. Thallus crustaceous or squamulose. Chiefly on soil or rock	**6**
3a	Thallus of coralloid, scaly lobes. On spruce in Scandinavia *Tholurna dissimilis* (p. 182)	
3b	Thallus crustaceous. Chiefly on bark, wood, or rock	**4**
4a	Spores simple..	**5**
4b	Spores one-septate .... *Calicium* (p. 180)	
5a	Spores colourless or pale; pale in the mass .... *Coniocybe* (p. 180)	
5b	Spores brown; dark in the mass .... *Chaenotheca* (p. 180)	
6a	Thallus crustaceous	**7**
6b	Thallus squamulose	**9**
7a	Apothecia black. On rock .... *Pilophorus* (p. 220)	
7b	Apothecia brownish. On soil or soft rock..	**8**
8a	Stalks branched; warted and inflated ... *Pycnothelia papillaria* (p. 220)	
8b	Stalks mostly simple; smooth .... *Baeomyces* (p. 210)	
9a	Stalks solid, with coralloid squamules (phyllocladia) *Stereocaulon* (pp. 222, 224)	
9b	Stalks hollow, with foliose squamules or naked *Cladonia* (pp. 210–20)	
10a	Thallus crustaceous	**11**
10b	Thallus of small squamules, small vesicles, or gelatinous, or foliose, or fruticose...	**45**
11a	Thallus wholly crustaceous, without marginal lobes	**12**
11b	Thallus with marginal lobes	**39**
12a	Fruiting bodies mazaedia .... *Cyphelium* (p. 182)	
12b	Fruiting bodies apothecia or pseudothecia, or absent........................	**13**
13a	Fruiting bodies pseudothecia (globose, with apical pore)	**14**
13b	Fruiting bodies apothecia (discoid or elongate) or absent	**16**
14a	Spores brown, 1- to 3-septate, thick-walled. On bark *Pyrenula* (p. 256)	
14b	Spores colourless (rarely tinged with brown), 1- to 5-septate, thin-walled	**15**
15a	Spores uniseriate in cylindrical asci .... *Acrocordia* (p. 260)	
15b	Spores massed in ovate asci .... *Arthopyrenia* (p. 260)	
16a	Fruiting bodies elongate (lirellae) or irregular	**17**
16b	Fruiting bodies round or absent..	**20**
17a	Fruiting bodies immarginate .... *Arthonia* (p. 258)	
17b	Fruiting bodies marginate	**18**
18a	Spores thin-walled. Paraphyses anastomosing. Lirellae sessile *Opegrapha* (p. 258)	
18b	Spores thick-walled. Paraphyses simple. Lirellae innate. Chiefly on bark	**19**
19a	Spores brown. Lirellae flat .... *Phaeographis* (p. 256)	
19b	Spores colourless. Lirellae with raised margins ...... *Graphis* (p. 256)	

39b Lobes grey, brownish, or yellowish; if yellowish K − **41**
40a Spores polarilocular .... *Caloplaca* (p. 246)
40b Spores simple. On rock and soil........................... *Fulgensia* (p. 248)
41a Apothecia without thalline margins; discs black. Thallus grey
Diploicia (p. 254)
41b Apothecia with thalline margins... **42**
42a Colour light greenish-yellow, of angular areolae. Spores brown, one-
septate. On rock .... *Dimelaena oreina* (p. 254)
42b Colour grey or yellowish-grey or greenish or brownish **43**
43a Spores one-septate. On rock and soil............... *Solenopsora* (p. 204)
43b Spores simple.. **44**
44a Cephalodia present, forming pink clumps on the surface. On rock
Placopsis gelida (p. 256)
44b Cephalodia absent.................................... *Lecanora* (pp. 204, 206)
45a Thallus of small black vesicles; growing with *Anthoceros* on soil. Rare
Geosiphon pyriforme (p. 260)
45b Thallus of small squamules or gelatinous or foliose or fruticose. Common **46**
46a Thallus gelatinous, swelling when damp. Dark; algae blue-green **47**
46b Thallus not gelatinous, but of small squamules, or foliose or fruticose ... **49**
47a Thallus fruticose. On maritime rocks in the tidal zone **Lichina** (p. 234)
47b Thallus usually squamulose or foliose. Above the tide-levels and inland **48**
48a Thallus with a well-defined upper cortex ... *Leptogium* (pp. 182, 184)
48b Thallus without an upper cortex .... *Collema* (p. 182) ·
49a Thallus of small squamules **50**
49b Thallus foliose or fruticose **61**
50a Squamules coralloid (phyllocladia). On rock and soil
Stereocaulon (pp. 222, 224)
50b Squamules foliose or adnate **51**
51a Lobes ascending at margins, with white undersides visible
Cladonia (pp. 210–20)
51b Lobes appressed, the undersides not visible **52**
52a Thallus with pseudothecia, only the minute dark ostioles visible. On soil
and bark.. *Catapyrenium* (p. 258)
52b Thallus with apothecia, or sterile **53**
53a Apothecia with thalline margins.. **54**
53b Apothecia without thalline margins, or sterile **56**
54a Thallus of minute squamules amongst mosses. Large apothecia with raised
crenate margins and reddish-brown discs normally present
Psoroma hypnorum (p. 234)
54b Thallus of large squamules **55**
55a Squamules umbilicate, greenish. On rock .... *Rhizoplaca* (p. 204)
55b Squamules cretaceous, thick and rounded. On rock and soil
Squamarina (p. 204)
56a Squamules rounded, shell-like.. **57**
56b Squamules thick and peltate or compact and adnate **59**
57a Lobes large, to 5 mm broad, greenish. Soredia absent. On acid soil
Coriscium viride (p. 260)
57b Lobes small, under 2 mm broad. Soredia often present. On bark and rock **58**
58a Lobes to 2 mm broad, grey. Amongst mosses
Normandina pulchella (p. 260)
58b Lobes to 1 mm broad, greenish, greyish, or brownish. On wood and bark:
Hypocenomyce (p. 208)

59a Squamules thick and peltate, pink to brown. On rock and soil
$$Psora \text{ (p. 208)}$$
59b Squamules compact and adnate, often forming an areolate thallus **60**
60a Apothecia innate. On rock .... *Acarospora* (p. 232)
60b Apothecia sessile. Squamules greyish, often dispersed. On rock and soil
Toninia (pp. 206, 208)
61a Thallus foliose, the upper side differing from the underside **62**
61b Thallus fruticose, the upper and lower sides undifferentiated **93**
62a Thallus rounded, attached at one central point (umbilicus). On rock ...   **63**
62b Thallus foliose, without an umbilicus. On rock, bark, wood, and earth   **65**
63a With immersed pseudothecia, visible only as dark ostioles
Dermatocarpon (p. 258)
63b With apothecia or sterile **64**
64a Thallus pustulate .... *Lasallia* (p. 230)
64b Thallus plane or ridged .... *Umbilicaria* (pp. 226–230)
65a Thallus and/or apothecia bright yellow, orange, or reddish **66**
65b Thallus pale to dark **68**
66a Thallus usually orange yellow, K + violet-red ...... *Xanthoria* (p. 248)
66b Thallus citrine yellow, K − **67**
67a Thallus minute. Chiefly on bark............ *Candelaria concolor* (p. 210)
67b Thallus large .... *Cetraria* (pp. 190–4)
68a Thallus subfruticose, fastened at one end **69**
68b Thallus foliose, fastened by most or all of the underside to the substrate   **73**
69a With long cilia along the margins **70**
69b Without cilia, or with only short cilia on the margins **71**
70a Spores thick-walled, smooth .... *Heterodermia* (pp. 250, 252)
70b Spores thin-walled, sculptured .... *Anaptychia* (p. 248)
71a Thallus antler-shaped, in one plane **72**
71b Thallus branching in all directions.................. *Cetraria* (pp. 190–4)
72a Underside whitish. Upper side greenish-grey, with sorediate margins
Evernia prunastri (p. 190)
72b Underside black on older branches. Upper side grey, with isidia
Pseudevernia furfuracea (p. 190)
73a Underside tomentose-pubescent, often also with veins **74**
73b Underside not hairy, either with rhizinae or glabrous **79**
74a Underside with holes or spots...   **75**
74b Underside without holes or spots **76**
75a Underside with cyphellae............................... *Sticta* (pp. 242, 244)
75b Underside with pseudocyphellae............... *Pseudocyphellaria* (p. 244)
76a Apothecia immersed in the surface. On soil amongst rock
Solorina (p. 236)
76b Apothecia sessile or stalked...   **77**
77a Apothecia (if present) on the undersides of erect lobe-ends
Nephroma (pp. 234, 236)
77b Apothecia at the lobe-edges or on the upper surface **78**
78a Apothecia formed along the edges of the lobe-ends, sometimes stalked.
Usually with veins on the underside. Chiefly on soil
Peltigera (pp. 238, 240)
78b Apothecia formed on the surface of the thallus. Without true veins on the
underside. Chiefly on bark and rock .... *Lobaria* (pp. 240, 242)
79a Thallus of large to medium lobes with upturned margins **80**
79b Thallus ± appressed **83**

52

100a Thallus of swollen radial branches, glabrous. Rare   *Dactylina* (p. 190)

100b Thallus of podetia, not swollen, often richly branched. Common
Cladonia (pp. 210–20)

101a Thallus strap-shaped.. **102**

101b Thallus filamentous, pendant to erect **104**

102a On soil. Thallus light yellow to dark brown, erect, glossy
Cetraria (pp. 190–4)

102b On bark or rock. Thallus greyish **103**

103a Thallus greenish-grey .... *Ramalina* (pp. 230, 232)

103b Thallus grey-brown to violet .... *Roccella* (p. 258)

104a Colour greenish-grey to greenish-yellow **105**

104b Colour olivaceous to brown or black **107**

105a Thallus with a tough, whitish, central strand (observed by pulling a branch
of the thallus apart). Fibrillae often present......   *Usnea* (pp. 186, 188)

105b Thallus without an axial strand **106**

106a Cortex continuous................................. *Alectoria* (pp. 184, 186)

106b Cortex segmented .... *Evernia divaricata* (p. 190)

107a Colour brown to olivaceous .... *Bryoria* (p. 186)

107b Colour dark brown to black **108**

108a Thallus sparsely branched, with apical black apothecia. On mountain rock
Cornicularia normoerica (p. 184)

108b Thallus richly branched. Often sterile **109**

109a Colour blackish, glossy. On mountain rock ......   *Pseudephebe* (p. 200)

109b Colour dark brown. On soil **110**

110a Cortex cartilaginous (hard and glossy). Colour uniform. Widespread
Coelocaulon (p. 184)

110b Cortex matt, not cartilaginous, dark above but usually light brown on
lower parts of the thallus. Arctic-alpine   ... *Alectoria nigricans* (p. 184)

Glossary

acid   referring to rocks or soils poor in mineral nutrients (pH less than 5.0) e.g. bogs and coniferous forests; sandstone and granite.

acrocarpous   archegonia and capsules borne terminally on main stems and branches (see pleurocarpous).

acumen   upper, tapering portion of a moss leaf.

acuminate   tapering distally.

acute   referring mainly to leaf tips which end in a more or less narrow, sharp point.

adnate   attached along the whole length.

alar   tissue at the leaf base at either side of the insertion, often differing in texture and colour from the upper lamina.

amphigastrium   reduced or modified leaf on the underside of the stem of a foliose liverwort.

antheridiophore   specialised outgrowth of the thallus of a liverwort that supports the male organs (antheridia).

antheridium   male reproductive organ: a small spherical or ovoid body containing the male gametes (antherozoids).

antical   pertaining to the upper surface of dorsiventral shoots.

apiculus   short, abrupt point or projection on an otherwise blunt or rounded leaf tip or lid of a moss capsule; also called a mucro, e.g. apiculate or mucronate leaves of *Pseudoscleropodium*.

aplanospore   vegetative cell formed with a wall within the mother cell and released without flagellae.

apophysis   lower, sterile portion of a moss capsule, mainly photosynthetic in function; enlarged and conspicuous in *Splachnum*.

apothecium   fruiting body with open hymenium, usually disc or cup-shaped (VI A, VIII B).

archegonium   female reproductive organ: a small, long-necked, flask-shaped structure containing the egg-cell.

areola   angular or rounded thallus division. An element of a network; e.g. the hexagonal pattern on the upper surface of a *Marchantia* thallus is composed of areolae (*Note* 'areolation' is sometimes used also to denote the cell pattern in leaves of bryophytes).

ascus   cell in which spores are formed.

autoecious   see monoecious.

axil   angle between a shoot axis or stem and the upperside of the attached leaf base.

basic   describing rocks and soil rich in mineral nutrients. Usually including calcium carbonate (pH more than 5.5), e.g. soils developed over chalk or limestone.

beard-lichen   pendant, richly branched, filamentous fruticose lichen.

calyptra   covering of the young sporophyte, developed from the archegonium, evanaescent in liverworts but in most mosses persisting in various forms as a cap on the unripe capsule.

capitiform   head-shaped.

carotenoid   orange, red or yellow colour pigments (unsaturated hydrocarbons) soluble in fats.

cartilaginous   like cartilage (i.e. tough and gristly).

cephalodium   tissue containing blue-green algae in the thallus of a green-algal lichen (VIII L).

chromosome   thread-like bodies, carriers of genetic information, contained in cell-nuclei undergoing mitosis and meiosis.

cilia   fine, hair-like processes; also refers to the fine threads between the inner peristome teeth of some moss capsules.

ciliate   margins fringed with hair-like teeth.

claviform   club-shaped.

complanate   shoots dorsiventrally flattened so that the leaves lie more or less in a single plane (e.g. *Neckera*).

conduplicate   bilobed leaves of foliose hepatics wherein one lobe is folded over, and lies against the other lobe. (e.g. *Scapania, Radula*).

conidium   asexual spore cut off at apex of specialised hypha.

coniocarp   lichen with a mazaedium fruiting body.

connivent   converging

convolute   leaves rolled together to form a tube, e.g. the leaves at the shoot tips of *Calliergon cuspidatum*; very frequent arrangement of perichaetial leaves.

coprophilous   growing on the dung of animals, e.g. *Splachnum*.

coralloid   resembling coral.

cortex   outer protective layer.

corticolous   growing on the bark of trees and shrubs.

crenulate   margins beset with very small, rather blunt teeth or notches.

crustaceous   crusty.

cygneous   curved like a swan's neck, usually applied to the seta of some mosses (e.g. *Grimmia pulvinata*).

cyphella   sharply delimited breathing pore on the underside of a thallus (VI B, VIII E).

decurrent   of leaves in which the lateral, basal portions continue for some distance on a stem, below the insertion.

deltate   delta shaped.

dentate   denticulate leaf margins beset with sharp, often very diminutive teeth.

dioecious   plants unisexual, hence antheridia and archegonia borne on separate plants.

diploid   pertaining to a cell containing a paired set of chromosomes as a result of fertilisation (e.g. cells of the actual fern plant).

dorsiventral   possessing both an upper side and a lower side.

ectohydric   mosses which absorb water over the whole plant, including the leaves, in contrast to *endohydric* mosses which absorb water through the rhizoidal system at the base of shoots. *Mixohydric* refers to plants which utilize both systems.

elater   long, narrow cell, with an internal spiral thickening, which is mixed with the spores in the capsules of liverworts, sometimes attached at one end to the capsule wall. The hygroscopic movements assist in spore dispersal.

endohydric   see ectohydric

entire   leaf margins which lack teeth, lobes or cilia, therefore having an unbroken outline.

epiphyte   growing on a living tree or other plant without absorbing nutrients directly from it.

excurrent   midrib of leaf extending beyond the end of the flat lamina, sometimes forming a long, terminal awn or hair-point.

falcate   leaves curved to resemble the blade of a sickle (see also *hamate* and *secund*), e.g. in *Dicranum scoparium*.

farinose   with a fine flour-like powdery covering.

fibrilla   a fibrous filament.

flagellum, flagellar   whip, whip-like: locomotory hair-like microscopical organelle (cilia are similar but always shorter); refers to many different structures in bryology,

56

including the 'tails' on the antherozoids. In the hepaticae, describes elongated shoots which have only vestigial leaves, such as those arising from the underside of the shoots of *Bazzania*.

fruticose   shrubby, in lichens those with a radial structure.

gametophyte   phase in a plant's life cycle that bears the sex organs (gametes), i.e. the leafy or thallose generation of a moss or liverwort (see also *sporophyte*).

gelatinous   resembling jelly, in lichens those with blue-green algae, which swell and become jelliform when damp.

gemmae   small, deciduous, one- to few-celled bodies that form a means of non-sexual reproduction (e.g. *Marchantia*, *Tetraphis*, *Lophozia*).

gemmiferous   producing gemmae, specialized bodies of non-sexual reproduction.

glabrous   hairless

granular   with fine, non-powdery particles.

gyrose   marked with wavy lines; spirally or contortedly ridged.

hair-point   leaf tips extended into a colourless hair, usually formed by a colourless extension of the midrib.

hamate   hooked, as in the strongly curved leaves of *Cratoneuron commutatum* or *Drepanocladus uncinatus*.

haploid   organisms whose cells each contain only a single set of chromosomes, e.g. spores and gametophytes of mosses (see *diploid*).

haustorium   organ connecting a parasite to its host.

heterocyst   a usually transparent but thick-walled cell found in certain algae.

heteromorphic   pertaining to plants or plant organs of different shape and structure.

heterophasic   pertaining to different phases of a cycle.

highland Britain   west and north of a line from the rivers Exe (Devon) to the Tees (Cleveland).

hyaline   cells or tissues which appear white or colourless due to loss of pigments or cell contents, e.g. the tissues forming the sheathing bases of some moss leaves.

hymenial disc   spore-bearing disc.

hymenium   spore-bearing layer of a fruiting body.

hypha   filament of a fungus.

imbricate   leaves largely overlapping one another and completely hiding the stems (opposite condition to *distant* where there is an appreciable gap between the leaves).

immersed   embedded; capsules of mosses borne on very short stalks and therefore completely or partially enveloped by leaves.

incubous   arrangement of leaves in leafy liverworts in which the older, lower leaves overlay the younger, upper leaves when shoots are viewed from above (see *succubous*).

indusium   a usually very thin protective cover of a sorus.

inflorescence   term borrowed from flowering plant terminology, used to denote the sex organs and associated structures (e.g. perichaetia, *q.v.*) in bryophytes.

innate   inborn

insertion   line of attachment of a leaf to a stem or branch.

involucre   outgrowths from the thallus of liverworts, associated with the sex organs *or* the enlarged leaves (bracts) surrounding the perianth of leafy liverworts.

isidium   outgrowth of thalline structure on a lichen, which is able to become broken off (VIII M).

labriform   lip-shaped (VI F, VIII O).

laciniate   cut into narrow lobes.

lamella   thin sheets or plates of green tissue growing at right angles from the surface of leaves or midribs, best known in the genus *Polytrichum* and its relatives.

lamina   flat, photosynthesizing part of a leaf, as distinct from the midrib.

lanceolate   shaped like the head of a lance, a common leaf shape in mosses.

lignicolous   living on wood (see *corticolous*).

ligulate   strap-shaped, describing leaves which are narrow, parallel-sided and, usually, blunt-tipped.

limb   spreading, upper part of a leaf, as distinct from a more or less erect, sheathing base, e.g. *Polytrichum* leaves.

lingulate   tongue-shaped: leaves which are broadest above the middle and have more or less rounded apices.

lirella   elongate apothecium (VI C)

lirelliform   in the shape of a lirella.

lowland Britain   east and south of a line from the rivers Exe (Devon) to the Tees (Cleveland).

macrolichen   lichen with a large thallus (i.e. foliose and fruticose species).

maculiform   spot-shaped (VI G).

maniciform   cuff-shaped.

marginal   on the edge.

mazaedium   fruiting body which disintegrates to form a powdery mass.

medulla   central portion, in lichens an inner layer of lax hyphae.

meristems   tissue in which active cell divisions are occurring, resulting in growth, as found in shoot tips and buds.

microlichen   lichen with a small thallus (i.e. crustaceous species).

mitosis   division of a chromosome into two identical pairs preceding cell division.

monoecious   plants bisexual, including *synoecious*, where archegonia and antheridia occur together, *paroecious*, where they occur separately on the same shoot, and *autoecious*, where they are borne on separate branches.

mucro   a minute, abrupt projection at a leaf tip or lid of a capsule.

muriform   multicellular with both transverse and longitudinal walls.

mycobiont   fungal partner in a lichen.

nitrophilous   preferring habitats rich in nitrogen or nitrates.

obdeltate   of inverted delta shape.

obovate   see *ovate*

ornithocoprophilous   favouring locations subject to bird excrement.

ostiole   small opening.

ovate   leaves etc. with an egg-shaped outline, broader below the middle; *obovate*, similar but broader above the middle.

papilla   very small (usually microscopic) protuberance, especially on the surface of a cell or spore (e.g. seta of *Brachythecium rutabulum*).

paraphyllium   very small, irregular, greenish 'leaflet' borne among the true leaves, e.g. on the stem of *Thuidium*.

paraphysis   minute, hair-like, sterile filament associated with the sex organs.

paroecious   see *monoecious*

peltate   shield-shaped, attached at the middle of the underside.

perianth   more or less tubular structure that encloses the female organs and young sporophyte in liverworts.

perichaetium   rosette of leaves surrounding the archegonia, often differing in form and size from ordinary leaves.

perigonium   leaves protecting the antheridia.

peristome   teeth or equivalent structures surrounding the mouth of a moss capsule, exposed after the lid has fallen.

perithecium   immersed fruiting body with an apical pore (VIII A).

pinnate   divided into two opposite rows of leaflets or branches along an axis (feather-like arrangement); *bipinnate* and *tri-* or *pluripinnate* refer to plants when the leaflets or branches are themselves again divided.

phycobiont   algal partner in a lichen.

phyllocladium   granular to squamulose outgrowth containing algae, occurring chiefly on the pseudopodetia of *Stereocaulon*.

pinnatifid   similar to *pinnatisect* but cut only some way towards rib.

pinnatisect   deeply pinnate but not cut to the midrib and not forming separate leaflets.

placoid   crustaceous and orbicular, with lobes at the margin; plate-like.

pleurocarpous   mosses in which the sex organs and fruit are borne on short, specialized branches, therefore appearing to arise laterally (see *acrocarpus*).

plicate   with narrow, longitudinal pleats, sometimes termed *striate*.

plumose   a version of pinnate branching in which the density of branching produces a plume- or feather-like effect.

podetium   lichenised stalk of a fruticose apothecium.

polarilocular   spore type of two lumina connected by a canal.

postical   pertaining to the lower side of dorsiventral shoots.

propagule   fragment of plant capable of effecting propagation.

prothallus   in ferns the gametophyte bearing antheridia and archegonia; in lichens the algae-free reticulum of fungal hyphae at the margin of the thallus.

protonema   preliminary stage of the gametophyte after germination of the spore: persistent systems of branched filaments in most mosses but short-lived and very inconspicuous in liverworts.

pruina   hoary surface of precipitated crystals or remnants of dead cells.

pseudocyphella   irregular simple breathing pore (VIII D).

pseudopodetium   thalline stalk bearing apothecia, soredia or phyllocladia.

pseudothecium   fruiting body resembling a perithecium, but with bitunicate asci.

pubescent   downy with short, soft hairs.

pycnidium   pear-shaped cavity, in which asexual spores (conidia) are formed (VIII C).

rachis (rhachis)   central rib of a fern frond.

recurved   refers either to leaves which are bent backwards, as in *Tortula ruralis*, or to the margins of leaves which are narrowly rolled back, as in most *Barbula* species.

reniform   kidney-shaped

retuse   with rounded shallowly notched end.

revolute   rolled back.

rhizina   bundle of hyphae projecting from the underside of a thallus, chiefly used for attachment (VII B, VIII G–K).

rhizoids   fine, thread-like appendages that attach mosses and liverworts to soil, rocks etc, and act in a manner analogous to the roots of higher plants.

rimiform   fissure-shaped.

rugose   leaves or other surfaces which are uneven, i.e. with irregular humps or undulations as distinct from regularly transversely undulate (*q.v.*), e.g. *Rhytidium rugosum* leaves.

saxicolous   growing on rocks.

secund   leaves all turned more or less in one direction, as in most species of *Dicranum*.

septate   multicellular with transverse walls.

serrate   sharply toothed (see *dentate*).

sessile   lacking stalks, e.g. the capsule of *Phascum*.

seta   stalk that supports the capsule of a moss or liverwort (in other contexts means bristle, e.g. the setae of earthworms). *Setose*, covered with bristles or stiff hairs.

shingled   overlapping (liverwort leaves), like roofing tiles.

siliceous   rocks composed mainly of silica, therefore poor in nutrients and giving rise to acid soils (e.g. granite and sandstone).

simple   of one cell or element.

sinuose   wavy, as opposed to straight or toothed; also refers to setae which are variously curved.

sinus   hollow between the lobes of a (liverwort) leaf.

soralia   aggregation of soredia (VIII N).

soredia   entwined algal cells and hyphae produced by lichens for vegetative reproduction (VIII P).

sorus   group of sporangia (plural sori).

spore   dust-like bodies produced in the capsules of mosses and liverworts, or by the sori of ferns, or the perithecia and apothecia of lichens, which are the main means of long-range dispersal of the species. They are *haploid* (*q.v.*) and produced by the *diploid* (*q.v.*) or sporophyte generation after so-called reduction-division (meiosis). Spores germinate to produce the haploid, gametophyte generation.

sporophyte   diploid phase in the life cycle of a plant, which produces sporangia and spores (see also *gametophyte, spore*).

squamule   scale or small thalline lobe.

squamulose   of scales or small lobes.

squarrose   rough with scales, hairs, etc., projecting at right angles.

subsessile   with very short stalks or setae.

succubous   leafy liverworts in which the upper, younger leaves overlay the lower, older leaves ehn shoots are viewed from above (see *incubous*).

terete   cylindrical, not ridged, grooved or angled.

terricolous   living on the ground.

thallus   plants lacking leaves, although sometimes broken up into irregular, leaf-like appendages. All lichens and some liverworts (e.g. *Marchantia* and *Pellia*) are thallose, while nearly all mosses, and the majority of liverworts are foliose.

tomentose   coated with a more or less dense mat of rhizoids or hairs.

tomentum   covering of thick and even short hairs.

umbellate   like an umbel, i.e. with stalks from the same point.

umbilicus   organ of central attachment of some foliose lichens.

umbonate   bearing a small boss or elevation in the centre.

undulate   having shallow, transverse waves or humps, as in the leaves of *Neckera crispa* and *Plagiothecium undulatum*.

urn   portion of a moss capsule containing the spores.

vaginule   ring or sheath of tissue enveloping the base of the seta of a moss sporophyte.

vascular system   pertaining to conducting tissue for water (*xylem*) and nutrition (*phloem*).

verrucose   warty.

vesicle   small globule.

vitta   distinct band of cells in a leaf which superficially resembles a midrib (e.g. *Diplophyllum albicans*).

wintergreen   fern fronds remaining green during winter.

Further reading

Ferns

CLAPHAM, A.R., TUTIN, T.G. and WARBURG, E.F., *Flora of the British Isles*, Cambridge, 1962, 2nd edition.
Excursion Flora of the British Isles, Cambridge, 1981, 3rd edition.
HYDE, H.A., WADE, A.E. and HARRISON, S.G., *Welsh Ferns*, Cardiff (The National Museum of Wales), 1978, 6th edition.
JERMEY, A.C. (editor), *Atlas of Ferns of the British Isles*, London, 1978.
TUTIN, T.G. et al. *Flora Europaea*, Vol I, Cambridge, 1964.

Lichens

DAHL, E. & KROG, H., *Macrolichens of Denmark, Finland, Norway and Sweden.* Universitetsforlaget, Oslo, 1973. Chemistry and keys.
DOBSON, F. (S.), *Lichens. An illustrated Guide*, Richmond, Surrey, 1979. Mostly black and white photographs; useful for beginners and students.
DUNCAN, U.K., *Introduction to British Lichens*, Arbroath, 1970. Standard work; keys and descriptions.
HALE, M.E., *The Biology of Lichens*, London, 2nd edition 1974.
HAWKSWORTH, D.L., JAMES, P.W. and COPPINS, B.J., Checklist of British lichen-forming, lichenicolous and allied fungi. *Lichenologist* **12**: 1–115, 1980. Interleaved reprints available from British Lichen Society, c/o Castle Museum, Norwich NR1 3JU.
HAWKSWORTH, D.L. and ROSE, F., *Lichens as Pollution Monitors* (*Stud. Biol.* 66), London, 1976.
HAWKSWORTH, D.L. & SEAWARD, M.R.D., *Lichenology in the British Isles 1568–1975. An Historical and Bibliographical Survey.* Richmond Publishing, Richmond, Surrey, 1977. Bibliography.
SEAWARD, M.R.D. (Editor), *Lichen Ecology.* Academic Press, London, 1977.
SEAWARD, M.R.D. & HITCH, C.J.B. (Editors) 1983, *Atlas of the Lichens of the British Isles. Volume 1*, Institute of Terrestrial Ecology, Cambridge, 1983.

Mosses and liverworts

MACVICAR, S.M., *The student's handbook of British hepatics*, Eastbourne, 1961 reprint. Out of date but the only available and still useful handbook to British liverworts.
SMITH, A.J.E., *The Moss Flora of Britain and Ireland*, Cambridge, 1978. Complete moss flora embodying recent ideas and views on the taxonomy of mosses.
WATSON, E.V., *British Mosses and Liverworts*, Cambridge, 1982, 4th edition Introductory work with full descriptions and figures of over 200 species and keys for the identification of all except the very rare species.
The Structure and Life of Bryophytes, London, 1971, 3rd edition. Comprehensive guide to morphology, biology and life history, with abundant references to aid the serious student.

Societies

BOTANICAL SOCIETY OF THE BRITISH ISLES, c/o Department of Botany, British Museum (Natural History), Cromwell Road, London SW7 5BD. The leading society in Britain devoted to the study of flowering plants; ferns are also included within its sphere of interest.

BRITISH BRYOLOGICAL SOCIETY, c/o Mr G.G. Geyman, 48, Gascoigne Gardens, Woodford Green, Essex 1GB 9NU. An international society for amateurs and scientists.

BRITISH LICHEN SOCIETY, c/o Department of Botany, British Museum (Natural History), Cromwell Road, London SW7 5BD. An international society which seeks to stimulate and advance interest in all aspects of lichenology. Anyone interested in lichens may become a member.

BRITISH PTERIDOLOGICAL SOCIETY, c/o Department of Botany, British Museum (Natural History), Cromwell Road, London SW7 5BD. For the study of ferns.

The Plants

Ferns

Mosses and Liverworts

Lichens

1. *Pteridium aquilium* (L.) Kuhn **Bracken** Bracken (see also p. 82), which forms the largest stands of all the European ferns, becomes dominant in certain habitats and often covers several hectares of ground. It occurs on light acid soils in neglected meadows, along edges and in clearings of forests, in parkland etc. and in open woodland it can grow up to 4 m in height. This plant requires plenty of light, moist conditions and relatively mild winters, and is therefore found only in areas with a predominantly atlantic climate. In many places it has become a weed difficult to eradicate.

2. *Blechnum spicant* (L.) Roth **Hard-fern** [×0.3] The leathery Hard-fern (see also p. 82), like many similar ferns, is wintergreen. This photograph was taken in spring and clearly shows the dark green leaves of the past year contrasting with the fresh green ones of the new season. In this species, in common with other ferns, the fertile leaves are different from the sterile ones. The illustration shows a rosette of spreading sterile leaves, and in the centre an erect young fertile leaf the apex of which is still inrolled.

3. *Polypodium vulgare* L. **Common Polypody** [× 13] Fern spores are contained in sporangia which form sori; in the majority of ferns they are found on the underside of the leaves. The dark ring of the anulus (see **13**) can clearly be seen on each of the globular sporangia. In contrast to many ferns the sori of this species are not protected by an indusium (compare **70**, **87** and **94**).

4. *Osmunda regalis* L. **Royal Fern** [×3] The illustration depicts the prothallia (gametophytes, see p. 9–10) as well as young shoots (sporophytes) of this species. The tiny prothallia are almost heart-shaped; the plant's sexual organs are borne on their lower surface. After fertilization the light green leaf appears; at this stage it is still undivided and does not display any similarity to the adult plant (**34**, **35**).

5. *Dryopteris filix-mas* (L.) Schott **Male Fern** [×0.2] As in many ferns, the young leaves of this species are inrolled (looking like bishop's crosiers) because at this stage the lower surface grows faster than the upper. Only when an equilibrium of growth is established do the leaves unfold (**43**). The leaves are arranged in dense rosettes (in many other species they may grow singly) on an underground rhizome. In this species almost all the leaf cells have already been developed in the previous autumn, which explains their rapid growth in spring.

1 △

2 △   ▽ 4

3 △   ▽ 5

Lycopodiaceae (6–16) A family of perennial herbs consisting of two genera with simple or dichotomously branched, trailing or rarely erect stems. Leaves small, undivided, arranged spirally or in whorls. Sporangia unilocular, compressed, opening by a slit, are either in the axils of normal leaves (**7**), greatly reduced leaves (sporophylls) or in spike-like terminal cones (**9, 10, 12**). In the past most of the species were assigned to the genus *Lycopodium*. Superficially they can be confused with *Selaginella* (**13–16**) or with Bryophythes (**113**), but the latter never possess roots! All species are protected.

6, 7. *Huperzia selago* (L.) Bernh. (*Lycopodium selago* L.) **Fir Clubmoss** [×0.7 and × 7] (in the background *Rhododendron ferrugineum* L. Alpenrose). Stem up to 25 cm tall, erect from a decumbent base, rooting below only. Leaves up to 8 mm long, suberect or spreading, not appressed to the stem, often with axillary gemmae. Sporophylls not differing from leaves and not in cones. Sporangia conspicuous, yellow (**7**). Found throughout most of Europe and the British Isles, including Ireland, mainly in mountain areas, heath, mountain grassland, and amongst rocks. Rare in some regions.

8. *Lycopodiella inundata* (L.) Hol. (*Lycopodium inundatum* L.) **Marsh Clubmoss** [× 1.5] (with Round-leaved Sundew *Drosera rotundifolia* L.) Stems 5–15 (20) cm long, creeping, little-branched, with only the tips ascending. Leaves arranged spirally, 3.5–6 mm long, suberect. Sporangia in not clearly defined terminal, ± sessile, 10–30 mm long cones. Found throughout most of Europe and the British Isles on moors, dunes and wet heathland. Localized and usually very rare (very rare in Wales, S Scotland and NE England and rare in Ireland).

9. *Lycopodium   clavatum* L. **Common   Clubmoss,   Stag's-horn   Clubmoss** [×0.7] Creeping, much-branched stems up to 100 cm long, with only the fertile branches ascending. Leaves arranged spirally, 2.5–5 mm long, tapering to a long, flexible, whitish hair-like point. Sporangia in paired cones (sometimes 3) set on a long stalk with appressed scale-like leaves. Found throughout Europe and the British Isles, including Ireland, locally common on mountain grassland, heaths, and moors and in conifer woods.

10. *Lycopodium annotinum* L. **Interrupted Clubmoss** [×0.5] Similar to the above but cones solitary and not stalked. Leaves without hair-like points. Found in conifer woods, and on moors, heaths, from N Europe to the Pyrenees; in Britain mainly on mountains in Scotland and (very rare) N England.

11. *Diphasiastrum tristachyum* (Pursh) Rothm. (*Lycopodium tristachyum* Pursh) [× 1.5] Stems underground. Erect shoots branched several times, forming tufts; the finer branches somewhat flattened, 1–1.5 (2) mm thick. Lateral leaves as wide as the dorsal ones; ventral leaves on the sterile branches $\frac{1}{3}-\frac{1}{4}$ as wide as the branches. Cones distinctly stalked. Found in Central Europe in dry conifer woods and on heaths. Local and very rare; not known in Britain. The closely related European species *Diphasiastrum complanatum* (L.) Rothm. occurs in similar habitats; its finer branches are distinctly flattened and 2–3 mm wide. The lateral leaves are wider than the dorsal ones.

12. *Diphasiastrum alpinum* (L.) Holub. (*Lycopodium alpinum* L.) **Alpine Clubmoss** [× 1] Stems much-branched, usually above ground, 10–30 (50) cm tall; finer branches cylindrical or only slightly flattened. Leaves usually blue-green; dorsal leaves of sterile branches lanceolate, stalked. Sporangia in sessile cones; sporophylls ovate-lanceolate, acute or drawn out to a point. In moors, heaths and mountain grassland. N and Central Europe, extending to the Pyrenees; in Britain in N and NW mountain areas. *Diphasiastrum × issleri* (Rouy) Holub (*D. alpinum × complanatum* (L.) Holub) has the finer branchlets distinctly flattened, and has purely green leaves; dorsal leaves linear,

6 △   ▽ 7   8 ▽

9 △   ▽ 10   ▽ 11

sessile; sporophylls ovate and upruptedly pointed. In similar habitats. Central Europe, Central and E France; in Britain confined to the Scottish Highlands (very rare).

Selaginella (13–16) Herbs with erect or creeping stems. Leaves numerous, ligulate, simple, small, one-veined, either all similar and arranged spirally or of two kinds and arranged in four ranks. Sporangia singly near the base of sporophylls in terminal cones.

13, 14, 15.   *Selaginella helvetica* (L.) Spring. [× 5.5, × 17, × 17] Herb with creeping stems up to 20 cm long, producing leafless rooting branches; fertile branches ascending (**13** left). Leaves of two kinds, four-ranked: those of the upper side smaller, appressed and erect; those of the lower ranks larger and spreading. Sporangia of two kinds, arranged in cones, with the microsporangia (containing very small spores) above (**15**) and the megasporangia (containing four large megaspores) (**14**-only three spores visible), see also p. 10. Found on moist loamy soils and on walls, mainly in alpine regions of Europe; not known in the British Isles.

16.   *Selaginella selaginoides* (L.) PB ex Schrank et Mart. **Lesser Clubmoss** [× 1.5] Markedly different from the above species. Stems up to 16 cm long, decumbent and with long ascending fertile branches. Leaves all alike, spirally arranged, finely ciliate-serrate. Cones sessile, solitary. Sporophylls larger than leaves and more brightly coloured. Microsporangia (few) in the upper, megasporangia in the lower part of the cone. Found in damp open grassland, steep mountain grassland and damp shrubby heathland from N and Central Europe to the Pyrenees; in Britain from N Wales and N Lincolnshire northwards, and in Ireland.

Equisetum (17–30) A very distinctive and easily recognisable genus of perennial herbs with creeping rhizomes. Aerial stems (strictly speaking stem-branches) are alike or of two kinds: green sterile stems and usually brownish fertile stems; all stems simple or branched from below, grooved, noded. Branches, similar to the stems, appear in whorls. Leaves greatly reduced, arranged in toothed sheaths above the nodes and usually equal in number to the stem-grooves. Spores of one kind, numerous, contained in sporangia suspended from the lower surface of the sporangiophores, which are arranged in whorls in a usually terminal cone (**18**, **19**). The species of this genus are often difficult to distinguish on account of both greatly varying characters and hybrid-formation.

17, 18, 19.   *Equisetum arvense* L. **Common Horsetail** [×0.2, ×0.3, × 10] Stems of two kinds: fertile stems in spring, short-lived, reddish-brown or cinnamon-coloured, up to 25 cm tall (**18**); sterile stems green, up to 50 (80) cm tall, extraordinarily variable; branches usually simple (rarely branched again as in *E. sylvaticum*), lowest branch-internode longer than adjacent sheath of stem (shorter in *E. palustre*). Teeth without a broad whitish margin (as in *E. palustre*). Silica cells between the nodes wider than high. Found throughout Europe and Britain, in fields, roadsides, meadows and in similar localities with sufficient supply of water, often a serious weed. Widespread and common.

14 △   15 △

16 △   ▽ 18   17 △   ▽ 19

20. *Equisetum pratense* Ehrh. **Shady Horsetail** [×0.2] Sterile stems very similar to those in *E. arvense*. Silica cells between the nodes taller than wide. Fertile stems at first pale and simple, later branching and turning green. Found in damp woods and on stream banks, infrequent, mainly in N Europe and alpine regions; in the British Isles locally in Scotland and N England, also in N Ireland.

21, 22. *Equisetum telmateia* Ehrh. **Great Horsetail** [×0.1, ×0.7] Short-lived fertile stems appearing in spring (**22** centre). Sterile stems (**22**, still young and simple) up to 120 (200) cm tall, much- and profusely branched (**21**). Fertile and sterile stems recognizable by ivory colouration between nodes. Found along mountain streams, in shady damp grassland and parkland, and valley fens, in alkaline soils. Widely distributed in Europe up to S Scandinavia and west to Ireland; rather local in the British Isles and rare in Scotland.

23, 24. *Equisetum sylvaticum* L. **Wood Horsetail** [×0.3, ×0.5] Fertile and sterile stems appear simultaneously. Stems at first pale, simple and terminated by a fertile cone; green and branching after spore-dispersal (cones then drooping, **24**). Can be mistaken for much-branched *E. arvense*. Found in damp woods and shady places in moist grassland, on acid soil. Widely distributed all over Europe; common in northern parts of Britain and becoming more local towards the South; also found in Ireland.

25, 26. *Equisetum hyemale* L. **Dutch Rush** [×0.3 (**26**)] Stems up to 150 cm tall, erect, thick, rough to the touch, usually simple, overwintering. Cones terminal, 8–15 cm long, usually pointed (**26**). In the past the rough stems of this plant were used for scouring tin ware. In damp woods, along streams in shade, often forming large stands. Widely distributed, but not frequent in Europe; in the British Isles local in northern parts, otherwise rare; scattered in Ireland.

27. *Equisetum palustre* L. **Marsh Horsetail** [×0.2] Fertile stems with a terminal blunt cone 10–30 mm long. Sterile stems very similar to those of *E. arvense*, usually of candelabra-like habit and irregularly branched, with the lowermost branch-internodes shorter than the relevant stem-sheath. Leaf margins scarious and whitish. In damp places, marshland, fens, damp pastures (poisonous to cattle). Widely distributed throughout Europe; common and widespread in Britain and Ireland.

28, 29. *Equisetum fluviatile* L. **Water Horsetail** [×0.1, ×0.3] Stems up to 150 cm tall, thick (up to 12.5 mm), smooth to the touch, almost simple or regularly branched in the middle (**29**), grooved but without prominent ribbs, branches simple, ascending. Found in shallow water around lakes and ponds and along ditches, sometimes in marshland. Widely distributed and common all over Europe, Britain and Ireland.

30. *Equisetum variegatum* Schleich. ex Web. & Mohr **Variegated Horsetail** [×0.7] Stems at first prostrate, later ascending, rarely erect, forming tufts *c.* 30 cm tall, simple or sparsely branched, persisting and green in winter. Cones short, tapering to a point. Found on wet ground, in marshes, banks, dunes and on mountains in N and Central Europe, extending to the Pyrenees; in Britain local in northern and western areas, otherwise rare; scattered in Ireland.

Similar are: *Equisetum ramosissimum* Desf., which is up to 80 cm tall and also branched above, with a central hollow of stem more than ½ its diam.; rare in Lincolnshire, where introduced; it is widely distributed in S Europe; and *Equisetum × trachydon* A. Br. (*E. hyemale × variegatum*) Mackay's Horsetail, with totally black sheaths and persistent teeth, very local in Ireland and N Scotland.

20 △   21 △   ▽ 22

23 △   ▽ 26

24 △

25 △   ▽ 27

28 △

29 △

30 △ ▽ 31

▽ 32

31.   *Isoetes lacustris* L.   Quill-wort [× 0.7]   The genus Isoetes is represented in N and Central Europe by three species. This submerged aquatic plant has a short stout stem and numerous roots. Leaves up to 20 cm long, subulate, subterete, arranged in a dense rosette, hollow and chambered, stiff and brittle, above upruptly narrowed to a point. Sporangia (megasporangia and microsporangia) embedded in the expanded leaf-base. Usually found on rocks or in sand in nutrient-poor cold lakes, at depths from 2–10 m. Rare in Central Europe, more frequent in N and SW. Found in Britain in SW England, Wales, Cumbria, Scotland and in Ireland. For the Spiny-spored Quill-wort (*I. echinospora* Dur.), local in SW England, Wales, the Lake District and N Scotland, see key (p. 31). The south European species *I. Histrix* Bory is very rare and only recorded from the Lizard area in Cornwall, Guernsey and Alderney. It grows terrestrial in sandy and peaty places and remains dormant and leafless in summer, and can be recognized by its glossy black leaf-bases.

Ophioglossaceae (32–33) A family characterized by plants with an underground rhizome producing leaves which consist of a sterile blade and a fertile (spore-bearing) spike or panicle. The sporangia all are of one kind and carried in two ranks.

32.   *Botrychium lunaria* (L.) Swartz **Moonwort** [× 1.5]   Leaves 3–15 (30) cm long; sterile blade pinnate; fertile part a panicle. Widespread in Europe in dry grassland and on rock ledges, especially in mountain areas, but never frequent; found throughout the British Isles.

33.   *Ophioglossum vulgatum* L.   Adder's Tongue [× 1]   Sterile blade of leaf (see also preceding species) undivided, reticulately veined. Sporangia in a spike (very young in **33**), usually longer than the blade. Widespread all over Europe in damp meadows, fens and scrub; widespread but rare in the British Isles. *O. azoricum* Presl (*O. vulgatum* subsp. *ambiguum* (Coss. et Germ.) E.F. Warb.) is very local in coastal areas of Dorset, Wales, Orkney and also on the Scilly and Lundi Islands. See key p. 00. *Ophioglossum lusitanicum* Dwarf Adder's Tongue is confined in Britain to the Scilly Isles (also known from the Channel Islands). See Key, p. 36.

34, 35.   *Osmunda regalis* L. Royal Fern [× 10, ×0.1]   The only European species of the genus and of the family Osmundaceae. Leaves tufted, up to over 250 cm long, 2-pinnate, bright green; fertile pinnules growing at the apex or from the middle of the leaf (sometimes the whole leaf fertile), up to 3 cm long, densely covered by brown sporangia. Outer leaves of tuft always sterile. Sporangia dehiscing by a slit (p. 13 and fig. II E); indusium absent. In moist woods, alongside lakes and watercourses, on cliff-edges, in fens, bogs etc. In Europe mainly of atlantic distribution, otherwise rare; in Britain local but widespread.

33 △   34 △   ▽ 35

Hymenophyllaceae (36–38) Plants with wiry, creeping rhizomes. Leaves very thin, filmy, consisting of only one cell-layer, translucent; ultimate segments single-veined. Sori marginal; indusium tubular, cup-like or bi-valved. Sporangia all alike. Ferns adapted to habitats with a high degree of humidity.

36, 37. *Hymenophyllum tunbrigense* (L.) Sm. **Tunbridge Filmy Fern** [× 1, × 5.5] Plant of very delicate habit. Leaves flat, perennial, 2–10 (12) cm long, thin and translucent; pinnae irregularly and dichotomously divided. Sori marginal at the apex of segments. Indusium with circular toothed valves. Found on trees and rocks in humid, sheltered situations. Distribution is oceanic (very rare in Central Europe); in Britain mainly in the West and northwards to Skye; also in W Ireland.

38. *Hymenophyllum wilsonii* Hooker **Wilson's Filmy Fern** [× 2] Similar to preceding species, but leaves less divided and not flat (pinnae bent backwards). Indusium with ovate, entire-margined valves. Found in habitats similar to those of the above species. Confined to western Europe; extremely rare, but more common in Britain, although absent from SW it is also found in Ireland. *Trichomanes speciosum* Willd., the Killarney Fern, found on damp shaded rocks and in the spray-zone of water falls, is similar (for differences see key, p. 32). Confined to the extreme West of Europe (very are); in Britain and Ireland it is extremely rare and extinct in most places, found in N Wales; protected by law.

39. *Adiantum capillus-veneris* L. **Maidenhair Fern** [× 1] Plant growing from a scaly rhizome. Leaves all alike, arranged in a close group, up to 30 cm long, born on a black glossy petiole. Leaf-segments light green, fan-shaped. Sori near the reflexed leaf-margins. Mediterranean plant; found in western Europe and in Britain and W Ireland in damp crevices of cliffs and rocks close to the sea, also on garden walls in sheltered positions.

40. *Matteuccia struthiopteris* (L.) Todaro **Ostrich Fern** [×0.05] Sterile leaves up to 100 cm long, bi-pannatifid (similar to *Dryopteris filix-mas*), growing from an erect stock and forming a funnel. Fertile leaves much smaller, growing inside the funnel, at first green, later brown, reminiscent of ostrich feathers. The only European species of the genus. Found in damp acid soil along watercourses. Very rare in Central Europe and Scandinavia; in Britain cultivated in gardens and very rarely naturalized.

41. *Cryptogramma crispa* (L.) R. Br. ex Hooker **Parsley Fern** [×0.3] Plant growing from a stout scaly rhizome. Sterile leaves (the outer ones) up to 20 cm long, tri-pinnatisect, with three pinnae on either side, in outline triangular-ovate, reminiscent of Parsley. Fertile leaves with longer petioles, tri-quadri-pinnate; segments with strongly reflexed margins hiding the confluent (when mature) sori. The only European species of the genus. Found in screes, acid rocks, stone walls etc. in mountain areas of Europe and Britain, locally common; rare in Ireland.

36 △

37 △

38 △   ▽ 40

39 △   ▽ 41

42, 43, 44. *Pteridium aquilinum* (L.) Kuhn **Bracken** [×0.05, ×0.1, ×17] Plant with a long creeping rhizome. Leaves all alike, very large, sometimes over 3 m long, (bi-)tri-pinnate (see also **1**), deltate in outline, erect but above bent horizontally, dying down in winter; pinnae inrolled when young (**43**). Sori continuous along the margins of leaf-segments; inner indusium present. Widespread but more frequent in western Europe, usually forming dominant stands on light acid or peaty soil in woods, moorland, heaths and pastures; very common throughout Britain and Ireland.

45. *Blechnum spicant* (L.) Roth **Hard-fern** [×0.3] Plant growing with a short, almost erect rhizome. Sterile leaves wintergreen, arranged in dense rosettes (see also **2**), 10–50 cm long, spreading, pinnate, comb-like. Fertile leaves longer and growing in the centre, erect; pinnae very narrow, beneath completely covered by sporangia. On acid soil in woods, heaths, rocks, mountain grassland, moors etc. Widespread and frequent in milder oceanic areas of Europe or in mountain areas with regular snow cover; Britain rare in lowland areas; common in Ireland.

46, 47. *Woodsia ilvensis* (L.) R. Br. [×0.5, ×7] Small plant with a scaly rhizome. Leaves all alike, 5–15 cm long, pinnate; longest pinnae oblong to ovate-oblong, $1\frac{1}{2}$–2 × as long as broad, densely covered with red-brown 2–3 mm long scales. Sori circular, with a deeply laciniate indusium (**47**). Found on sunny silica rocks and in crevices. Rare on Central European mountains and in the Alps; very rare in N England, N Wales and Scotland. *Woodsia alpina* (Bolton) S.F. Gray, the Alpine Woodsia, is usually smaller. Largest pinnae triangular-ovate, 1–$1\frac{1}{2}$ as long as broad; scales shorter ($\pm$ 1 mm). In the Arctic and on high European mountains; in Britain in Scotland and N Wales. Both are protected plants in UK.

48, 49, 50. *Cystopteris fragilis* (L.) Bernh. **Brittle Bladder-fern** [×0.7, ×7, ×13] Delicate plant, creeping with a short rhizome in soil of rock-crevices. Leaves densely arranged, 5–30 (45) cm long, bi(rarely tri)-pinnate, lanceolate in outline, with the longest pinnae in the middle; petiole very fragile, dark brown. Sori in two rows on either side of the midrib, circular, at first covered by a pale, inflated indusium (**49**). Common throughout Europe on alkaline rocks and on stone walls in damp situations; found in Scotland, N England (rarer southwards or absent), Wales and N Ireland. *Cystopteris montana* (Lam.) Desv., the Mountain Bladder-fern, grows with a long rhizome. Leaves below tri-pinnate, with the lowest pinnae longest. Rare in the Alps and on mountains in Central Scotland. *Cystopteris dickiena* R. Sim has overlapping pinnae. Very rare in arctic Europe and only known in Britain in sea-caves in Kincardine (Scotland) and there protected by law.

42 △   ▽ 43   · ▽ 44

45 △   ▽ 46   ▽ 47

48 △   ▽ 49   ▽ 50

51, 52. *Phyllitis scolopendrium* (L.) Newman **Heart's-tongue Fern** [×0.3, ×7] Plant growing with a short, scale-clad rhizome. Leaves in dense tufts, 10–50 (60) cm long, oblong or narrowly oblong, entire or slightly lobed, cordate at the base, tapering to an obtuse apex, at first beset with scales later glabrous. Sori arranged in pairs along the veins, linear, stretching over more than one half of the leaf, partly covered by the lateral indusium (**52**), indusia of correlated sori opening face to face. Widespread in damp situations, on limestone walls, on rocks in woods and hedgebanks, but rare in Europe, common in the wetter parts of the British Isles but rare in drier regions and in N Scotland, widespread in Ireland.

Asplenium (**53–63**) All species of this genus grow with a short rhizome, which usually has firm scales, characterized by a network of dark cell-walls (visible only through a strong lens). Sori attached to a lateral vein, not paired; indusium present, shaped like the sorus, opening towards the centre of the pinna.

53, 54. *Asplenium viride* Hudson **Green Spleenwort** [× 0.2, × 0.5] Similar in habit to *A. trichomanes* (**58, 59**) but distinguished as follows: Petiole green (brown at the lower surface near the base). Rhachis green, not winged; pinnae circular to ovate-circular, paler green, more distinctly toothed, not deciduous. Sori closer to the midrib. Widespread in crevices of alkaline rocks and on walls, but often only local in Europe; in Britain local and more frequent in northern and western districts. Specimen displaying a partly brown petiole may represent *Aspleniun adulterinum* Milde (or possibly a hybrid: *A. viride × trichomanes*).

55, 56. *Asplenium adiantum-nigrum* L. **Black Spleenwort** [×0.7, ×2] Leaves in dense or loose rosette-like tufts, 8–35 (50) cm long, triangular in outline, dark green and glossy above, persistent, fairly robust; petiole as long as the leaf-blade, blackish, scaly at the very base; rhachis blackish on the underside, winged; pinnae up to 15 on each side, pinnate or lobed, decreasing in size upwards; segments with a narrow base, acutely serrate. Sori closer to the midrib than to the margin, about 2 mm long, narrowly oblong, often confluent when old and then covering most of the segment. Found on alkaline rocks in woods, on walls and on hedgebanks in shade. Very rare in Central Europe, more frequent in the atlantic regions; found throughout Britain and Ireland and in places common. *Asplenium onopteris* L. (*A. adiantum-nigrum* subsp. *onopteris* (L.) Luerss.) is similar. Leaves tri-pinnate; petiole usually longer than the leaf-blade; pinnae curved towards the apex. Very local in SW Ireland; also perhaps in SW England.

51 △

52 △

53 △   ▽ 55   54 △   ▽ 56

57. *Asplenium ruta-muraria* L. Wall-Rue [×0.7] Leaves in irregular tufts, 4–10 (15) cm long, persistent, dark green, not glossy, coriaceous, bi (tri)-pinnate, triangular-ovate to triangular-lanceolate in outline; petiole often longer than the leaf-blade, green from a blackish base; pinnae stalked; pinnules 3–5, rarely divided, with a cuneate base, obtuse at the apex, without a visible midrib. Sori confluent when mature. Widespread on walls (especially in mortar) and alkaline rocks and common in Europe and Britain. *Asplenium billotii* F. W. Schultz (*A. obovatum* auct. non Viv.) is characterized by having the basal pair of pinnae a little shorter than those nearer the middle of the lanceolate, bi-pinnate, tough leaf; pinnules with sharp-pointed teeth. Found on rocks, walls, hedgebanks etc. usually close to the sea. In western Europe, extending eastwards to Germany and Italy; in Britain in W England, W Scotland and Wales; very local; also very local in Ireland.

58, 59. *Asplenium trichomanes* L. Maidenhair Spleenwort [×0.5, ×7] Leaves in dense rosette-like tufts, 5–25 (40) cm long, linear to narrowly oblong in outline, pinnate, deep green, persistent; petiole short, blackish; rhachis blackish, glossy, narrowly winged; pinnae up to 40 on each side, broadly elliptic or oblong, or equal size over most of the leaf, slightly asymmetric, crenate or toothed, deciduous. Sori linear to oblong-linear, 1–2 mm long, usually situated on the upper branch of the veins in the middle between midrib and margins. Widespread in crevices and on walls all over Europe. In the British Isles this species is represented by two not always easily identifiable subspecies. Subsp. *quadrivalens*, Common Maidenhair Spleenwort (illustrated) is frequently found in mortar of old walls and on rock rich in lime and is common throughout Britain and Ireland. Subsp. *trichomanes* Delicate Maidenhair Spleenwort is more delicate in appearance with fronds of an arching habit and found locally in Wales, Lake District and Scotland, mainly on acid rocks.

60, 61. *Asplenium septentrionale* (L.) Hoffm. Forked Spleenwort [× 1, ×7] Leaves 4–15 cm long, irregularly dichotomously divided, dark dull green, persistent; petiole usually much longer than the leaf-blade; segments of unequal length, narrowly linear or linear-cuniform, tapering towards the base. Sori linear, covering almost the entire segment-surface (**61**); indusium entire, whitish. Widespread in rock-crevices and on walls, in dry situations all over Europe but rarely common; in Britain rare in SW England, the Lake District, Scotland and Wales; very rare and local in W Ireland.

62. *Asplenium × alternifolium* Wulfen (*A. septentrionale × trichomanes* subsp. *trichomanes*) **Alternate-leaved Spleenwort** [× 1.5] In habit and colour like the preceding species. Leaves simply pinnate or the lowermost pair of pinnae split into three pinnulas; pinnae oblanceolate-cuniform, sometimes lobed. Found on dry rocks and walls, often growing where parent-species occur together. Rare in Britain (SW England, Lake District, Scotland and Wales).

57 △

58 △

59 △

▽ 61

60 △

▽ 62

63. *Asplenium marinum* L. **Sea Spleenwort** [× 1] Leaves in tufts, 5–40 (100) cm long, persistent, intense green, coriaceous, simply pinnate, lanceolate in outline, glabrous; petiole up to ½ as long as the leaf-blade; Rhachis brown below, with green wing; pinnae elliptic or oblong from an asymmetric base, deciduous. Sori narrowly oblong; indusium brownish. Found in crevices of sea cliffs and on coastal rocks along the atlantic coast of Europe; in Britain along the south and west coast and on the east coast from Yorkshire northwards; also in Ireland.

64, 65. *Ceterach officinarum* DC. **Rusty-back Fern** [× 0.4, × 7] Leaves in dense tufts, persistent 3–12 (20) cm long, coriaceaous, simply pinnate, dull green above, densely covered by overlapping brown scales beneath; petiole short; pinnae ovate to oblong, up to 20 mm long, rounded at the apex, involute in very dry and hot conditions. Found in crevices of dry limestone rocks and on mortared walls in Central Germany, the Rhineland and Belgium; in Britain (mainly in S and W England and Wales) and in Ireland.

Dryopteris (66–77) The species of this large genus are characterized by the reniform shape of the indusium (**70**). They usually grow from a short, erect or ascending (rarely creeping) rhizome. The leaves are usually arranged to form a crown. The frequent occurrence of hybrids makes identification sometimes difficult.

66, 67. *Dryopteris cristata* (L.) A. Gray **Crested Buckler-fern** [×0.1, ×0.2] Leaves 30–70 (100) cm long, pinnate with deeply pinnatifid pinnae: sterile leaves on the outside of the crown, more or less expanded; fertile leaves on the inside, larger and usually erect and with the pinnae turned horizontal (**67**), lanceolate or oblanceolate, with 10–20 pinnae on either side; all leaves dying down in the autumn; petiole up to half as long as the blade, deeply grooved scaly; pinnae and pinnules serrate, often as the inwardly curved bristly teeth. Found in marshes, wet heaths and riverine woods, in Europe from Norway to France; in Britain very rare and local in S England, and E Anglia.

68. *Dryopteris aemula* (Aiton) Kuntze **Hay-scented Buckler-fern** [×0.03] Leaves up to 60 cm long, long persistent, tri-quadri-pinnate, bright green, triangular-ovate or triangular-lanceolate in outline, scaly on both rhachis and midribs below, with very small secreting glands (coumarin), fragrant; petiole dark brown-purple, with lanceolate reddish-brown scales; pinnae about 15–20 on either side, the lowest pair the longest and with the first pinnule on the lower side significantly longer than the one on the upper side. Indusium irregularly fringed with glands as well as dentate. Found in shady woods, shaded rocks and hedgebanks in western Europe only; in Britain rare, mainly in western counties (also in Sussex and Kent); also in Ireland.

69, 70. *Dryopteris filix-mas* (L.) Schott **Male Fern** [×0.07, × 12] Leaves in one or in a few crowns, 50–120 (150) cm long, dark green, soft-textured, without glands, usually dying in winter; simply pinnate with the pinnae deeply pinnatified; pinnae-lobes or pinnules flat and regularly denate all round, with 3–6 sori along either side of the midrib; rhachis and midribs sparsely scaly or glabrous. Indusium without glands, greyish-blue when young (**70**). In woods, screes, hedgerows etc. Widespread and common throughout Europe, Britain and Ireland. *Dryopteris oreades* Fomin, the Dwarf Male Fern has an atlantic-montane distribution and occurs in W Europe and Britain on screes, walls and in rock-crevices in western mountain areas (incl. Wales) and very local in Ireland. See Key (p. 34); it also differs from *D. filix-mas* in its grey-green leaf-colour and the obtuse apex of the pinnule-teeth.

63 △

64 △

65 △   ▽ 67   66 △   ▽ 68

69 △   ▽ 70   ▽ 71

72 △   ▽ 73   ▽ 74

71, 72. *Dryopteris affinis* (Lowe) Fraser-Jenkins (*Dryopteris pseudomas* (Wollaston) Holub et Pouzar; *D. borreri* Newman) **Scaly Male Fern** [× 1, × 0.1] Very similar to *D. filix-mas* but petiole and rhachis with dense orange-brown scales. Leaves wintergreen, firm, yellowish green; pinnae with a blackish blot close to the rhachis; pinnules subtruncate and without teeth at sides. Frequent in western Europe in woods, screes and hedgerows, mostly on acid soil; fairly common in Britain; frequent and common in Ireland.

73, 74. *Dryopteris submontana* (Fraser-Jenkins & Jermy) Fraser-Jenkins. (*Dryopteris villarii* (Bellardi) Woynar ex Schinz et Thell. **Limestone Buckler-fern** [× 0.3, × 4] Leaves in tufts, 20–45 (60) cm long, bi-pinnate (lowermost pair of pinnules more or less equal), dull green, on both surfaces with stalked yellowish-white glands; pinnules somewhat concave; lobes with acute teeth. Found on calcareous rocks and in clefts in limestone pavements of European mountains (mostly Alps). Very rare and local in N England and N Wales.

75, 76, 78. *Dryopteris dilatata* (Hoffm.) A. Gray **Broad Buckler-fern** [× 0.1, × 7] Leaves densely tufted (30) 40–150 cm long, ovate-triangular in outline, tri-quadri-pinnate, not particularly stiff but firm, somewhat spreading, wintergreen, below often with scattered glands; pinnule-lobes with pointed or bristle-like teeth; petiole-scales dark brown in the centre and pale brown at the margins. Indusium fringed with stalked glands. Widespread and common in Europe and the British Isles in damp woods, hedgerows, moorland, rock-crevices, usually in nutrient-rich soils; also found in Ireland.

77. *Dryopteris carthusiana* (Vill.) H.P. Fuchs **Narrow Buckler-fern** [× 1] In habit similar to the above species. Leaves not densely tufted, narrowly lanceolate in outline, bi-pinnate, with deeply pinnatifide pinnules; petiole with uniformly coloured scales. Indusium rarely fringed with a few glands. Found in similar localities as the above but usually in nutrient-poor soils. Common throughout Europe and Britain; also found in Ireland. *Dryopteris expansa* (C. Presl) Fraser-Jenkins & Jermy, the Northern Buckler-fern, is an arctic-alpine species and grows in crevices on rocks in N England, Wales and Scotland, and in Europe from Scandinavia to Spain. See Key p. 34; it can also be distinguished by having the indusium toothed and fringed with stalked glands.

79, 80. *Phegopteris connectilis* (Michx.) Watt (*Thelypteris phegopteris*) (L.) Slosson [× 4, × 0.5] Plant growing with a creeping rhizome, slender, covered with golden-brown scales. Leaves 10–60 cm long, single, triangular-ovate in outline, simply pinnate with pinnatifid pinnae (the lowest pair a little removed from the rest and pointing forward and downward). Sori close to the margins of the pinnae-lobes; indusium absent. In acid soil in damp woods and shade of rocks. Widespread and common all over Europe; in Britain mainly in the west and north; scattered and rare in Ireland.

81. *Thelypteris palustris* Schott (*Thelypteris thelypteroides* Michx.) **Marsh Fern** [× 0.2] Rhizome slender, long creeping, with a few small scales near the apex. Leaves singly, not in dense tufts (stands often appear 'untidy'), simply pinnate with deeply pinnatified pinnae, lanceolate in outline, at first sparsely hairy beneath and inconspicuously glandular; sterile leaves (appearing earlier) (15) 20–65 cm long, longer petioled, firmer and stouter, with the pinnule margins usually recurved. Sori in the middle between midrib and margins; indusium more or less reniform, deciduous. Widespread in Europe along watercourses, in marshes, fens and fen-woods, but only locally frequent; in Britain frequent in E Anglia, elsewhere scattered and rare; scattered in Ireland.

94

75 △   ▽ 76   ▽ 77

78 △

79 △　　　　　　　　　▽ 80

81 △   82 △   ▽ 83

Gymnocarpium (82–83) Ferns with creeping, slender rhizomes. Leaves never tufted or arranged in a crown, solitary, erect, bi-tri-pinnate, triangular in outline (the two lowermost pinnae each almost as large as the rest of the leaf and distinctly jointed to the rhachis), Sori close to the lobe-margins, circular, sometimes confluent; indusium absent.

82.   *Gymnocarpium robertianum* (Hoffm.) Newman (*Thelypteris robertiana* (Hoffm.) Slosson) **Limestone Fern**[× 7] Similar in habit to the following species but lowermost pinnae a little smaller than rest of the leaf. Leaves with short glandular hairs, dull green, rolled-up (ball-like) when young. On limestone scree, rocks and on walls (in Britain often in artificial habitats such as disused railway stations). Widespread in Europe (mainly in mountain areas); scattered and local in Britain; very rare in Ireland.

83.   *Gymnocarpium dryopteris* (L.) Newman (*Thelypteris dryopteris* (L.) Slosson) **Oak Fern** [× 1] Lowermost pinnae each more or less as large as the rest of the leafblade. Leaves bright green, without glands. In damp woods in acid soil, along streams, near shaded rocks. Widespread and common in Europe; in Britain frequent in northern counties and Wales; very rare in Ireland.

84, 85.   *Oreopteris limbosperma* (All.) Holub (*Dryopteris oreopteris* (Ehrh.) Maxon; *Thelypteris limbosperma* (All.) H.P. Fuchs) **Mountain Fern** [×0.05, ×8] Rhizome erect, short, stout. Leaves in a crown, erect to spreading, (30) 50–100 (120) cm long, lanceolate in outline, firm, fragrant when rubbed, simply pinnate with deeply pinnatifid pinnae, with yellow glands on the lower surface; lowest pinnae the smallest, the largest (5–12 cm) in about the middle of the leaf. Sori very close to the margins of the pinnae-lobes; indusium soon deciduous. Found in damp woods, fen-woods, streamsides, hedgebanks, pastures, banks etc. (not on limestone). Widespread and fairly common in Europe and Britain; scattered in Ireland.

Athyrium (86–89) Ferns with short rhizomes. Leaves large, arranged in a crown, bi-tri-pinnate, broadly lanceolate in outline, delicate in appearance. Sori circular to elongate; indusium present, reniform or horse-shoe-shaped.

86, 87.   *Athyrium filix-femina* (L.) Roth **Lady Fern** [×0.1, × 16] Leaves large, 25– 100 (150)cm long, spreading and often with the ends drooping, dying in autumn; petiole reddish, scaly; rhachis green or purplish sometimes scattered scaly. Sori elongate, often hook-like; indusium narrow, conspicuous. In damp woods, deciduous woodland, screes, marshes, hedgebanks, shady rocks, on acid soil. Widespread and common in Europe, Britain and Ireland.

88, 89.   *Athyrium distentifolium* Tausch ex Opiz (*A. alpestre* (Hoppe) Rylands) **Alpine Lady-fern** [×4, ×0.05) Leaves similar in appearance and size to above species but with a thick straw-coloured petiole. Sori circular; indusium soon deciduous. Rocks, galleys and screes. A species of arctic-alpine distribution; in Britain confined to Scotland northwards to Argyll and Angus and very local.

Polystichum (90–94) Ferns similar in habit to *Dryopteris* but leaves stouter; pinnae and pinnules asymmetrical marginal teeth with spiny or bristly points. Indusium typically shield-like, fixed in the centre (**94**). Hybrids between the following species are frequent.

90.   *Polystichum lonchitis* (L.) Roth **Holly Fern** [×0.2] Leaves in tufts, (10- 15–50 (60) cm long, coriaceous, simply pinnate, narrowly oblong to oblong-lanceolate in outline, tough, wintergreen; pinnae 20–40 on each side, sicle-like and pointing upwards, stiff, with spine-pointed teeth. Sori in a row close to each side of the midrib but in a double-row on the basal pinnae-lobe, usually to be found only in the upper half

84 △   85 △   ▽ 86

87 △

88 △

89 △   ▽ 91

90 △   ▽ 92

of the leaf. Found on basic rocks, in rock-crevices in Europe in higher mountain areas; in Britain on mountains in N Wales, N England, Scotland, usually local; also in western Ireland.

91.   *Polystichum setiferum* (Forssk.) Woynar (*P. angulare* (Willd.) Presl) **Soft Shield-fern** [×0.5] Leaves in tufts, bi-pinnate, soft, rarely wintergreen (only in sheltered positions), arching, 30–100 (150) cm long, lanceolate in outline, deep green above, pale green below; petiole and rhachis densly scaly and pilose; pinnae 30–40 on each side, the lowermost only a little shorter than the following; pinnules of lower pinnae shortly stalked. Found in woods and on hedgebanks in southwestern Central Europe and western Europe; in Britain common in southern and western counties, local to rare in the East and North; found in most parts of Ireland.

92.   *Polystichum braunii* (Spenn.) Fée [×0.3] Leaves tufted, 30–100 cm long, bi-tri-pinnate, light green, soft, with a greasy gloss, not overwintering; lowermost pinnae much shorter than the middle ones; pinnules sessile, whitish pilose on both surfaces, margins with spiny teeth. In Europe found in mountainous woodland in damp shady situations as far as southern Scandinavia; not known in Britain and Ireland.

93, 94.   *Polystichum aculeatum* (L.) Roth (*P. lobatum* (Hudson) Cheval) **Hard Shield-fern** [×0.2, × 16] Like *P. setiferum* but leaves stiff, subcoriaceous, wintergreen, dark green, somewhat glossy, 20–100 cm long; pinnae 25–50 on each side, the lowermost much shorter; pinnules of lowermost pinnae mostly sessile, the lowermost one usually much longer than the rest. Widespread in Europe and Britain in shady woods and on hedgebanks; more scattered in Ireland.

Polypodium **Polypody (95–96)** Ferns with a densely scaly rhizome, creeping below or above the surface. Leaves singly, arranged in two ranks along the rhizome, pinnate or very deeply pinnatifid, wintergreen. Sori circular or elliptic, arranged in a single row on each side of the pinna-midrib; indusium absent. This genus is, strictly speaking, represented in Europe and Britain by one species only (*P. vulgare*) but it can be subdivided into three microspecies, the characters of which all overlap; they also hybridize. A precise determination is sometimes difficult.

95.   *Polypodium interjectum* Shivas **Intermediate** (Western) **Polypody** [×0.3] Leaf-blade ovate-lanceolate, longest pair of pinnae usually the 4th–6th from below; between or around sori minute unbranched glandular hairs. Sori elliptic, when young; thickened cells of annulus pale buff to gold-brown. In Europe of atlantic distribution on limestone, calcareous dunes and mortared walls, scattered in NW Germany; throughout the British Isles; more scattered in Ireland. This species is hexaploid. Not illustrated but found in western Britain northwards to Argyll is the diploid *Polypodium cambricum* L. (P. australe Fée) Southern Polypody. Leaf-blade triangular-ovate or broadly ovate; the longest pair of pinnae usually the 2nd–4th from below; with large, many-branched hairs around the sori. Sori elliptic when young; thickened cells of annulus bright yellow. Found in similar habitats to *P. interjectum* but also on basalt and basic rocks.

96.   *Polypodium vulgare* L. **Common Polypody** [×0.4] Leaf-blades oblong to lan-ceolate in outline; pinnae usually of same length for some distance from below, often with an obtuse apex. Sori circular when young; annulus usually red-brown, the thick-walled cells with thin-walled ones between them (large, many-branched hairs between sori absent). Widespread and common throughout Europe, Britain and Ireland usually, but not exclusively, on calcareous ground. This species is tetraploid.

97.   *Azolla filicoides* see p. 104
98.   *Salvinia nataus* see p. 104

96 △   ▽ 97   ▽ 98

97. *Azolla filicoides* Lam. [×2] Small free-floating aquatic plants with branched stems and true roots, 1–5 cm in diam. Leaves bi-lobed, arranged in two ranks, imbricate; the upper lobe about 1 mm wide, ovate, obtuse, floating, densely hairy; lower lobe submerged, thinner, bearing pairs of sori (each pair either both with megasporangia or each with mega- or microsporangia). Found in ditches and ponds. Most probably introduced from America but naturalized in S and Central Europe, in southern England, and in eastern Ireland.

98. *Salvinia natans* (L.) All. [×2] Free-floating aquatic plant. Stems sparingly branched. Leaves three, arranged in a whorl: the upper two ovate, floating, with large intercellular spaces, hairy and unwettable on both surfaces (hairs on the upper in tufts); the lower one split into numerous filiform root-like segments (functional roots). Sporangia (mega- and microsporangia) enclosed in globular sporocarps situated at the base of the submerged leaf. Found in warm ponds and ditches in Central and SE Europe, extending to Holland and Spain; absent from Britain and Ireland.

Marsileaceae (99–101) A family of perennial herbs. Rhizome creeping, often long and much-branched. Leaves arranged in two rows, alternate, spirally inrolled when young, entire and subulate or with two or four palmately arranged (clover-like) leaflets. Sporangia contained in hard, globose, hairy or glabrous sporocarps born singly or in groups at the base (rarely higher up) of the petiole. Sporangia of two different kinds (mega- and microsporangia) within the same sorus.

99, 100. *Marsilea quadrifolia* L. [×1, ×2] Rhizome slender, far-creeping, branched. Leaves with four clover-like leaflets, glabrous; petiole (5) 8–20 cm long; leaflets (0.8) 1.2–1.8 (2.2) cm long, obdeltate, with entire margins and rounded apex. Sporocarps two, ellipsoid, attached above the base of the petiole, 3–5 mm long, with small teeth at the base, stalked. Found in S and SW Europe, extending to France, in shallow water of periodically flooded localities such as water-meadows or ricefields, with the leaves floating and the sporocarps usually developing in the mud when the water-level is lowered. Extinct in Germany; absent from Britain and Ireland.

101. *Pilularia globulifera* L. Pillwort [×2] Leaves arising from a creeping rhizome with nodes 1–4 cm apart, 3–10 (15) cm long, subulate. Sporocarps singly at the leaf-base, four-chambered (two chambers containing microspores, the other two megaspores), about 3 mm in diam., erect, almost sessile, brown when mature. Found in western Central Europe and scattered throughout the British Isles in shallow water at edges of ponds, ricefields, marshy ground, wet heaths, often submerged, in acid substrata; very local and absent from many counties; local in Ireland. Because of the subulate leaf this species is often overlooked and mistaken for a *Juncus* or *Carex*. An endangered species in Europe as the habitat is being destroyed for agriculture etc.

99 △   ▽ 100   ▽ 101

102. Humid forests in hilly districts provide ideal habitats for vigorous moss growth, often supporting large cushions such as those shown here. The coniferous woodland in the background of the picture produces an acid soil which many bryophytes prefer. Such acid conditions, combined with shade, suit relatively few higher plants, so the mosses do not have to contend with serious competition. Large hummocks of *Polytrichum* (**108**–**117**), *Pleurozium* (**258**) and *Bazzania* (**313**) dominate the ground flora in this example, with a few fronds of the fern *Dryopteris dilatata* (**75**).

103. Some mosses are adapted to open habitats which are subject to drying out. This plate shows a horizontal limestone exposure with large, brownish tufts of moss. Mosses in such habitats are frequently strongly pigmented and may have hair-pointed leaves, such as *Tortula* (**158**). Other genera include *Tortella* (**162**), *Pleurochaete* (**161**), *Barbula* and *Schistidium* (**168**), commonly in association with variously coloured lichens.

104. Some mosses demand aquatic, or at least permanently wet habitats. Here a small cascade in the Black Forest, running in a limestone ravine, makes an ideal habitat for the calcicolous, semi-aquatic moss, *Cratoneuron commutatum* (**243**). The stems and leaves of this moss frequently become coated in calcium carbonate.

105. Bryophytes, particularly peat mosses (*sphagna*) may dominate the flora on moors and bogs. The *Sphagnum* shown here is growing in a large bog pool and is associated with the Cotton Sedge (*Eriophorum angustifolium*). In the more oceanic regions of Western Europe, *Sphagnum* may occur above the water table, often forming large hummocks, but in Central Europe the genus tends to be confined to lakes and lake margins. The water-holding capacity of *Sphagnum* makes it a very important genus ecologically.

106. *Funaria hygrometrica* [×25] Has thin, thread-like protonema, seen here with buds and young plantlets.

107. *Mnium punctatum* [×25] A section of male 'flower' with ovoid antheridia (green) mixed with the swollen-ended, reddish, sterile hairs (paraphyses).

102 △

103 △

104 △

▽ 106

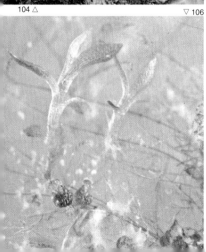

105 △

▽ 107

109. *Pogonatum urnigerum* (Hedw.) P. Beauv. [× 1.5] Plants about 2–8 cm tall, erect, frequently once or twice branched, in colonies or patches of a distinctly greyish-green colour. Leaves as in *Polytrichum commune* (below), but differing in colour. Setae reddish, 2–4 cm long; capsules shortly cylindrical, erect or inclined, at first concealed by the pale, fibrous calyptras. Common on sandy or stony banks and ledges in hilly and mountainous areas, uncommon in the lowlands; often occurring only as short, immature plants on banks by mountain streams. Differs from *P. alpinum* (**117**) in its paler, greyish green colour.

110. *Pogonatum aloides* (Hedw.) P. Beauv. [× 4] Plants short, under 2 cm tall, dull green, scattered or in patches, often with persistent, bright green protonema. Leaves spreading when moist,incurved when dry, sheathing at base with narrow, denticulate lamina ending in a rather blunt tip. Seta redish; mature capsules greyish, cylindrical, with conspicuous white diaphragams across the top after the lids have fallen. Frequent on steep or vertical sandy clay banks by paths, streams and woodlands. *P. nanum* (Hedw.) P. Beauv. is a very similar plant but is smaller on average and has a short ovoid to more or less hemispherical capsule. It is not uncommon in hilly areas on acid, stony soils.

111. *Atrichum undulatum* (Hedw.) P. Beauv. [× 3.5] Rather large, erect plants with unbranched stems up to 10 cm high, in lax tufts or patches, dull green or yellowish. Leaves long and tapering, strongly transversely undulate, shrivelled when dry, tapering to sharp tips and with bordered and toothed margins and usually with diagonal lines of minute teeth on the underside. Midrib reaching leaf apex, with 4–7 longitudinal lamellae on the upperside. Setae long, brownish, bearing curved, cylindrical, inclined capsules with long-beaked lids. Calyptra small, not fibrous. Common on damp sandy or clay soils in fields, woodlands and heathlands throughout Britain and Europe. *Oligotrichum hercynicum* (Hedw.) Lam. & Cand. is much smaller, with deep green, rather solid leaves covered by wavy lamellae on the upperside. Frequent on acid, stony soils in hilly and mountainous districts.

108. *Polytrichum commune* Hedw. [× 1] Plants very large, deep green with erect, mainly unbranched shoots forming lax tufts or extensive colonies up to 40 cm tall. Leaves stiff, widely spreading when moist, appressed to the stems when dry, elongate and tapering gradually to acute points, with sharply toothed margins; basal part of leaf forming an erect sheath around the stem, the spreading portion, as in the other species of *Polytrichum* and *Pogonatum*, with longitudinal lamellae covering the upper surface. Male plants with cup-shaped 'inflorescences' formed of perigonial bracts. Setae up to 12 cm long; capsules mostly four-angled, horizontal, at first covered by the yellowish, fibrous calyptras. Common in wet, acid, peaty habitats such as fens, margins of bogs, wet heathlands and birchwoods at all altitudes. (Plant in foreground is *Sphagnum pulustre*, see **123**)

112, 113, 114. *Polytrichum formosum* Hedw. [× 4, × 3, × 6] Robust, dark green plants with mainly unbranched, erect shoots up to 12 cm tall. Often distinguishable from *P. commune* (**108**) only by microscopic examination, but typically much shorter, growing in drier habitats. Capsules are 4–5 angled, covered at first by pale, fibrous calyptras (**112, 113**). The conspicuous male 'flower' is shown in **114**. Common in acid woodlands and heathlands.

115. Polytrichum alpestre Hoppe [×2] (syn. *P. strictum* Brid.). Plants with erect, unbranched shoots in lax tufts, up to 20 cm tall. Leaves dark green, spreading when moist, appressed to stems when dry, narrow and acute, ending in sharp, brownish points but without apical 'hairs'; margins hyaline and folded over the upper surface. Lower parts of stems coated with conspicuous, off-white felt-like tomentum. Capsules on yellowish, rather thin setae, 4–5 angled, about $\frac{2}{3}$ covered by the yellowish, fibrous calyptra. Frequent on peaty moors and drier areas of bogs, especially in the north and in hilly districts. The even more common *P. juniperinum* Hedw. is very similar but shorter, rarely over 8 cm tall and without the basal tomentum. It grows in large patches on well drained, acid soils. The greenish male 'flowers' and fruits are often very conspicuous in spring on heaths and pathsides.

116. Polytrichum piliferum Hedw. [×3] Plants simple, in lawns or lax tufts, usually under 6.0 cm tall. Leaves greyish green, narrow, erect-spreading when moist, with folded-over margins which entirely cover the lamellae on the upper surface of the leaves. Leaf apices mostly drawn out into white, glassy hair points. Male 'flowers' cup-shaped, usually bright red. Calyptra bright red near apex when young. Common throughout Europe on exposed, well drained, gritty or sandy soils; often a primary coloniser and sand-binder on dunes.

117. Polytrichum alpinum Hedw. [×3] Plants dark green, in low tufts or colonies up to 15 cm tall, often with shoots branched. Leaves stiff, with toothed margins. Capsules erect, not sharply angled, borne on setae 3–5 cm long. Found on dryish, acid humus in hilly and mountainous districts. (Distinguished from other dark green spp. by the ovoid, papillose end cells on the lamellae).

118. Diphyscium foliosum (Hedw.) Mohr [×3] Plants very short, up to 1 cm, brownish or dark green, inconspicuous except in fruit. Lower leaves narrow, strap-shaped with blunt ends; upper (perichaetial) leaves ending in a long hair and with long cilia on the upper margins. Capsules pale, large and conspicuous, ovoid, asymmetrical and tapered above with pointed lids. Peristome membranous, not composed of teeth. Widely distributed on sandy or peaty soils, it is frequent in mountain districts but rare elsewhere.

120. Buxbaumia aphylla Hedw. [×4] Plants leafless except for very inconspicuous vestiges at base of setae. Capsule large and conspicuous, very asymmetrical, plano-convex with very narrow mouth. A saprophyte found on organic soils, humus and rotting wood. Rare, scattered throughout Europe.

119, 121. Schistostega pennata (Hedw.) Web. & Mohr [×13] 'Luminous Moss'. Plants in small, flat, light green fronds about 1 cm tall, arising from a persistent, glistening protonema (**119**, ×250). Leaves nerveless, in two rows on sterile stems. Seta thin; capsule small, oval, lacking a peristome. Cells of protonema very convex, acting as lenses and refractive so that it gives an impression of luminosity. Occasional, found in dark caves, rock clefts and rabbit burrows in non-calcareous areas.

115 △   116 △

117 △   118 △   ▽ 120   119 △   ▽ 121

122.   *Tetraphis pellucida* Hedw. [×6] Plants in tufts up to 3 cm tall, with ovate to rotund leaves. On many of the stems, the uppermost leaves are enlarged to form cup-shaped rosettes containing numbers of discoid, green gemmae. The rather uncommonly produced fruit is oval cylindrical and is remarkable in having a peristome composed of only four large teeth. Common on rotting wood, especially old stumps, and humus among acidic rocks.

123.   *Sphagnum palustre* L. [×2] Large, pale green or whitish plants with youngest branches forming a dense head (capitulum) which is often brownish or purplish. Branches in clusters (fascicles) along the stem and of two kinds: thicker, spreading branches with convex, hooded leaves and pendent, thin and very pale branches lying against the stem. Stems brown with hyaline cortex and thin, spatulate leaves. Common and widespread plant often in large, pale cushions among sedges and rushes in acid fens and fen-woods and by lakes and streams; not on bogs.

124.   *Sphagnum rubellum* Wils. [×1.5] Plants in rather large cushions formed of elongated stems and clusters of 4–5 narrow branches; green with flecks or flushes of red or the whole plant deep wine-red. Common on moors and drier parts of bogs and in open areas in acid woodlands. (Considered by some authorities to be only a form of *S. capillifolium*, **133**.)

125.   *Sphagnum magellanicum* Brid [×2] Robust plants, resembling *S. palustre* (**123**) and *S. papillosum* (**130**) but coloured red or pink. Spreading branches blunt, with spreading, very concave, hooded leaves. Grows on bogs, often in very large hummocks, mainly in western and parts of Central Europe.

126.   *Sphagnum fimbriatum* Wils. [×2] Plants elongated, with thin, long branches. Capitulum with a hard, conical bud in the centre. Branch leaves small, more or less acute, never in five rows. Plants and stems green or yellowish. Stem leaves closely appressed to stems and difficult to see (pull off capitulum and observe leaves projecting beyond broken stem end), broadly spathulate and fringed. Frequent, in tall, soft cushions in acid fens and fen-woods; fairly shade tolerant.

127.   *Sphagnum compactum* DC [×1.5] Plants in low, dense, orange or red-brown tufts. Branches usually upwardly directed and concealing the capitula, so that plants resemble true mosses such as *Leucobryum*, rather than other peat-mosses. Branch leaves large, 2–3 mm long, but stem leaves minute and difficult to observe. Frequent and widespread on shallow peat on heaths and drier areas of bogs.

128.   *Sphagnum cuspidatum* Hoffm. [×3] Green, yellowish or whitish plants with pale stems; young branches sometimes brown. Recognized by the very narrow, often more or less tubular branch leaves which may be over 3 mm long but only 0.5 mm wide. Common and widespread, forming soft, low carpets in wet hollows and pools on bogs, heaths and acid mires; submerged forms have a very characteristic appearance, often likened to 'drowned cats'.

129.   *Sphagnum fallax* Klinggr. [×5] (syn. *S. recurvum* auct.). Plants green, yellowish or pale brown-orange, with pale stems. Leaves of spreading branches small, sometimes in five rows which curl outwards when dry. Stem leaves small, more or less triangular and reflexed. In acid fens, ditches and pool margins, often forming very extensive 'lawns' in wet hollows, with sedges and rushes. This is one of a complex of closely related species, some of them common, which may be difficult to identify without experience. The illustration shows the large perichaetium and spherical capsule characteristic of all peat-mosses.

122 △   123 △

124 △   ▽ 127   125 △   ▽ 128   126 △   ▽ 129

130.   Sphagnum papillosum Lindb. [× 1.5] Robust plants with dark stems and tumid, olive-brown or ochre branches, rarely green throughout; branches blunt, not tapering at their ends as in *S. palustre* (**123**). In low hummocks or extensive lawns, often with *S. capillifolium* (**133**). Locally abundant, mainly on peat bogs and wet areas in heathland, sometimes in acid fens.

131.   Sphagnum squarrosum Crome [× 1] Robust, pale green plants with dark stems and large capitula. Branch leaves abruptly turned outwards from their middles (squarrose) and appearing more or less sharply pointed with incurved upper margins, so that branches look 'prickly'. Unlike most sphagna, this species prefers richer habitats such as slightly basic mires and fens, associated with herbs, sedges and rushes. Frequent throughout Europe.

132.   Sphagnum auriculatum Schimp. [× 3] Very variable, but usually large, plants which may grow in hummocks, scattered, erect stems, or more or less prostrate and flaccid. Green in shade, orange, brown or dull purple-red in strong light. Branches usually plump, sometimes curved and horn-like, with large, ovate, not hooded leaves. Stems commonly almost black, cortex almost invisible. Common in very wet, acid habitats; ditches, mires and bog pools at all altitudes.

133.   Spagnum capillifolium Brid. [× 3] (syn. *S. nemoreum* Scop.) Relatively small and rather compact plants with neat, rounded capitula and tapering branches, nearly always with red tints. Leaves small, more or less erect, not five-ranked. Found in large, often compact cushions above the water-table in bogs, heathlands and acid wood-lands; also on exposed hillsides in the more oceanic regions of western Europe.

134.   Campylopus fragilis (Brid.) BSG [× 2] Short, erect stems in green, compact tufts 1–4 cm high. Leaves rather stiff, finely tapering to very narrow, channelled apices, white below and slightly narrowed, with very broad midribs. Leaves and young shoot apices readily detach and act as propagules. Scattered and locally frequent on dry, sandy humus and rotting wood. *C. pyriformis* (Schultz) Brid., a rather more common species in most areas, is a smaller, yellowish plant with more finely drawn out leaves which are exceedingly deciduous. *C. flexuosus* (Hedw.) Brid. is larger, usually deep green, with felted stems and small reddish auricles at the leaf bases. It is a common plant in similar, but wetter habitats.

135.   Campylopus atrovirens De Not. [× 4] Relatively robust plants, usually in dull brown to blackish tufts up to 15 cm tall. Leaves erect-spreading, very long-tapering and the upper with distinct glassy hair-points. Stems not felted with tomentum. Found on wet, non-basic rocks and thin peat: most frequent in western Europe, especially Scandinavia and the British Isles.

136.   Campylopus introflexus (Hedw.) Brid. [× 4] Plants in greyish green, rather hoary tufts up to 10 cm high. Stems erect and commonly with clusters of short branches forming dense heads. Leaves stiff, narrowed above to conspicuous white hair-points which, in the dry state, bend sharply outwards. A common and increasing species (first introduced from the southern hemisphere *c.* 1940) on disturbed peat, sandy humus and occasionally on rotting stumps.

130 △   131 △

132 △   ▽ 134   ▽ 135   ▽ 136   133 △

137. *Dicranoweisia cirrata* (Hedw.) Milde [× 7] Small plants in neat, green, compact cushions 1–2 cm high. Leaves narrowly lance-shaped, tapering gradually to acute tips, flexuose-spreading when moist, strongly curled when dry. Capsules oval-cylindrical, erect, on pale setae, very pale when old and empty. Common and widespread on trunks and branches of trees, logs, fenceposts and occasionally on sandstone rocks.

138. *Cynodontium strumiferum* (Hedw.) De Not. [×2] Plants in compact, green tufts up to 4 cm high. Leaves erect-spreading, tending to be secund; lanceolate with lower margins narrowly recurved. Capsules usually present, asymmetrical, curved, grooved and with a small protruberance (struma) on one side of the apophysis. Rare in Britain but widespread and locally frequent in Europe on acidic rocks and screes in mountainous districts. (One of a number of similar species that may be found in the mountains, none of them common.)

139. *Dichodontium pellucidum* (Hedw.) Schimp. [×4] In small to rather large bright, light green or yellowish tufts 1–6 cm tall. Leaves more or less flat, with rather broad, abruptly tapering, toothed tips, reflexed or widely spreading when moist, rather shrivelled when dry. Capsules short, inclined (immature in picture). Frequent in consistently moist, usually fairly calcareous habitats: streamsides, on rocks and silt, mainly in hilly districts.

140. *Orthodicranum flagellare* (Hedw.) Loeske [×8] Plants in low, compact tufts up to 6 cm high, yellowish green, with tomentose stems. Leaves long and very narrow except at bases. Recognised by the production of short-leaved, straight, brittle shoots near the ends of the stems, which act as propagules. Found on rotting wood; uncommon, rare in Britain. The related *O. montanum* (Hedw.) Loeske lacks the propaguliferous shoots. It very closely resembles *Dicranoweisia cirrata* (**137**) but has minutely toothed leaves and is nearly always sterile. Found on trunks and exposed roots of trees in south-east England; scattered in lowland Europe.

141. *Paraleucobryum longifolium* (Hedw.) Loeske [×6] Plants in low, silky tufts up to 8 cm high, dull green when moist, whitish and bleached-looking when dry, with narrow, curved leaves composed mainly of the broad, almost hyaline midribs. On acidic rocks in the higher mountains and far north. Rather rare in Europe and possibly extinct in the British Isles.

142. *Dicranodontium denudatum* (Brid.) Broth. [×3] Plants in low, silky, green or yellowish tufts or patches, up to 10 cm tall. Leaves curved to one side, long and finely drawn out from broader, sheathing bases. Midrib very broad, with red-brown patches on either side at the base. Stems with rust-brown tomentum. Found in the mountains on damp, acidic rocks, wood and peat. Frequent at high altitudes but not always distinguishable by the novice from *Campylopus* spp.

143. *Dicranella heteromalla* (Hedw.) Schimp. [×4] In low, silky, deep green or occasionally yellowish tufts up to 4 cm tall. Stems mainly simple, not tomentose. Leaves narrow, hair-like, curved and turned in one direction. Capsules oval, asymmetrical, inclined, on yellowish setae, at first with finely pointed lids which fall to reveal reddish teeth. Abundant on acid, mineral or humus-rich soils in woodlands throughout Britain and Europe. *D. varia* (Hedw.) Schimp. has shorter leaves and reddish setae. It is frequent in calcareous habitats. *D. rufescens* is a smaller, usually reddish plant and occurs in scattered colonies on acid, sandy soils by streams.

137 △

138 △

139 △

140 △   ▽ 142

141 △   ▽ 143

144. *Dicranum scoparium* Hedw. [×2.5] Very variable, usually rather robust plants in green, yellowish to brownish tufts up to 12 cm tall. Leaves gradually tapering to fine, toothed apices, not undulate, with small brownish patches at the base. Nerve narrow, at apex toothed on the underside. With curved, secund leaves, resembles giant forms of *Dicranella heteromalla* (**143**) but stems are tomentose. Dioecious: a peculiar feature of this species and its relatives is that male plants are very small and found among the matted rhizoids on the stems of female plants. Very common on lime-free soils in woodlands, heathlands and coarse grasslands throughout Britain and Europe. The related *D. fuscescens* Sm. has generally more narrowly tapering leaves with roughened but not toothed apices. It grows in dull green tufts on rocks, wood and peaty soils and is common in hilly districts.

145. *Dicranum bonjeanii* De Not. [×3] Robust, pale or yellowish, soft tufts up to 15 cm tall. Leaves erect-spreading or turned to one side, narrow and tapering to flat, toothed apices, transversely undulate. Stems with more or less conspicuous tufts of pale, not rust brown, tomentum. Frequent in marshes, damp grasslands and woodlands, especially in calcareous districts.

146. *Dicranum polysetum* Sw. [×3] (syn. *D. rugosum* (Funck) Brid.) Robust, erect, yellow-green plants in large tufts or patches up to 10 cm high. Leaves erect-spreading, sometimes slightly secund, strongly transversely undulate, with long and narrow, flat, toothed apices. Midrib with two low lamellae on the underside, near leaf apex. Stems with conspicuous, brown tomentum. Scattered distribution up to 1,500 m altitude on acid humus, mainly in coniferous woodlands and heathlands.

147. *Dicranum spurium* Hedw. [×2] Plants typically in low, lax tufts or patches, yellowish, about 6 cm tall or less. Leaves erect-spreading, transversely undulate, when dry incurved and forming rather dense, ovoid apical tufts (plants pictured here in dry condition). On acid, sandy humus in heathlands and open woodlands; mainly lowland.

148. *Dicranum majus* Sm. [×3] Large, green plants often over 10 cm tall, in lax tufts. Stems with pale brown or white tomentum. Leaves very long, 9–15 mm, strongly curved and turned in one direction, very finely tapering into setaceous, denticulate apices. Often difficult to distinguish from robust *D. soparium* (**144**) but has longer, narrower leaves and the fruits, when produced, are usually several together (single in *D. scoparium*). Frequent and widely distributed in mature woodlands on damp humus and peaty soils, common in the west.

149. *Dicranum undulatum* Brid. [×3] (syn. *D. bergeri* Bland.) Plants large, with tall, erect stems forming matt yellow-green cushions up to 20 cm high. Leaves lance-shaped, transversely undulate, erect or slightly curved and secund; midrib more or less smooth on the underside. Stems matted with rust-coloured tomentum. Uncommon plant of undisturbed bogs; rare in Britain.

144 △

145 △

146 △ ▽ 148

147 △ ▽ 149

150. *Leucobryum glaucum* (Hedw.) Angstr. [× 1] Shoots simple or forked, closely packed into more or less hemispherical, whitish or pale blue-green hummocks, white and bleached-looking when dry but otherwise unaltered. Leaves with ovate bases and long, narrow, channelled apices composed mainly of large, water-holding cells. Hummocks can hold quantities of water, like *Sphagnum*. Common and widely distributed on acid humus in woodlands and heathlands; sometimes found as completely detached, but living, plants or 'moss balls'.

151. *Ceratodon purpureus* (Hedw.) Brid. [× 1.5] Unremarkable moss when barren, in low, green, brownish or reddish tufts up to 3 cm tall. Leaves erect-spreading, lance-shaped, tapering to acute points which, in the upper leaves, may have a characteristic slight lateral twist when viewed from above. Conspicuous in young fruit because of the massed, bright red or purple setae (shown enlarged × 16 in **152**). Capsules ovoid, inclined, grooved, with conical lids. Very common on lime-free soils, rocks, pathsides, roofs of houses, heathlands, leached sand-dunes and sites of old fires throughout Europe.

153. *Distichium capillaceum* (Hedw.) BSG [× 4] Plants in compact or rather tall and soft, bright green, silky tufts. Stems matted below with brown rhizoids. Leaves, from erect, sheathing bases, suddenly contracted into long, very narrow apices, in strictly two rows. Capsules oval-cylindrical, erect, on setae 1–3 cm long. Frequent on basic rocks in montane regions; rare in the lowlands except in the north and west.

154. *Fissidens adianthoides* Hedw. [× 11] Flat, erect shoots up to 7 cm tall, in green or yellowish tufts. Leaves, as in all species of the genus, in two ranks, oblong-lanceolate, finely denticulate near tips; with the lower part of the leaf, above the midrib, duplicated to form a sheath. Leaf margins often paler but not distinctly bordered. Midrib not running beyond leaf tip. Frequent and widespread; in wet meadows, rocks by streams and waterfalls.

155. *Fissidens cristatus* Mitt. [× 3] In tufts or scattered stems, up to 4 cm tall, usually yellowish. Very similar to *F. adianthoides* (**154**) and sometimes indistinguishable without microscopic examination, but usually smaller; leaf margins with more distinct pale marginal band. Common in calcareous grasslands (e.g. chalk downlands) and among limestone rocks.

156. *Fissidens taxifolius* Hedw. [× 3] Shoots flat, dull green, simple, up to *c* 3 cm tall. Leaves unbordered, very minutely crenulate but not toothed. Midribs projecting beyond leaf tips in minute mucros. Seta, as in the previous species, arising from near the base of a shoot. Common on damp, shaded banks in woodlands, on non-calcareous soils, from sea-level to 2000 m alt. *Fissidens bryoides* Hedw. is smaller, and is distinguished by the narrow, clearly defined border of colourless, narrow cells on the leaf-margins. Setae and capsules, which are common, are produced from the tips of the shoots. Very common, rather glossy plants, in patches up to 1.5 cm tall, on earth banks, usually in shade; throughout Europe. (See p. 262)

150 △   151 △

152 △   153 △   ▽ 155   154 △   ▽ 156

157.   Tortula muralis Hedw. [× 4] Plants small, in low tufts or wide patches up to 1 cm tall, deep green or bright yellow-green. Leaves widely spreading when moist, twisted when dry, tongue-shaped, with narrowly recurved margins; midribs extended beyond the blunt leaf-tips in long, white hairs. Seta yellow, about 2 cm long; capsules narrow and cylindrical, erect, with elongated, tapered lids. Peristome teeth long and spirally twisted. Abundant throughout Europe, even in towns; on rocks and walls. *T. subulata* Hedw. is a larger plant, lacking hair points to the leaves and having much larger fruit. It is frequent, especially in limestone regions.

158, 159.   Tortula ruralis (Hedw.) Gaertn. [× 3,   × 13] Plants up to 8 cm tall, in tufts or wide patches, yellowish to reddish brown. Leaves tongue-shaped, spreading and recurved when moist, spirally twisted around stems when dry, with narrowly recurved margins; midrib extended in a long, toothed, glassy hair. On walls, roofs and calcareous soils from sea level to the lower mountain zone. *T. ruraliformis* (Besch.) Ingham, often considered to be a variety of *T. ruralis*, is larger, with more tapering leaves. It is a common, sand-binding species on dunes. *T. intermedia* (Brid.) De Not. is very similar to *T. ruralis* but has less recurved, duller leaves and smoother hair points. It is frequent on rocks and walls. *T. laevipila* (Brid.) Schwaegr. is also very similar, but is found on the bark of trees.

160.   Barbula recurvirostra (Hedw.) Dix. [× 4] Plants in small, green tufts up to 3 cm high. Interior of tufts a characteristic bright, brick red. Leaves narrow, tapering to narrow, sometimes toothed tips. Capsules cylindrical erect, on reddish setae *c* 1.5 cm long. Common on basic walls, rocks and soils. Many other species of *Barbula* are to be found in similar habitats: *B. fallax* Hedw., a brownish plant, in lax colonies or tufts on walls and soil, has shorter leaves and lacks the rust-red colouration in its lower parts (See p. 263) *B. convoluta* Hedw. with wavy, tongue-shaped, light green leaves with blunt tips, is a common 'weed' on paths and walls, as is the similar *B. unguiculata* Hedw. which has shortly projecting midribs (see p. 263); *B. cylindrica* (Tayl.) Schimp., yellowish, with longer, narrowly tapering leaves.

161.   Pleurochaete squarrosa (Brid.) Lindb. [× 7] Plants 3–6 cm tall, yellowish or green, in lax tufts. Leaves spreading-recurved or squarrose, usually finely toothed, with tapering, acute tips, leaf bases colourless and a hyaline band borders the lower part of the blades. Found in dry, sandy and calcareous grasslands, scrub and woodlands. Common in the Mediterranean region. Local in southern Britain.

162.   Tortella tortuosa (Hedw.) Limpr. [× 7] Plants in compact, yellow tufts up to 8 cm deep. Leaves long and tapering, variously curved and rather contorted and undulate, strongly curled and contorted when dry, with glossy midribs. Basal leaf tissue colourless, with an abrupt, oblique transition to the upper, green tissue. Found on calcareous rocks and soil, mainly in montane areas.

163.   Encalypta streptocarpa Hedw. [× 7] Low plants, up to 4 cm tall, in lax tufts or colonies, dull or light, matt green. Leaves spreading when moist, incurved and crisped when dry, tongue-shaped with broad tips. Midrib not reaching extreme leaf tip, rough on the underside. Leaf axils sometimes have clusters of reddish, stiff 'brood filaments' or gemmae. Widely distributed on calcareous rocks, mortar and stony soil in damp or shaded habitats.

164.   Encalypta vulgaris Hedw. [× 3] Plants small, up to 1 cm, in dull green or yellowish tufts. Leaves tongue-shaped, obtuse, usually with projecting midribs. Midribs smooth on the underside. Capsules common, cylindrical, erect, completely covered by the conspicuous, whitish, conical calyptras (sometimes called 'extinguisher moss' because of similarity of calyptras to candle snuffers). Found on basic rocks and walls from sea level to the forest zone; frequent.

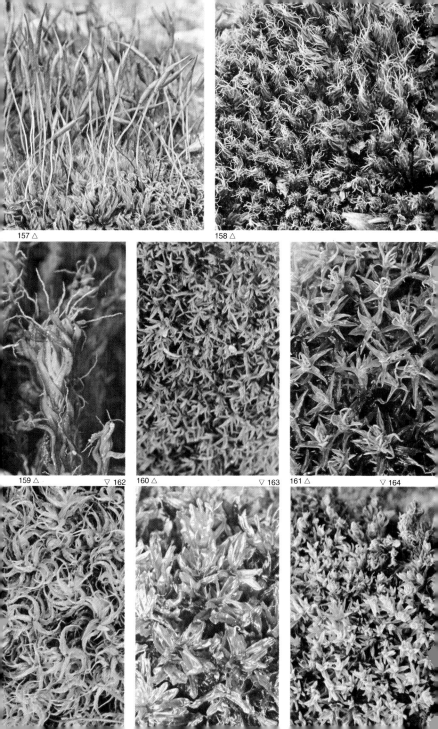

157 △

158 △

159 △   ▽ 162

160 △   ▽ 163

161 △   ▽ 164

165. *Cinclidotus aquaticus* (Jacq.) BSG [× 5] Dark green, elongated plants up to 20 cm long. Leaves stiff, lightly curved downwards, narrow and tapering above. Midrib strong and running into the leaf apex. Leaf margins only slightly thickened. Grows on limestone rocks submerged in fast flowing streams at medium to high altitudes. Not found in the British Isles.

166. *Cinclidotus fontinaloides* (Hedw.) P. Beauv. [× 2] Straggling or tufted plants up to 10 cm long, green to more or less blackish. Leaves flat, with thickened margins; midrib extended beyond the obtuse leaf tip in a short mucro. Capsules borne on extremely short setae and hidden among the leaves. Grows on rocks by waterfalls and margins of lakes and streams where periodically flooded. Locally frequent, up to 1,500 m altitude. The somewhat similar *Schistidium alpicolum*, which grows in similar habitats, lacks the thickened margins to the leaves and has conspicuous, radiating peristomes.

168, 169. *Schistidium apocarpum* (Hedw.) BSG [× 5, × 8] Partly creeping plants forming mats or low tufts, stems up to 4 cm long, brownish, hoary when dry. Leaves erect-spreading when moist, appressed to stem when dry, oval lanceolate, tapering into short or long hair points. Capsules erect, short and wide-mouthed, with very short setae and partly immersed among the upper leaves, at first green with red, umbonate lids. Peristome teeth conspicuous, bright red, radiating when dry. Common and widespread on rocks and walls, especially where calcareous.

167. *Grimmia trichophylla* Grev. [× 3] Plants in rather dense tufts, green to blackish green, up to 3 cm tall. Leaves spreading when moist, lightly recurved, when dry more or less erect, lanceolate, tapering to a longish hair point. Gemmae sometimes produced on the lower part of the leaf upperside. Seta arched when moist; capsules pale, grooved. Widely distributed on siliceous rocks.

170. *Grimmia pulvinata* (Hedw.) Sm. [× 10] Short, erect stems packed together into neat, rounded tufts up to 3 cm deep, greyish green, hoary, mouse-like when dry. Leaves broadly lanceolate with abrupt tips from which project the long hair-points. Capsules ovoid, grooved, on setae which are strongly curved when moist (straighter when old and dry) so that the capsules are tucked among the leaves. Common on rocks and walls below *c* 1,000 m alt.

171. *Grimmia incurva* Schwaegr. [× 8] Plants up to 3 cm high, in close tufts up to 10 cm wide, green above, dark below. Leaves lanceolate, usually only the upper leaves shortly hair-pointed; hairs short. Midribs strong. Fruit rare, on short, curved setae. Occasional on dry siliceous rocks in mountainous regions. Rare in Britain.

165 △   166 △

167 △   168 △   ▽ 170   169 △   ▽ 171

172.   *Rhacomitrium lanuginosum* (Hedw.) Brid. [×3] Robust, ascending or sprawl-ling, branched shoots up to 20 cm long, in yellowish or hoary, white patches. Leaves erect-spreading, commonly turned to one side, lanceolate, tapering gradually to long, irregularly toothed, rough hair points. Locally abundant and often dominant on mountains throughout Europe. Rare in the lowlands except in arctic regions.

173.   *Rhacomitrium canescens* (Hedw.) Brid. [×1.5] Yellowish plants up to 8 cm. Stems with clusters of short branches. Leaves broadly lanceolate, spreading, tapered above to flat, rough, minutely denticulate hair points. Frequent and widely distributed, up to 3,500 m alt., on sandy soils and detritus, silt by upland rivers and dunes, occasionally on basic sandstone rocks.

174.   *Rhacomitrium aquaticum* Brid. [×3] Plants erect, up to 10 cm high, in yellow-ish tufts. Stems forked but without short branchlets. Leaves erect-spreading, lanceolate, with narrowly recurved margins and tapered above to rather narrow but very blunt tips, never with hair points. Capsules erect, cylindrical, or erect setae. On moist, lime-free rocks, mainly subalpine and northern. Frequent in montane parts of Britain. *R. aciculare* (Hedw.) Brid. is a dark or blackish green plant forming low patches on wet or shallowly submerged rocks in streams. The leaves are rounded and irregularly toothed at their apices. The cylindrical, erect capsules are common. Frequent by small streams and rivers, especially in hilly districts.

175.   *Rhacomitrium affine* (Web. & Mohr) Lindb. (syn *R. sudeticum* (Funck) BSG) [×4] Stems ascending or prostrate, dull green to blackish, branched but not with short branchlets. Leaves lanceolate, with or without short hair-points. Seta short, up to 4 mm long; capsules short and ovoid. Grows in low tufts on acidic rocks; alpine and subalpine (barren plants readily confused with forms of *R. heterostichum* (**177**).

176.   *Rhacomitrium fasciculare* (Hedw.) Brid. [×3] Creeping or ascending, yellow or brownish plants with many small branchlets on the shoots. Leaves lanceolate, narrowed to fine, but not sharp, tips that never have hair-points. Common on lime-free rocks up to 2,100 m alt.

177.   *Rhacomitrium heterstichum* (Hedw.) Brid. [×3] Much-branched plants in low tufts or mats, greyish green to blackish. Leaves erect-spreading, lanceolate, usually with longish hair-points. Capsules cylindrical, on setae more than 4 mm long. Common on lime-free rocks, especially in hilly districts.

178.   *Tetraplodon angustatus* (Hedw.) BSG [×9] Plants in tufts up to 5 cm tall, yellow green. Leaves rather distant, recurved-spreading, tongue-shaped, tapering to short or longish filiform points; margins toothed. Capsules short cylindric, on larger, wider, cylindrical apophyses; seta short and thick, less than 5 mm long. Grows on animal dung in the higher mountains. Rare in Britain. *T. mnioides* (Hedw.) BSG is similar, but has untoothed leaves and longer (more than 10 mm) setae, and grows in similar habitats but is much more frequent.

179.   *Splachnum ampullaceum* Hedw. [×3] Plants in tufts up to 3 cm high, fresh green. Leaves broadly oval from narrow bases, spreading, tapered and often coarsely toothed above. Seta thin; up to 6 cm long, reddish-yellow to purplish. Capsules cylindrical, much narrower than the broadly top-shaped apophysis. Grows on dung on moors; lowland to subalpine; frequent.

172 △

173 △

174 △   ▽ 177

175 △   ▽ 178

176 △   ▽ 179

180, 182.   *Splachnum sphaericum* Hedw. [× 1,   × 13] (syn. *S. ovatum* Hedw.) Green plants up to 3 cm tall, in close tufts. Leaves broadly ovate, narrow at base, tapered above but not toothed. Seta thin, reddish below, yellow above, usually not more than 8 cm long. Urn of capsule small and cylindrical, set on a larger, ovoid, glossy, dark brown apophysis. Found on dung of ungulates on moors, mainly in hilly and mountainous districts.

183.   *Splachnum luteum* Hedw. [× 1] Plants 2–4 cm high, in tufts. Leaves widely oval, almost untoothed. Seta up to 12 cm tall, yellow or reddish. Capsules very small, dark, set on a very wide, skirt-shaped, flattish, bright yellow apophysis. Grows on animal dung. Rather rare except in areas of northern Scandinavia. A spectacular plant but unfortunately not known to occur in Britain. The apophysis is said to attract coprophilous insects which distribute the spores to other animal droppings.

181.   *Physcomitrium pyriforme* (Hedw.) Brid. [× 3] Small and usually rather scattered plants up to 5 mm tall. Leaves ovate-lanceolate, broadly acute, toothed and forming lax rosettes from which arise the setae, about 1 cm tall. Capsules almost spherical or shortly pear-shaped, the convex lids having small, central umbos; after the lid falls, the mouth of the capsules are wide, without peristome teeth. Grows on damp soil in fields and by streams and paths. Frequent throughout Europe below 1,500 m altitude.

184.   *Funaria microstoma* BSG [× 4] Very similar to *F. hygrometrica* (**185**) but typically smaller. Lid of capsule narrower. Grows on damp, sandy soils. Rare, mainly in the north-west.

185.   *Funaria hygrometrica* Hedw. [× 3] Plants up to 3 cm tall, green or yellowish, in low tufts or sometimes extensive colonies. Upper leaves of female plants forming large, ovoid buds. Male plants with upper leaves forming a rosette containing the cluster of yellow, ovoid antheridia. Seta up to 7 cm long, straight or sometimes strongly curved and cygneous; Young calyptras swollen and conspicuous. Capsules asymmetrical, curved and conspicuously grooved when old; lid shallowly convex. Peristome double, the teeth remaining arched and usually attached at their tips. An abundant, cosmopolitan species, especially in man-made habitats: soil, often in flower pots and gardens; a characteristic colonist of sites of old bonfires.

186.   *Orthodontium lineare* Schwaegr. [× 9] Plants in low, green, silky tufts (resembling *Dicranella*, **143**). Leaves soft and flexuous. Seta green to yellow, curved so that the narrow, club-shaped capsules are held horizontally. Locally common and increasing; on trunks and roots of trees, rotting wood and dry peat. Introduced from the southern hemisphere about 1910, first recorded in England in 1922 but now recorded for almost every county.

180 △   181 △

182 △   183 △   ▽ 185   184 △   ▽ 186

187.   *Bryum pallens* Sw. [×8] Plants small to medium sized, in tufts up to 6 cm deep, green, tinged with red or whole plant pink or deep red. Leaves ovate, acutely pointed, with strong, excurrent midribs and distinct narrow borders of long, narrow cells. Male plants with terminal rosettes of leaves enclosing clusters of ovoid antheridia. Capsules club-shaped, pendulous, on long setae. Frequent up to 3,500 m alt. on damp, sandy or clay soils and wet rocks by rivers, streams and springs.

188, 189.   *Bryum capillare* Hedw. [×3] Plants in mounds up to 6 cm tall, deep green. Upper leaves concave, erect-spreading when moist, spirally twisted around stems when dry, ovate-spathulate, with narrow borders and broadly acute tips which are abruptly contracted to long, filiform, flexuose hair points. Capsules large, pendulous, reddish brown at first, pale when old and empty, borne on setae 2–4 cm long. Very common throughout Britain and Europe on rocks, walls and trees.

190.   *Bryum pseudotriquetrum* (Hedw.) Schwaegr. [×4] Medium to large plants up to 10 cm tall, green, brown or reddish, matted with brown rhizoids below. Leaves spreading, not crowded on stems, shrivelled when dry, ovate-lanceolate to broadly lanceolate, acute, with bordered, narrowly recurved margins. Common and widely distributed in marshes, wet meadows and wet rocks and silt by streams and lakes.

193.   *Bryum argenteum* Hedw. [×5] Plants small, less than 1.5 cm, in compact tufts or mats with a characteristic silvery sheen. Leaves small and very concave, densely arranged and overlapping so that shoots have a string-like appearance, short and wide, abruptly narrowed to tips which are devoid of chlorophyll (except in plants from wet, shaded habitats). Capsules pendulous, ovoid, on rather short setae; young capsules bright red. Found on soil, paths, crevices in walls, particularly in nitrogen-rich places. Resistant to pollution and found in the largest cities. Cosmopolitan. *Bryum bicolor* Dicks. has a similar, but less compact form. It grows in similar habitats but is entirely green. Gemmae are often found among the upper leaves. *Bryum rubens* Mitt. is laxer, and often reddish. It is recognised by the production of globose, orange gemmae or tubers among the leaves and rhizoids. It is a frequent plant of disturbed soils where not too acid, including gardens and mole-hills.

191, 192.   *Pohlia nutans* (Hedw.) Lindb. [×3] Green plants in tufts up to 4 cm deep. Leaves lanceolate, unbordered, minutely toothed near tips, usually making a narrow angle with stems. Midrib strong but not running through the leaf tip. Setae reddish when young, becoming straw-coloured, often very long in proportion to the short, oval-cylindrical, pendulous capsules. Often produces stiff, erect shoots with smaller leaves, these acting as propagules, being brittle and easily detached. Common on acid humus on moors and bogs, also on rotting wood, lime-free rocks and tree-roots.

187 △   188 △

189 △   190 △   ▽ 192   191 △   ▽ 193

194, 195. *Rhizomnium punctatum* (Hedw.) Kop. [× 5, × 7] Stems erect, up to 10 cm tall, in lax tufts; stems matted at base with brown rhizoids. Leaves translucent deep or brownish green, broadly oval with very widely rounded apices and narrow bases, often with a tiny mucro at apex; margin bordered with a thick, usually red-brown border of narrow cells. Antheridia produced in the centre of a rosette of large leaves at the shoot apices. Seta reddish-yellow, 2–4 cm long; capsules ovoid, pendulous. Grows on damp or wet soil, rocks and tree roots. Sometimes found as scattered, small shoots arising from extensive, perennial, thin carpets of rust-coloured protonema. Common and widespread.

196. *Rhizomnium pseudopunctatum* (BSG) Kop. [× 1.5] Very similar to the previous species, but midrib usually ceasing below leaf apex and border less strongly developed. Capsule shorter, with shorter lid. Found in mires and spongy vegetation by springs and lakes. Local in Britain; in Europe, mainly in the north and northwest.

197. *Pseudobryum cinclidioides* (Hüb.) Kop. [× 7] Plants green and rather glossy, in tufts up to 10 cm high, very similar to *Rhizomnium pseudopunctatum* (**196**) but with unbordered leaves. Midrib ceasing well below leaf apex. Found in very wet, peaty vegetation in mires and by lakes. Rather rare, mainly in northern, lowland swamps; rare in Britain. *Mnium stellare* Hedw. is a somewhat similar, but smaller, bluish green plant and has unbordered leaves. It is locally frequent in Britain and Europe, occurring as compact tufts on damp, shaded rocks and soil.

198. *Mnium marginatum* (With.) P. Beauv. [× 7] Plants up to 4 cm tall, in lax tufts or scattered shoots, usually with red colouration of the older parts. Leaves rather widely spaced on stems, broadly lanceolate to ovate, with well defined, usually reddish borders and paired teeth. Midrib ending in, or just below leaf tip. Grows on damp, lime-rich rocks. Uncommon.

199. *Mnium spinosum* (Voit.) Schwaegr. [× 3] Robust plants up to 8 cm tall. Stems dark red-brown in lower parts, there with vestigial leaves. Upper leaves large, more or less in terminal rosettes, up to 8 mm long with strong, doubly serrate, often reddish borders. Midrib reddish towards leaf base, green above, shortly excurrent, smooth or toothed on the underside. Setae often several together, orange, up to 2 cm long. Capsules club-shaped, pendulous. Occurs on humus among rocks in mountain woods. Generally rare, very rare in Britain.

200. *Plagiomnium undulatum* (Hedw.) Kop. [× 3] Usually robust plants with erect or arching stems up to 15 cm long, unbranched or with a crown of radiating branches. Leaves translucent green, elongate and more or less strap-shaped, with rounded, apiculate apices, strongly transversely undulate; leaf margins bordered and toothed. Fruit rather uncommon, often borne several together from one perichaetium; capsules ovoid, pendulous. Very common on rich soils in shade under trees or tall herbs.

194 △   195 △

196 △   197 △   ▽ 199   198 △   ▽ 200

201, 202. *Mnium hornum* Hedw. [× 3, × 20] Dark green plants with dark stems, up to 10 cm tall, in tufts or very wide cushions. Leaves erect-spreading, elongate, not undulate and more or less uniform in size, strongly bordered with paired teeth. Midrib strong, almost reaching the leaf apex, toothed on the underside. Setae produced singly, tall, up to 6 cm long, green above, reddish brown below; capsules oval-cylindric, pendulous. Antheridia in dense, dark clusters in terminal rosettes (**202**). Occurs on lime-free soil, rocks and tree roots. Abundant and often dominant in acid woodlands.

203. *Plagiomnium affine* (Funck) Kop. [× 3] Sterile shoots more or less flat, prostrate or arched, with broadly oval, often apparently 2-ranked leaves. Stems usually with copious red-brown rhizoids. Fertile shoots short and erect, with leaves all round the stem, the terminal in rosettes. Leaves bordered and often toothed, teeth single. Widely distributed in marshy ground and mires. *P. affine* belongs to a complex of species which are often difficult to identify. The commonest of these, *P. rostratum* (Schrad.) Kop. is to be found on damp soils in woodlands, wet grasslands and shaded banks throughout Europe.

204. *Rhodobryum roseum* (Hedw.) Limpr. [× 2] Shoots scattered, erect, 4–10 cm tall, pale green. Lower leaves small, upper leaves very large, in conspicuous rosettes, up to 10 mm long, spatulate, broadly acute, with margins narrowly recurved below, toothed above. Midrib strong, ending in leaf tip. Locally frequent on damp, basic soils in meadows and woodlands from sea-level to the subalpine zone.

205. *Aulacomnium androgynum* (Hedw.) Schwaegr. [× 13] Small, bright green plants up to 3 cm tall. Leaves erect-spreading, about 1.5 mm long, lanceolate, denticulate above. Shoots often extended into leafless, stalk-like 'pseudopodia' which bear spherical clusters of green gemmae at their tips. Common and widespread on lime-free rocks, bark, rotting wood and occasionally dry peat.

206. *Aulacomnium palustre* (Hedw.) Schwaegr. [× 2] Robust, yellowish plants up to 15 cm or more long; shoots densely matted with brown tomentum. Grows in lax tufts or scattered stems among mosses, especially among *Sphagnum*, in acid fens and bogs. Frequent in suitable habitats up to 3,000 m alt.

201 △

202 △

203 △   ▽ 205

204 △   ▽ 206

207. *Bartramia hallerana* Hedw. [×3] Plants in deep, soft tufts up to 15 cm tall, green, matted below with copious brown tomentum. Leaves more or less erect-spreading, sometimes secund, with sheathing bases and long, very narrow and finely tapered limbs; margins finely toothed. Seta short, up to 4 mm long, from the sides of the shoots so that the spherical capsules may be hidden among the leaves. Found on rocks in damp shaded places on mountains.

208, 209. *Bartramia pomiformis* Hedw. [×3, ×5] Plants in low, glaucous-green or brownish tufts up to 8 cm high, matted below with rhizoids. Leaves widely spreading when moist, crisped when dry, long and finely tapering but scarcely sheathing at bases, margins toothed. Setae up to 2 cm long, from the ends of shoots. Capsules bright green at first, ripening to brownish-red, more or less spherical. On mainly lime-free rocks and thin soils in rock clefts. Frequent and widespread up to 2,100 m altitude. *B. ithyphylla* Brid. is very similar but has white, sheathing leaf bases. Frequent in similar habitats. *B. stricta* Hedw. is smaller, with stiff, erect leaves, and grows on dry, sandy soils among rocks in central and southern Europe (rare in Britain).

210. *Breutelia chrysocoma* (Hedw.) Lindb. [×4] Robust, usually prostrate plants; shoots more or less branched, golden green and profusely matted with brown tomentum. Leaves widely spreading, narrowly triangular and tapering to sharp points, longitudinally pleated. Seta curved and cygneous; capsule rarely produced, ovoid. Rare except in western Europe; on damp ledges; frequent in upland Britain.

211. *Philonotis marchica* (Hedw.) Brid. [×1.5] Plants with narrow, string-like shoots, pale green, frequently with clusters of branches above, in tufts up to 8 cm tall. Leaves erect, occasionally slightly secund, oval-triangular to lanceolate, acute, toothed, with flat margins. Midrib rather thin, ending in leaf apex. Grows on damp, shaded sandy or clayey soils and gravel. Occasional in lowland districts, rare in the north and subalpine zone. Very rare in Britain.

212, 213. *Philonotis fontana* (Hedw.) Brid. [×2] Shoots erect, simple or with radiating clusters of branches above, pale or glaucous green, matted with brown tomentum below, up to 14 cm tall. Leaves erect or slightly but regularly turned to one side, oval-triangular and tapering to sharp points through which the midrib runs; margins toothed and narrowly recurved below. Setae up to 5 cm long; capsules at first bright green and spherical, becoming brown and grooved when old. Male organs in a terminal rosette of leaves that have blunt to rounded apices. Found in springs, mires and by streams. Common and widely distributed.

214. *Philonotis calcarea* (BSG) Schimp. [×2] In pale or yellowish green tufts, very similar to *P. fontana* but leaves usually longer, more strongly secund and leaves of male 'flowers' are tapered to acute apices. Frequent and widespread in calcareous mires, from sea-level to 3,000 m alt.

207 △   208 △   209 △

210 △   211 △   ▽ 213   212 △   ▽ 214

215. *Orthotrichum stramineum* Brid. [× 4] Plants in low, green or yellow-green tufts up to 2 cm tall. Leaves erect-spreading, lanceolate, acute, with recurved margins. Capsules pale brown to yellowish, tapered into the short setae but held more or less clear of the upper leaves; base of seta surrounded by hairs; old capsules constricted below the mouth and with eight longitudinal ridges. Peristome teeth erect to spreading-reflexed. Calyptra conical, with or without sparse hairs, dark at apex. Widely distributed, up to 1,700 m alt., on bark of trees.

216. *Orthotrichum cupulatum* Brid. [× 7] Olive green, tufted plants up to 3 cm tall. Leaves erect-spreading when moist, lanceolate, shortly acute or blunt at tips, margins recurved. Seta about 2 mm long; capsules ovoid, slightly inflated, held almost clear of the upper leaves, smooth or almost so. Calyptra conical, with sparse hairs. Frequent, on walls and basic rocks. *O. anomalum* Hedw., common in similar habitats, has longer setae, 3–4 mm, holding the darker capsules clear of the leaves.

217. *Orthotrichum affine* Brid. [× 6] Short, bushy, dark green plants in close tufts up to 3 cm high. Leaves erect-spreading, lanceolate, with recurved margins. Setae very short; capsules partly hidden among the upper leaves. Capsules short-cylindrical, with eight ridges; peristome usually reflexed when dry. Calyptra greenish, sparsely hairy. Common on the bark of trees in damp woodlands.

218. *Orthotrichum speciosum* Nees [× 7] Rather robust plants in brownish-green, lax tufts up to 5 cm tall; shoots with matted, brown rhizoids below. Leaves narrowly lanceolate, acute, with recurved margins. Capsules half-exserted above the upper leaves, almost smooth, more or less spindle-shaped. Calyptra hairy, sometimes profusely so. Occurs on trees, rarely on rocks. Occasional in Europe but very rare in Britain.

219. *Ulota crispa* (Hedw.) Brid. [× 3] Green to brownish plants in small tufts. Leaves spreading, strongly curled when dry, with oval basal part and narrower, elongate upper part, tapering to acute apices. Seta yellowish, short but holding the capsules clear of the leaves; capsules elongate, furrowed below the mouth when dry. Common on trunks and twigs of trees and shrubs in shaded, humid areas. *U. phyllantha* Brid. is a similar, yellowish plant but very rarely fruits. Instead, characteristic tufts of brown, elongated gemmae are produced at the ends of the upper leaves. Found on trees and rocks in western Europe; frequent around the coasts of Britain except in the south.

220. *Leucodon sciuroides* (Hedw.) Schwaegr. [× 3] Erect, leafy shoots arise from inconspicuous creeping stems, up to 10 cm long, dull green to olive-brown. Leaves erect-spreading, appressed to stems when dry, oval-triangular, acute, streaked with longitudinal pleats but without midribs. Grows on trees and rocks; occasional to frequent.

221. *Antitrichia curtipendula* (Hedw.) Brid. [× 3] Robust, rather shaggy moss up to 20 cm long, branched, dull or olive green. Leaves erect-spreading, ovate, acute, with irregular, rather coarse and often recurved teeth (sometimes producing minute but characteristic anchor-like tips); margins recurved. Midrib reaching almost to leaf apex. Found on bark of trees and shaded rocks in humid atmospheres; widespread but decreasing, probably due to air pollution.

138

215 △

216 △

217 △

218 △   ▽ 220

219 △   ▽ 221

222. *Hedwigia ciliata* (Hedw.) BSG [× 4] Plants in mats of branched, prostrate or ascending shoots up to 10 cm long, with red-brown stems, yellow-green when moist, white and hoary when dry. Leaves erect-spreading, sometimes turned to one side, ovate, tapering to toothed, hyaline tips which turn out when dry so that shoots appear prickly; midrib lacking. Capsules ovoid, on extremely short setae and immersed among the leaves. Frequent and widely distributed on dry, exposed, siliceous rocks.

223. *Climacium dendroides* (Hedw.) Web. & Mohr. [× 1.5] Plants resembling miniature trees; erect shoots arising from creeping, thin rhizomes, more or less leafless below, supporting a dense head of spreading branches; up to 10 cm tall. Leaves of branches yellowish, slightly spreading, ovate with rather broad tips, longitudinally pleated and with toothed margins. Frequent in colonies of scattered stems in damp grasslands and marshy ground.

224, 225. *Fontinalis antipyretica* Hedw. [× 4, × 8] Large, soft, branched, flexuose plants, often more than 40 cm long, deep green to brown. Leaves without midribs but folded longitudinally and arranged in three strict ranks so that shoots appear three-sided. Capsules rare, on short setae and half enclosed in the perichaetia, arising from the sides of the shoots. Aquatic plants, attached to stones in clear streams and rivers. Frequent.

226. *Leskea polycarpa* Hedw. [× 13] Small, creeping plants with prostrate stems and ascending branches, in low, dull or brownish green mats. Leaves small, often turned to one side, with strong midribs reaching almost to apex. Usually copiously fertile: capsules cylindrical, erect or slightly curved, with conical lids. Grows on silt-covered tree roots, sometimes on rocks, by streams and rivers where liable to periodic flooding. Lowland to subalpine.

227. *Pseudoleskeella nervosa* (Brid.) Nyholm [× 11] Shoots more or less decumbent, irregularly branched, forming dull green to brownish mats. Leaves widely spreading when moist, often more or less secund, erect and appressed to stems when dry, lanceolate with narrowly tapering apices into which the midribs run. Recognised from similar species by the presence of clusters of small branchlets at the shoot tips. Found on basic rocks, mainly in mountain woods and scrub. Very rare in Britain (a few sites in the Scottish Highlands). There are several, very similar, related species which require the use of a microscope for positive identification.

228. *Hookeria lucens* (Hedw.) Sm. [× 3] Shoots usually rather short, sparingly branched, flat, glistening and translucent. Leaves large, up to 5 mm long, untoothed, broadly oval and obtuse, lacking midribs. Leaf cells very large, discernible with the aid of a lens. Setae dark red-brown below; capsules small, dark and shining, horizontal when mature and finely beaked. Grows on damp, heavily shaded earth banks in woodlands, mainly in the more southern and western regions of Europe, and frequent in Britain.

222 △   223 △

224 △   ▽ 226 ▽ 227   225 △   ▽ 228

229. *Neckera crispa* Hedw. [×2] Plants silvery green, yellow or brown, robust, remotely pinnately branched, up to 20 cm long, glossy and somewhat curled when dry. Shoots flat, with leaves more or less rectangular in shape, abruptly pointed to almost truncate, strongly transversely undulate; midribs short or apparently absent. Seta short, under 12 mm long; capsule oval-cylindrical, erect, long-beaked. Frequent and widespread on basic rocks, dry calcareous soils and occasionally on trees. *N. complanata* (Hedw.) Hub. is smaller, paler and more profusely branched. Leaves smaller and not undulate. Common around tree roots, rocks and walls. (See p. 265)

230. *Thamnium alopecurum* (Hedw.) BSG [×6] Shoots up to 15 cm tall, deep green, resembling miniature trees but with flattened, frondose heads of branches. Leaves oval, bluntly tapered, toothed, with strong midribs. Common and widely distributed on wet, shaded, more or less vertical rock faces, usually near water, occasionally forming loose mats in calcareous woodlands.

231. *Homalia trichomanoides* (Hedw.) BSG [×6] Leafy shoots yellowish green, complanate, with deflexed leaves. Leaves oblong, asymmetrical, with more or less rounded, minutely denticulate tips; Midrib short, reaching to mid-leaf. Seta up to 1.5 cm long; capsule ovoid, erect. Frequent and widely distributed in damp, shaded places on rocks and bases of trees.

232. *Leptodon smithii* (Hedw.) Web. & Mohr [×3] Shoots ascending, yellow-green, densely pinnately or bipinnately branched, the whole shoot strongly inrolled when dry. Branch leaves small, short-oval with widely rounded tips and short midribs. Found on rocks and tree trunks, mainly in southern and western Europe; southern Britain.

233. *Isothecium myurum* Brid. [×2] Plants in extensive mats of arching, sub-dendroid, much-branched stems, greyish green with a dull sheen. Leaves oval, concave, rather abruptly pointed, minutely denticulate near apex. Capsules short-cylindrical, erect and symmetrical. Frequent and widely distributed on shaded rocks and trees in woodlands. *I. myosuroides* Brid. is similar in habit and dimensions but has narrower, more acute leaves and slightly asymmetrical and inclined capsules. Found in similar habitats. Abundant in western Europe, including Britain, sometimes the dominant epiphyte.

234. *Myurella julacea* (Schwaegr.) BSG [×7] Plants in small, dense patches or scattered, slender shoots up to 4 cm long; branches slender, cylindrical and string-like, with closely set, silvery green leaves. Leaves very small, concave, more or less orbicular with rounded ends, sometimes with a filiform apiculus. Found on basic soils and calcareous rocks, mainly in the higher mountains.

235. *Abietinella abietina* (Hedw.) Fleisch. [×2.5] Yellowish green to brownish, decumbent or ascending plants with stiff stems and regularly disposed but not complanate (flattened) branches. Stem leaves spreading, broad at base and finely tapering; branch leaves small, oval, with broadly acute tips. Small, yellow-green paraphyllia occur on the stems, among the true leaves. Frequent and widely distributed in open, usually calcareous, grasslands.

229 △   230 △

231 △   232 △   ▽ 234   233 △   ▽ 235

236. *Thuidium tamariscinum* (Hedw.) BSG [× 1] Plants regularly and profusely bi- or tripinnately branched, the resulting fronds matt green to yellowish, up to 10 cm or more long. Stems densely clothed with paraphyllia among the leaves. Stem leaves triangular, with narrow apices. Branch leaves minute, oval, minutely toothed. Common throughout Europe on the ground and around stumps and rocks.

237. *Thuidium philibertii* Limpr. [× 2] Plants almost identical to *T. tamariscinum* (**236**) but stem leaves ending in long, hair-like, reflexed, filiform tips. Frequent, but much less common than the preceeding species, on calcareous soil and rocks.

238. *Calliergon stramineum* (Brid.) Kindb. [× 4] Plants pale green or yellowish, rather glossy, slender and with few branches, up to 15 cm long. Leaves oval, concave, with blunt, often slightly hooded tips, untoothed. Midrib reaching above mid-leaf. Frequent on wet moors and acid mires, often among *Sphagnum*. *C. sarmentosum* (Wahlenb.) Kindb. differs in its rich, purple-red colour. It is less common; in mires and on irrigated rocks in the mountains.

239. *Calliergon cordifolium* (Hedw.) Kindb. [× 1.5] Plants green or yellow, erect or more or less prostrate, up to 15 cm long, rather sparingly branched. Leaves erect-spreading, oval, concave, with rounded tips. Midrib ending near leaf apex. Frequent, in fens, mires and lake margins, sometimes partly submerged. *C. giganteum* (Schimp.) Kindb. is more robust, often brownish, with many, radiating branches. The leaves have distinct patches of hyaline tissue at the base and stronger midribs that reach almost to the leaf tips. Found in similar habitats but less frequent.

241. *Calliergon cuspidatum* (Hedw.) Kindb. [× 1.5] Green, yellow or brown plants, pinnately branched, up to 15 cm long, the ends of stems and branches formed into characteristically sharp points due to the tightly convolute young leaves. Leaves oval, very blunt or rounded at tips; midribs lacking. Abundant and locally dominant moss in damp grasslands and marshy ground. Sometimes a nuisance in lawns.

240. *Scorpidium scorpioides* (Hedw.) Limpr. [× 2] Plants large, soft, turgid, sparingly branched, up to 20 cm long, red-brown to blackish-purple. Leaves broad and concave, asymmetrical and turned in one direction, with blunt or broadly pointed apices. Midrib absent or short and double. Found in very wet fens, mires and pool margins, often partly submerged. Frequent, especially in hilly districts.

242. *Amblystegium varium* (Hedw.) Lindb. [× 3] Small, creeping, irregularly branched stems forming dull or yellowish green patches. Leaves small, lanceolate, up to 2.0 mm long, tapering. Midrib often reaching nearly to leaf apex. Capsules cylindrical, curved, on long, erect setae; lids conical with a small apiculus. Grows on damp, shaded rocks, tree-roots and soil. Occasional; widely distributed. *A. serpens* (Hedw.) BSG, a much commoner species, is smaller, growing in thin, greenish to brownish mats on damp stones, mortar, tree bark, etc. The leaves are scarcely more than 1.1 mm long with inconspicuous midribs. Young fruits have conspicuous, pale, shining calyptras. (See p. 265)

144

236 △   237 △

238 △   239 △   ▽ 241   240 △   ▽ 242

243. *Cratoneuron commutatum* (Hedw.) Roth [×2] Plants stiff, up to 10 cm long, with regularly pinnately branched stems, olive green, brown or orange-brown, usually in large cushions. Leaves triangular-lanceolate, strongly curved and turned downwards, with distinct auricles at base, longitudinally pleated. Midrib thick, running into leaf tip. Older parts of plants are often encrusted with calcium carbonate. Found in basic or calcareous mires and streamside rocks. Frequent and widely distributed, it sometimes occurs as little-branched plants (var. *falcatum*), then easily confused with *Drepanocladus* spp.

245. *Cratoneuron filicinum* (Hedw.) Spruce [×5] Very variable, sometimes resembling *Amblystegium* (**242**) or larger; typically erect shoots, pinnately branched but branches often radiating; green, yellowish or yellow-brown. Leaves curved but not sickle-shaped, secund, with strong midribs. Common and widely distributed on wet rocks and in mires.

244. *Drepanocladus uncinatus* (Hedw.) Warnst. [×3] Shoots erect or ascending, up to 10 cm long, irregularly pinnately branched, yellowish green with brown stems. Leaves narrowly and finely tapering, strongly curved into almost full circles, pleated. Midrib rather thin. Setae long, purplish when young; capsules curved, short-cylindrical. Fruit common. Occurs on siliceous rocks and damp, sandy soils in woodlands, by streams and on moors. Frequent, especially in hilly districts.

246. *Drepanocladus fluitans* (Hedw.) Warnst. [×4] Shoots shorter and pinnate or much elongated, up to 25 cm or more long, green, yellowish or brown. Leaves very long, tapering to very narrow, often toothed, flexuose points, not plicate, often curved and secund. Common and widely distributed in acid mires, pools and sluggish streams on heaths and moors. *D. exannulatus* (BSG) Warnst. is similar, but often purple-red with hamate leaves. Locally frequent in alpine and subalpine, acid mires. *D. aduncus* (Hedw.) Warnst. has straighter, untoothed leaves. It grows in richer, lowland habitats, in dull green to olive brown patches.

247. *Drepanocladus revolvens* (Sw.) Warnst. [×5] Plants up to 10 cm long, simple or pinnately branched, orange to deep purple-red. Leaves narrow and finely tapering, strongly curved into almost full circles and turned in one direction, not pleated; leaf bases narrow, not decurrent and without auricles. Frequent and widely distributed in acid to moderately basic mires.

248. *Drepanocladus vernicosus* (Mitt.) Warnst. [×4] Yellowish green to brownish plants, very similar to forms of *Cratoneuron commutatum* (**243**) but leaves untoothed and often red-brown across the base. Occurs in fens and marshes. Uncommon.

249. *Pseudoscleropodium purum* (Hedw.) Fleisch. [×2] Plants pale green to pale yellow, pinnately branched, with pale stems and lacking rhizoids. Leaves broadly oval and very concave, apices rounded with minute, recurved filiform tips; leaves closely set and overlapping, so that shoots are tumid and cylindrical. Midribs short, reaching to about mid-leaf. Abundant in grasslands, open woodlands and scrub.

243 △   244 △

245 △   246 △   ▽ 248   247 △   ▽ 249

250. *Cirriphyllum crassinervium* (Tayl.) Loeske & Fleisch. [×2] Plants green, in close, low tufts; shoots branched, the branches often all pointing in one direction. Leaves erect-spreading, concave, broadly oval and abruptly tapered at tips; margins minutely toothed. Midrib thick below, sometimes kinked, ceasing well below leaf tip. Grows on damp, shaded, calcareous rocks, occasionally on tree roots, mainly in hilly districts in Europe but not rare in limestone districts in lowland Britain. *C. piliferum* (Hedw.) Grout is very dissimilar. It is pinnately branched, green with pale, cylindrical shoot apices and leaves abruptly tapered to long, flexuose hairs. It is a common plant, usually as scattered stems among grass, etc., in base rich woodlands. (See p. 266)

251. *Camptothecium lutescens* (Hedw.) BSG [×5] Robust, straggling, laxly pinnately branched plants, yellowish, brown in older parts. Leaves erect, appressed to stems when dry, elongate triangular with finely drawn out tips, strongly pleated. Midrib thin and inconspicuous. Frequent in calcareous turf on dunes, limestone and chalk.

252. *Rhynchostegium riparioides* (Hedw.) BSG [×3] Typically deep green or olive green plants, sparingly branched with robust, parallel shoots up to 15 cm long. Leaves broadly oval, short-pointed, erect or slightly secund, toothed all round. Midribs strong, not reaching leaf tips. Common and widely distributed on wet or shallowly immersed rocks in streams and waterfalls.

253. *Brachythecium mildeanum* (Schimp.) Milde [×3] Green or yellowish, branched shoots, rather robust. Leaves erect-spreading, broadly lanceolate and acute. Midrib reaching to beyond mid-leaf. Seta long, smooth; capsule inclined, short-cylindrical. Found on wet soil in marshy ground. Rather rare. Sometimes considered to be a variety of *B. salebrosum* (Web. & Mohr) BSG.

254. *Brachythecium velutinum* (Hedw.) BSG [×3] Small, green plants in low silky tufts. Leaves lanceolate, acute, with minutely toothed margins. Midrib ending well below apex of leaf. Seta long, rough with papillae; capsules ovoid, inclined, with conical lids. Grows on rocks and trees. Lowland to subalpine, frequent and widely distributed; common in lowland Britain.

255. *Brachythecium albicans* (Hedw.) BSG [×2] Plants very pale, silky, in lax tufts, irregularly branched. Leaves broadly lanceolate, erect when dry, finely tapering to long, almost filiform tips, slightly pleated. Stems without or with only scattered, not matted rhizoids. Common and widely distributed in dry turf or soil on neutral to acid soils, especially on dunes.

256. *Brachythecium rutabulum* (Hedw.) BSG [×3] Green to yellowish, robust, pale and often shining plants, branched, often in extensive carpets. Leaves oval, concave, sharply pointed and finely toothed. Midrib ending above mid-leaf. Setae red-brown, very rough with papillae. Capsules oval, brown when mature, more or less horizontal, with conical lids; peristome conspicuous, double. Abundant, often very fertile, on soil, trees, rocks and walls, especially where rich in nitrogen; sometimes an annoying weed in gardens. *B. rivulare* BSG is very similar, but has wider, more abruptly tapered, usually more strongly pleated leaves. It is found in marshy ground and among wet rocks by streams, springs and in fens and mires. Frequent.

250 △   251 △   252 △

253 △   ▽ 255

254 △   ▽ 256

257. *Orthothecium rufescens* BSG [×3] Plants erect or decumbent, golden or coppery, usually with strong tinges of pink or wine-red, sparingly branched, up to 10 cm long. Leaves erect-spreading, triangular-lanceolate, finely tapering and markedly pleated. Midribs lacking. Uncommon to rare species of damp, shaded ledges and crevices of calcareous mountain rocks.

258. *Pleurozium schreberi* (Brid.) Mitt. [×2] Plants robust, regularly pinnately branched, translucent yellow with red stems, rather stiff. Leaves oval, concave, erect and overlapping so that shoots are tumid, without visible midribs or marginal teeth; apices rounded-obtuse. Grows in deep, loose cushions or scattered stems among grasses and dwarf shrubs in acid woodlands and heathlands. Common and widely distributed.

259. *Homalothecium sericeum* (Hedw.) BSG [×4] Green to brownish plants with creeping stems and dense, ascending branches, in patches up to 20 cm or more across. Leaves triangular, finely tapering, spreading when moist but erect when dry so that the, usually slightly curved, branches have a silky appearance; strongly pleated so that the thin midrib is difficult to distinguish. Seta rough; capsule cylindrical, erect. Common on walls, rocks and old trees throughout Britain and Europe.

260. *Eurhynchium angustirete* (Broth.) Kop. [×4] Very similar to *E. striatum* (below) but with shorter and wider leaves. Rare, with a more eastern or continental type of distribution.

261. *Eurhynchium striatum* (Hedw.) Schimp. [×3] Plants rather robust, irregularly or pinnately branched with stiff, arching, dark green or yellowish shoots. Leaves spreading, broadly oval-triangular, shortly acutely pointed, strongly pleated, with denticulate margins. Midrib narrow, reaching to below leaf tip. Occurs on base-rich soils in woodlands; rather more common in the west. Common and widespread in Britain.

262. *Eurhynchium praelongum* (Hedw.) Hobk. [×4] Plants creeping or arched, bright green or yellowish, regularly pinnately, sometimes bipinnately, branched, up to 15 cm long. Stem leaves very broad at base, triangular, cordate, finely tapering above to spreading-recurved, narrow points. Branch leaves oval-lanceolate, smaller, erect-spreading, acutely pointed with finely toothed margins. Midrib ceasing below leaf tip. Long-beaked, oval-cylindrical, inclined capsules occasionally produced on long, rough setae. Common on wood, rocks and soil in shaded places throughout Europe. *E. swarzii* (Turn.) Curn. differs in its broader, less diverse leaves. It is frequent on damp, base-rich soils in similar habitats.

263. *Dolichotheca seligeri* (Brid.) Loeske [×3] Plants creeping with arched branches, green, glossy when dry, in close tufts or patches. Leaves spreading, sometimes slightly secund, flexuose when dry, oval-lanceolate and tapering to acute, finely denticulate tips. Midrib faint, short and double. Capsules usually abundant, smooth, cylindrical and inclined, with conical lids. Grows on stumps and bases of trees. Mainly lowland in Europe; southern England, especially in *Castanea* coppice.

150

257 △   258 △

259 △   260 △   ▽ 262   261 △   ▽ 263

264. *Plagiothecium curvifolium* Schlieph. [×1.5] Plants glossy, green, with narrow, prostrate, sparingly branched shoots up to 6 cm long. Leaves complanate, curved downwards on either side of stems, asymmetrical, mostly with one margin curved and the other more or less straight, tapering to acute, almost entire tips. Midrib short and double. Capsules short-cylindrical, inclined, smooth. Occasional to locally frequent in woodlands on humus-rich soils, logs and tree roots.

265. *Plagiothecium denticulatum* (Hedw.) BSG [×5] Shoots flat, prostrate, glossy, bright green, up to 10 cm long, only slightly shrunken when dry. Leaves ovate, asymmetrical but both margins curved, acute at apex and often faintly toothed. Midrib short and double. Capsules cylindrical, curved, strongly inclined. Common and widely distributed on damp rocks, soil and wood in shade. *Isopterygium elegans*, a very common species on shaded, acid woodland banks, is very similar, but smaller. It can often be recognized by the clusters of tiny propaguliferous branches among the upper leaves.

266. *Plagiothecium latebricola* BSG [×6] Plants weak, slender, with flat, pale or yellowish shoots, in small patches. Leaves elongate-triangular, symmetrical, tapering to narrow, acute tips. Midrib absent or short and single. Occurs on tree bases and stumps, uncommon, mainly lowland; in Britain mainly in the southern counties.

267. *Plagiothecium nemorale* (Mitt.) Jaeg. [×3] (syn. *P. silvaticum* (Brid.) BSG). Very similar to *P. denticulatum* (**265**) but leaves, on average, more abruptly pointed and much more shrivelled when dry. Found on damp, shaded rocks and trees, mainly in the forest zone. Frequent in Britain.

268. *Plagiothecium undulatum* (Hedw.) BSG [×2] Plants robust, flat, very pale or almost white, sparingly branched, the complanate shoots up to 15 cm long, often in very extensive mats. Leaves ovate, strongly transversely undulate, abruptly tapered to acute or obtuse tips. Common and widely distributed on acid humus, logs and lime-free rocks in coniferous forests, birchwoods and heathlands.

269. *Plagiothecium succulentum* (Wils.) Lindb. [×3] Very similar to *P. nemorale* (**267**) and cannot be distinguished with certainty without a microscope. Usually glossy, golden green plants on moist soil among rocks and shrubs. Occasional to locally frequent.

270. *Ctenidium molluscum* (Hedw.) Mitt. [×3] Shoots golden and silky, densely pinnately branched and plumose, up to 8 cm long, forming extensive soft carpets. Stem leaves spreading and lightly secund, broadly cordate-triangular with fine, often crimped apices. Branch leaves lanceolate, strongly curved and turned downwards, with toothed margins. Midribs short and double. Common and widely distributed on calcareous soil and rocks, sometimes on walls.

264 △   265 △   266 △

267 △   ▽ 269   268 △   ▽ 270

271. *Pylaisia polyantha* (Hedw.) BSG [×6] Small, dull or yellow-green plants in silky tufts. Shoots pinnately or irregularly branched, with short, often curved, ascending branches. Leaves secund, upswept, ovate at base then tapered to fine apices; margins untoothed; midribs lacking. Young setae purplish; capsules narrowly ellipsoid, erect, with acute, conical lids. Occurs on bark of trees, from sea-level to 1,400 m alt. Rather rare in Britain. Easily confused with *Hypnum cupressiforme* var. *resupinatum*.

272, 273, 274. *Hypnum cupressiforme* Hedw. [×1, ×4, ×3] Very polymorphic species; typically prostrate, pinnately branched, with glossy, green, yellowish to orange-brown shoots up to 8 cm long. Leaves oval-lanceolate, concave, curved and turned downwards, sometimes appearing as if two-ranked when viewed from above, usually minutely toothed; midrib absent or short, faint, double. Setae red-brown or orange. Capsules inclined, short-cylindrical, lids conical and usually drawn out into short beaks. Very common on rocks, walls, trees, logs and soil. The var. *lacunosum* Brid. is a robust form with bronze colouration and more turgid shoots. The leaves are larger, more concave, with only the tips turned down. It is common on lime-rich soils, rocks and walls. Var. *resupinatum* (Tayl.) Schimp. is a small, compact form with narrow, upturned leaves and branches, resembling *Pylaisia* (**271**). It is frequent on bark, rocks and walls. Var. *filiforme* Brid. (**274**) has thin, irregularly branched, parallel, downward growing shoots. It is an abundant epiphyte on tree trunks. According to some authorities, this form should be transferred to *H. mamillatum* (Brid.) Loeske.

275. *Hypnum jutlandicum* Holmen & Warncke [×4] (syn. *H. cupressiforme* var. *ericetorum* BSG). Resembles *H. cupressiforme* but the pinnately branched shoots are pale, whitish green, almost devoid of rhizoids, and distinctly flattened. It grows in large, soft, glossy cushions on acid humus and litter in woodlands and heathlands. Common and widely distributed.

276. *Rhytidium rugosum* (Hedw.) Kindb. [×1.5] Robust, brownish or golden, prostrate plants, irregularly or sometimes pinnately branched; main shoots up to 12 cm long. Leaves rather glossy, rugose, secund, closely overlapping so that shoots appear rather turgid, ovate at base then tapering to narrow points; margins narrowly recurved to beyond the middle, apical margins toothed. Midrib short, reaching more or less to mid leaf, often forked above. Occurs on exposed, sandy, usually calcareous soils on rock ledges, hillsides and dunes. Widely distributed but uncommon; up to 3,000 m altitude.

277. *Ptilium crista-castrensis* (Hedw.) De Not. [×2] Elegant, plumose plants with shoots up to 15 cm long, densely and very regularly pinnately branched. Leaves tapering from broader bases, strongly curved and turned downwards, longitudinally pleated, entire; midrib lacking or very short and double. Grows on damp, acid humus under trees, especially conifers, or ericaceous shrubs. Widespread but uncommon; locally frequent in mountain woods.

271 △   272 △

273 △   274 △   ▽ 276   275 △   ▽ 277

278. *Rhytidiadelphus squarrosus* (Hedw.) Warnst. [×3] Plants up to 15 cm long, green or yellowish, with reddish stems and rather translucent leaves, remotely pinnately branched. Leaves of main shoots strongly recurved (squarrose) from erect bases, broad at base then tapered to finely pointed, reflexed tips; margins minutely toothed. Midrib double, ceasing below mid-leaf. Growing in extensive carpets in grasslands; common, locally abundant and often a serious pest in lawns.

279. *Rhytidiadelphus triquetrus* (Hedw.) Warnst. [×3] Large plants, up to 20 cm tall, with erect, stiff stems and radiating branches. Stems red-brown. Leaves pale, widely spreading and of a chaff-like rigidity, neither squarrose nor secund, oval-triangular, tapered to acute points, pleated and sometimes slightly rugose; margins toothed. Midrib double, thin, reaching a little beyond mid-leaf. Common and widely distributed from sea-level to 2,000 m altitude on base-rich soils in open woodlands, scrub and coarse grasslands.

280. *Rhytidiadelphus loreus* (Hedw.) Warnst. [×3] Plants robust, rigid, up to 30 cm long, arching-decumbent, regularly but not closely pinnately branched, yellowish to brown with reddish-brown stems. Leaves spreading, curved and turned in one direction (secund), firm, drawn out into long, fine apices; margins toothed; midrib more or less absent. Occurs on acid humus and litter among rocks, screes, and in acid woodlands, mainly in montane or northern districts. Common in upland Britain.

281. *Hylocomium splendens* (Hedw.) BSG [×1.5] Robust, frondose plants up to 20 cm long, with ascending, flat, profusely bi- or tripinnately branched shoots, translucent yellowish-green with red stems. Leaves ovate, concave, those of the stem much larger than those of the branches, interspersed with minute, branched paraphyllia; leaf apices shortly acute or obtuse, toothed, lightly pleated. Midrib double, reaching more or less to mid-leaf. Common and widely distributed in acid woodlands, heathlands and coarse grasslands.

282. *Hylocomium pyrenaicum* (Spruce) Lindb. [×1.5] Plants up to 10 cm long, simply and rather irregularly pinnate; shoots cylindrical and worm-like, yellowish with red stems, in rather compact cushions. Leaves ovate, with short, acute or obtuse apices, strongly pleated and with coarsely toothed upper margins. Midrib usually single, ending in mid-leaf. Occurs on basic soils among rocks and in open woodland in the subalpine and alpine zones. Locally frequent in Europe; rare and local in Britain. *H. brevirostre* (Brid.) BSG is a similar but rather coarser plant but has widely spreading stem leaves with longer apices and normally double midribs. In Britain, at least, it is much more frequent, especially in the west and north.

283, 284. *Andreaea rupestris* Hedw. [×10, ×25] Plants small, in low, dense, brown to almost black tufts, usually under 1.5 cm tall. Leaves small, ovate, narrowed to acute tips, often asymmetrical and slightly secund, lacking midribs. Perichaetial leaves much larger than ordinary leaves, erect. Capsules on short stalks, very small, opening by four longitudinal slits. Found on exposed siliceous rocks from sea level to 3,000 m altitude; common in hilly districts. *A. alpina* Hedw. is larger, with leaves waisted below the middle (i.e. panduriform). It grows in similar habitats and also on wet, compact soils, sometimes in extensive mats. Frequent in the alpine and subalpine zones. *A. rothii* Web. & Mohr has narrow, curved and secund leaves, black when dry. On rocks, sometimes slightly basic, and usually with a more or less southerly aspect. Frequent in mountainous districts.

156

278 △   279 △

280 △   ▽ 282

281 △   ▽ 283

284.   *Andreaea rupestris* see p. 156

285.   *Anthoceros punctatus* L. [× 7] Thalli small, bright green, blackened when dry, in irregular rosettes up to 1.2 cm in diameter, irregularly lobed, the lobes divided into numerous, very small segments; dorsal surface more or less rough with several lamellae and having a crisped appearance. Scattered, dark dots in the thallus tissue are colonies of the blue-green alga *Nostoc*. Capsules long and narrow, elongating from basal growth, arising from cylindrical involucres, green, becoming blackish towards the apex where they split into two ribbon-like valves. Spores black when mature. Locally frequent on moist soil in fields, by paths and rivers; widely distributed.

286.   *Phaeoceros laevis* (L.) Prosk. [× 13] Thalli up to 1.2 cm long, flat and smooth, green, blackening when dry, without colonies of blue-green algae. Thallus lobes short or sometimes elongated and forked, with undulate but not laciniate margins. Capsules as in the previous species but usually olive or brownish. Spores pale brown or yellowish. Locally frequent on soil in fields, etc.

287.   *Preissia quadrata* (Scop.) Nees [× 10] Thalli simple or forked, pale or slightly glaucous green with purplish margins, up to 3 cm long, 5–10 mm wide, rounded and notched at the ends. Upper surface with a distinct hexagonal pattern of areolae and minute white pores. Underside reddish brown to purple, with a row of scales on either side of the midline, and copious rhizoids. Carpophores up to 5 cm long, the heads convex, rounded-squarish. Antheridia in smaller, hemispherical heads on stalks up to 2 cm long. Found on rock ledges, on more or less basic soils. Frequent and widespread in hilly districts. Absent from southern England. *Reboulia hemisphaerica* (L.) Raddi is somewhat similar but lacks the regular pattern of areolae. The male organs are not produced on stalked structures. On dry rocks and soil, mainly in the south.

288, 289.   *Conocephalum conicum* (L.) Lindb. [× 1.5, × 25] Large plants; thalli fresh green, occasionally yellowish, up to 15 cm long and 2 cm wide, without a darker or coloured median zone. Upper surface with large areolae and conspicuous pores (**289**); underside greenish, with long rhizoids and 2 rows of small, distant, colourless scales. Carpocephala conical, borne on long stalks up to 6 cm tall. Antheridia embedded in green to dark purple discs or pads, becoming apparently lateral on the main thallus, not stalked. Common and widespread in large, flat patches on damp, shaded rocks and walls.

290, 291.   *Sphaerocarpus michelli* Bellardi [× 16, × 10] Dioeceous plants of more or less annual duration. Thalli small and delicate, seldom more than 6 mm across. Female plants with archegonia and developing capsules enclosed in more conspicuous, inflated, ovoid or club-shaped involucres about 2 mm long. Male plants smaller, the antheridia enclosed in smaller involucres. Occurs on bare soil. Frequent in the warmer regions of Europe, elsewhere rare and often of spasmodic occurrence.

284 △   285 △   286 △

287 △   ▽ 289   ▽ 290   288 △   ▽ 291

292, 293, 294. *Marchantia polymorpha* L. [×½, ×13, ×7] Flat, branching thalli, often forming extensive mats, dull green with darker, brownish or purplish median zone, up to 10 cm long and 1.3 cm broad. Upper surface areolate and with moderately conspicuous pores, usually here and there with cup-shaped structures containing discoid gemmae (**294**). Underside with copious rhizoids and two rows of colourless scales. Female carpophores on long stalks, more or less umbrella-shaped with a median disc and 8–10 narrow rays; capsules at first enclosed in thinly textured perianths, in clusters from the underside of the disc. Antheridiophores also stalked, the heads flat-topped and with 6–9 short, rounded lobes. Grows on soil; common by paths and in gardens; often a weed in greenhouses.

295. *Riccardia pinguis* (L.) Lindb. [×7] Plants thallose, thalli rather small, irregularly or pinnately branched, deep green, fleshy and smooth. Underside with rhizoids but no scales. Male plants with antheridia inside small, rough, cylindrical side branches. Capsules elongate, oval-cylindrical, splitting into four valves, on white, short-lived setae up to 1 mm long, springing from a fleshy perianth. Found in patches or creeping among vegetation on wet, peaty soils by streams, in mires and fens and on wet moorland. Common and widespread. *R. multifida* (L.) Gray has very narrow, stiff, bipinnately branched, dark thalli up to 2 cm long but only 0.5 mm wide. It is frequent in wet, shaded places in fens and by streams. *R. palmata* (Hedw.) Carruth. forms small, velvety green cushions of ascending thalli, 1 cm long, 1 mm wide. It is occasional on rotting wood in dense shade.

296. *Riccia fluitans* L. [×4] Thalli elongate, narrow, forked, either floating and lacking rhizoids or on mud and thicker, with dense rhizoids; light green, up to 5 cm long, 2 mm wide, without pores but with internal air-chambers. Capsules rarely produced, and then only in terrestrial forms, seen as black spheres within the body of the thallus. Occurs in floating colonies in pools and ditches, or on mud by lakes and rivers; mainly in southern and western, lowland districts. Often grown in freshwater aquaria.

297. *Riccia glauca* L. [×3] Plants growing in more or less circular rosettes of small, forked thalli, pale or bluish green, closely attached to compacted soils by abundant rhizoids. Thallus lobes 1–3 mm wide, channelled only near the notched apices; underside with colourless, evanescent scales. Capsules spherical, immersed in the thallus, black when mature and ultimately disintegrating to release the spores. Frequent and widely distributed on damp soils in fields and by paths, etc. *R. sorocarpa* Bisch. is similar but has erect thallus margins and more or less acute apices. Frequent in similar habitats. *R. crystallina* L. has spongy thalli with abundant air-spaces, appearing white and crystalline when dry. Widely distributed, especially in the south. *R. nigrella* DC has narrow thalli, blackish purple beneath and with conspicuous, persistent scales. Frequent in southern Europe but rare in Britain.

298. *Lunularia cruciata* (L.) Dum. [×3] Rather robust, bright green, furcate thalli, similar to *Marchantia* but without a darker median zone and with gemma cups that are crescent-shaped. Fruit is rarely produced: carpocephala on long, weak, short-lived stalks, cross-shaped; male organs produced on dark, blackish pad-like outgrowths of the main thallus, not stalked. Very common near habitation, on soil, damp rocks and walls, rare in the north.

160

292 △

293 △

294 △

295 △   ▽ 297

296 △   ▽ 298

299.   *Blasia pusilla* L. [× 2] Thallose plants; thalli prostrate or ascending, more or less tongue-shaped with lobed margins, very thin except for broad midrib; translucent green with darker dots (*Nostoc* colonies, as in *Anthoceros*). Upper surface with flask-shaped vesicles containing gemmae. Underside of midrib with colourless rhizoids and two rows of inconspicuous scales. Occurs on damp soil on banks, roadsides and in open woodlands. Widely distributed but uncommon.

300.   *Metzgeria furcata* (L.) Dum. [× 7] Thalli narrow and ribbon-like, furcate, to 1 mm wide, very thin (one cell thick) except for the narrow, sharply defined midrib; green or yellowish. Wings of thallus more or less hairless, the margins usually with a fringe of non-paired, more or less straight cilia. Spherical capsules, on short setae up to 2.5 mm long, arise from hollow, hairy, inflated involucres on the underside of the midrib. Common and widely distributed on trees, rocks and walls.

301.   *Metzgeria pubescens* (Schrank) Raddi [× 7] Similar to *M. furcata* but the whole plant is more or less densely clothed with short hairs. Found in patches or creeping among mosses among shaded, calcareous rocks. Uncommon.

302.   *Metzgeria conjugata* Lindb. [× 7] Plants very similar to *M. furcata* but generally longer, and marginal cilia mostly in pairs. Locally frequent on damp, shaded rocks, rarely on trees, mainly subalpine and western.

303.   *Pallavicinia lyellii* (Hook.) Gray [× 4] Thalli thin, pale green, 3–4 cm long, 3–4 mm wide; branches arising from the underside of the narrow, sharply defined midrib. Female 'perianth' smooth and cylindrical, arising from a laciniate, cup-shaped involucre on the dorsal side of the midrib. Antheridia mixed with small, laciniate scales on the dorsal side of the thallus. Capsule cylindrical, 4 mm long. Occurs on wet soil in marshy ground at low altitudes. Uncommon to rare; very local in Britain.

305.   *Pellia endiviifolia* (Dicks.) Dum. [× 3] (syn. *P. fabbroniana* Raddi). Plants very similar to *P. epiphylla* (below) but female 'involucre' is an erect, cylindrical tube about 4 mm long. The thallus is usually pure green and much crisped about the margins. Frequent and widely distributed in mats on damp, calcareous rocks and soil.

304, 306.   *Pellia neesiana* Gottsche [× 3, × 4] Plants indistinguishable from forms of *P. epiphylla* except when fertile. Thalli fleshy, thin towards margins, deep green with often purple overtones, up to 10 mm wide. Dioecious; capsules spherical, borne on abruptly elongating, white setae which arise from cylindrical involucres and pseudo-perianths. Antheridia embedded in the upper side of the thallus, visible as small, often reddish pustules. Occurs in usually extensive patches on wet, peaty soils on marshy ground. Frequent and widely distributed; sea-level to subalpine. *P. epiphylla* (L.) Lindb. is a much commoner plant. It is monoecious, with antheridia scattered in the upperside of the thallus behind the female 'involucre' which in this species is in the form of a small, green flap, not tubular. Common and locally abundant on shaded, damp, lime-free soils on banks by ditches and in woodlands.

299 △   300 △

301 △   ▽ 304   302 △   ▽ 305   303 △   ▽ 306

307. *Fossombronia* species [×20]. Small, usually green plants, up to 1.5 cm long, creeping, with fleshy stems closely attached to soil by, usually, reddish-violet rhizoids. Leaves in two lateral rows, the insertion parallel to the long axis of stem, irregular in form and variously crisped and lobed. Antheridia naked, on the upper side of stem. Capsules spherical, on short setae. Grows on soil, often of annual duration. The species of *Fossombronia* are mainly identified on characters of spore ornamentation, requiring a microscope. The genus is common and widely distributed.

308. *Trichocolea tomentella* (Ehrh.) Dum. [×10] Plants pale, almost white, pinnately to bipinnately branched, prostrate or ascending. Leaves and amphisgastria more or less identical, almost entirely divided up into hair-like filaments so that the whole plant has a woolly texture. Found in marshy ground, fens and saturated vegetation by streams and lakes. Uncommon, mainly subalpine but descending to sea level in the west (including Britain).

309. *Anthelia juratzkana* (Limpr.) Trev. [×13] Small, compact plants; shoots narrow, dull slate-coloured with a curious white 'bloom', especially when dry. Amphigastria more or less identical to leaves, hence appearing tristichous, all erect and overlapping, deeply cleft to two-thirds into two acute lobes. Perianth broadly ovoid, toothed at mouth. Monoecious and usually fertile. Grows on rock ledges and soil in the mountains, mainly above the forest zone and locally common in snow-bed vegetation. *A. julacea* (L.) Dum. is very similar but is dioecious and often barren. A much commoner species, often in extensive grey or blackish carpets on wet, acid soils and rocks in the alpine zone.

310. *Ptilidium pulcherrimum* (Web.) Hampe [×4] Plants creeping, densely pinnately branched, in compact, low, orange to red-brown mats; shoots to 3 cm long. Leaves divided into 3–4 unequal lobes, cleft to beyond two-thirds; margins profusely ciliate. Amphigastria similar to leaves but only half as large and more or less symmetrical. Found on trunks of trees, rarely on rocks; frequent in hilly districts but sensitive to air pollution.

311. *Ptilidium ciliare* (Hedw.) Hampe [× 10] Plants similar to the preceeding species but larger, up to 8 cm long, and more lax. The ciliate leaves are divided only half way. Fruit rare; perianth cylindrical, inflated, pleated above and ciliate around the mouth. Frequent and widely distributed on peaty soils and litter on heathland and in open woodlands.

312. *Bazzania tricrenata* (Wahl.) Trev. [×3] Plants erect or ascending, simple or forked, yellowish green, 2–8 cm long. Shoots arched; rhizoids few, confined to older parts. Leaves incubously shingled, to 1.5 mm long, deflexed, asymmetrical, at apex with 2–3 short, acute or blunt teeth. Amphigastria twice as wide as stem, wider than long, with 3–4 irregular, blunt lobes, partly connate with the leaves. Grows in cushions or among other bryophytes among lime-free rocks. Mainly subalpine and alpine. Frequent in the west and north-west.

313. *Bazzania trilobata* (L.) Gray [×4] Robust, whitish-green to pale olive plants with ascending, dichotomously branched shoots up to 15 cm long. Leaves 3–4 mm long, deflexed, ending in three short, broadly acute lobes or large teeth. Amphigastria wider than long, irregularly lobed or dentate. Long, thin, flagellar branches, having only vestigial leaves, grow downwards from the underside of the stem. Frequent, except in the lowlands, in damp, shaded woodlands, among rocks and on stumps, etc.

307 △   308 △

309 △   310 △   ▽ 312   311 △   ▽ 313

314. ***Blepharostoma trichophyllum*** (L.) Dum. [× 16] Small, delicate, pale yellowish plants, irregularly branched, up to 2 cm long. Leaves composed of 3–4 hair-like lobes. Amphigastria smaller, but otherwise similar to leaves, of 2–3 lobes. Perianths terminal, elongate cylindrical, inflated, rounded-triangular and ciliate at mouth. Occasional, mainly in hilly districts, among mosses on humus, rocks and tree roots in shaded places where not very acid. *Kurzia pauciflora* (Dicks.) Grolle (syn. *Lepidozia setacea* (Web.) Mitt.) is similar but dark green to brownish and is confined to very acid habitats such as peat in bogs and acid heathlands. (See p. 267)

315, 316. ***Lepidozia reptans*** (L.) Dum. [× 7, × 20] Small, regularly branched, green, creeping plants up to 5 cm long, in compact mats. Leaves rectangular, curved and deflexed, divided to the middle into 3–4 narrow lobes, rather remote and not hiding the stems; incubously shingled. Amphigastria slightly wider than the stem, 3–4 lobed, about as wide as long. Common and widely distributed on acid humus, tree roots, stumps and rocks in woodland.

317. ***Chiloscyphus pallescens*** (L.) Corda [× 6] Shoots yellowish green, 2–5 cm long, 3 mm wide, sparingly branched, creeping or ascending. Leaves succubously shingled, obliquely inserted, arched-spreading, more or less rectangular in outline with rounded-truncate to shallowly retuse ends. Amphigastria well developed, deeply bilobed, lobes acute and usually with a tooth at the side. Grows in cushions on wet, peaty soils, occasionally on wet rocks. Occasional. *C. polyanthus* (L.) Corda is very similar but usually duller, green to brownish. It is common in and by streams.

318. ***Lophocolea cuspidata*** (Nees) Dum. [× 4] Superficially almost identical to *L. bidentat* (below), but monoecious and commonly fertile. Common. especially on rotting wood and damp rocks in shade.

319. ***Lophocolea bidentata*** (L.) Dum. [× 10] Plants creeping, pale or yellowish green, up to *c.* 5 cm long, 3 mm wide, irregularly branched. Leaves succubously arranged, with broad, almost longitudinal attachment to stem, decurrent, $\frac{1}{4}$ divided into two acutely tapering lobes; sinus more or less rounded. Amphigastria well developed, bifid with tapering, acute lobes and a large tooth at each side above the insertion. Dioecious and fruits rather rare. Perianths elongate, three-sided and laciniate at the mouth. Common and widely distributed on damp, usually acidic soils, in woodlands, grasslands and heaths.

320. ***Lophocolea heterophylla*** (Schrad.) Dum. [× 8] Plants creeping, usually dark green, irregularly branched; shoots up to 3 cm long, 2.5 mm broad. Older leaves distinctly bilobed, the lobes acute or commonly blunt to rounded; younger leaves variously rounded, truncated or shallowly bilobed. Amphigastria acutely bilobed, with lateral teeth, as in the previous species. Perianths usually abundant, erect, long-cylindrical becoming three-sided above and toothed at the mouth. Grows on shaded, moist tree trunks, rotting wood and rocks. Resistant to pollution and the commonest epiphytic foliose liverwort near towns. Common throughout Europe.

314 △   315 △

316 △   317 △   ▽ 319   318 △   ▽ 320

321. *Sphenolobus saxicola* (Schrad.) Steph. [× 16] Brown, rigid and brittle, sparingly branched plants up to 5 cm long, 2.5 mm wide, creeping or ascending. Leaves almost transversely inserted, divided into two unequal lobes. Upper lobe concave, bent over the larger, convex lower lobe, the apices incurved and often concealed. Amphigastria absent. Found on siliceous rocks, especially isolated blocks, in mountainous areas. Local, rare in Britain.

322. *Barbilophozia lycopodioides* (Wallr.) Loeske [× 5] Shoots robust, mostly unbranched, up to 8 cm long, 4–5 mm wide, creeping, with scattered, colourless rhizoids. Leaves four-lobed, broader than long, undulate, the lobes broadly triangular, ending in a long, fine tooth; lower leaf margin with 2–5 cilia at the base. Underleaves small, two-lobed, with occasional cilia. Grows in patches or scattered shoots on base-rich soils in the alpine and subalpine zones.

323. *Barbilophozia hatcheri* (Evans) Loeske [× 2] Very similar to the preceeding species but smaller and terminal leaves often gemmiferous. On soil among rocks and in subalpine woodlands. Locally frequent. *B. floerkii* (Web. & Mohr) Loeske is similar but smaller, usually with three-lobed leaves. It is locally common in similar habitats. *B. attenuata* (Mart.) Loeske also has three-lobed leaves but is recognised by its ascending, narrow, catkin-like shoots with gemmiferous leaves. Locally frequent on thin, acid humus among rocks and on bark of old trees.

324. *Barbilophozia barbata* (Schreb.) Loeske [× 6] Yellowish green to brownish, creeping plants, 2–6 cm long, 2–3 mm wide. Leaves almost longitudinally inserted, with four obtuse, shallow lobes, without cilia at the base. Amphigastria absent or vestigial. Occurs in grasslands and on rock ledges, usually on base-rich soils. Subalpine and alpine, locally frequent.

325. *Barbilophozia kunzeana* (Hüb.) K. Müll. [× 6] Green or yellowish plants with erect or ascending, mostly unbranched shoots up to 5 cm long, with long colourless rhizoids. Leaves obliquely inserted, heart-shaped and basically bi-lobed, with 1–3 cilia above the postical base. Amphigastria small, with two narrow, acute lobes and a tooth at the side. Tips of young leaves often gemmiferous. Found among other bryophytes in wet, acid habitats, occasionally on rocks or rotting wood. Frequent in the mountains of Europe, rare elsewhere.

326. *Tritomaria quinquedentata* (Huds.) Buch [× 8] Rather robust, creeping plants, green or yellowish, 2–5 cm long, 2–3 mm wide, with numerous rhizoids. Leaves obliquely inserted, with three unequal lobes, the adaxial lobe and margin much larger than the abaxial. Amphigastria lacking. Grows on thin soil among rocks. Common in mountainous regions, elsewhere rare.

327. *Leiocolea heterocolpos* (Thed.) Buch [× 7] Plants greenish, sparingly branched, the shoots up to 2 cm long, slender, erect, with numerous long rhizoids. Leaves obliquely inserted, spreading, oval and bilobed to about one-third; lobes obtusely pointed, with a narrow sinus. Usually producing catkin-like gemmiferous shoots with erect, reduced leaves and enlarged underleaves; gemmae brown. Amphigastria on normal shoots very small, simple or bifid. Grows on ledges of calcareous rocks in the mountains. Rare in Britain.

328. *Leiocolea gillmanii* (Aust.) Evans [× 6] Plants green, tufted; shoots 2–3 cm long, 2–3 mm wide, with brownish rhizoids. Leaves closely set, spreading and slightly recurved, shallowly bilobed. Amphigastria small, lanceolate, often with a lateral tooth. Gemmae lacking. Found on damp, sometimes inundated limestone. Northern Europe; rare or local in Britain. *Lophozia ventricosa* (Dicks.) Dum. differs from *Leiocolea* in its acute, symmetrical leaf lobes. It lacks underleaves but produces gemmae at the tips of the young leaves. It is common on acid humus in heathlands.

321 △   322 △

323 △   ▽ 326   324 △   ▽ 327   325 △   ▽ 328

329.   *Pedinophyllum interruptum* (Nees) Lindb. [× 3] Plants more or less prostrate and matted, yellowish green to olive brown; stems leafy from the base and with rhizoids all along the underside. Leaves succubous, rounded-quadrate, 1–2 mm long, not decurrent at antical base, convex and deflexed. Amphigastria absent or vestigial. Grows on damp, shaded calcareous rocks, mainly in central and southern Europe; rare in Britain.

330.   *Plagiochila asplenioides* (L.) Dum. [× 2] Robust, mainly unbranched, ascending, stiff shoots arise from more or less leafless, prostrate stems; leafy portion lacking rhizoids. Leaves ovate, decurrent, usually toothed around the margins. Amphigastria vestigial. Grows on damp, slightly acid to more or less basic soils in shaded places. Common and widely distributed.

331.   *Plagiochila porelloides* (Nees) Lindb. [× 5] Very similar to the preceeding species but smaller, under 7 cm long, and branching rather frequently. Leaves of similar shape but usually lacking marginal teeth. Grows on damp, shaded rocks and walls, occasionally on tree bases. Common and widely distributed.

332.   *Jungermannia lanceolata* L. emend Schrad. [× 6] Plants bright pale green to brownish, in patches; stems fleshy, irregularly branched; shoots up to 3 cm long, 2 mm wide, with copious brownish rhizoids. Leaves succubous, obliquely inserted, spreading, slightly decurrent, oblong oval and about twice as long as wide. Amphigastria lacking. Monoecious: perianth long and cylindrical, depressed at the narrow mouth. Grows on wet rocks, humified soils and trunks of trees in shade. Uncommon to locally frequent in Europe; very rare in Britain.

333.   *Solenostoma triste* (Nees) K. Müll. [× 10] Plants typically in dark green patches; shoots creeping with ascending apices and colourless to pale brown rhizoids; small-leaved 'stolons' usually present. Leaves obliquely inserted, closely set, broadly ovate with rounded apices. Amphigastria lacking. Dioecious: antheridia in the axils of more concave leaves (**333**); perianth club-shaped, strongly pleated at mouth. Frequent on damp or wet, shaded rocks. *S. cordifolium* (Hook.) Steph. is larger, with soft, cordate leaves. It grows in large, almost black cushions up to 15 cm deep, in alpine streams and springs. Locally frequent.

334.   *Solenostoma crenulatum* (Sm.) [× 16] Plants creeping or ascending, shoots up to *c.* 2 cm long, in reddish-brown patches, often with abundant, small-leaved, attenuated shoots. Leaves orbicular, the largest with a narrow, pale marginal band of cells. Common and widespread on moist soils by paths and on hillsides. Similar to *Nardia scalaris* (p. 267).

335.   *Mylia taylori* (Hook.) Gray [× 7] Plants in compact cushions of erect shoots up to 8 cm long; yellow-green with shades of brown and purple-red; rhizoids scattered. Leaves obliquely inserted but almost transverse at shoot apices, concave at base then recurved-spreading, rotund. Amphigastria minute and usually hidden among the rhizoids. Normally lacking gemmae. Locally common on drained, acid humus and peat in mountainous districts. *Mylia anomala* (Hook.) Gray has shorter, loosely tufted or scattered, creeping stems. The uppermost leaves are elongated and strongly gemmiferous. Locally frequent in peat bogs and on wet heathlands, among *Sphagnum* and other mosses. Frequent in lowland and subalpine regions.

329 △   330 △

331 △   332 △   ▽ 334   333 △   ▽ 335

336. **Cephalozia macrostachya** Kaal. [× 10] Plants slender, branched, creeping, forming green patches; without flagellar branches. Leaves slightly concave, ovate but deeply bifid with straight or curved and connivent, acute lobes. Amphigastria absent or vestigial. Perianths large, oval-cylindrical with cilia at the mouth. Antheridia on distinctive, catkin-like shoots. Occasional among *Sphagnum* in lowland bogs. *C. bicuspidata* (L.) Dum. is similar but lacks the catkin-like male shoots and the perianths are longer. It is a common and widespread species growing in thin mats on lime-free soils in damp, shaded places. *C. connivens* (Dicks.) Lindb. has strongly connivent, pincer-like leaf lobes. It is common in *Sphagnum* bogs and on wet, acid humus by streams, etc. (See p. 267)

337. **Nowellia curvifolia** (Dicks.) Mitt. [× 13] (shown mixed with *Lophocolea heterophylla*). Plants slender, branched, creeping, in thin, reddish-yellow to rust-coloured mats. Leaves broad, asymmetrical, deeply two-lobed, narrow at the base; lobes very concave, the upper much larger, both lobes abruptly drawn out very narrow, tapering and connivent apices. Amphigastria absent. Found on rotting wood in shade in damp woodlands. Frequent in hilly districts, rare in the lowlands.

338. **Cladopodiella fluitans** (Nees) Buch [× 10] Slender, branching plants, green to brownish, lower parts of stems with reduced leaves; flagellae numerous. Leaves distant, small, 2–3 times as wide as stem, ovate or heart-shaped and bifid, with rounded lobes. Amphigastria very small, simple or bifid. Widely distributed in very wet, acid mires and bog pools. *Gymnocolea inflata* (Huds.) Dum. is very similar but usually darker. It lacks amphigastria but is recognised mainly by its balloon-like, inflated, usually barren perianths. It is common in similar habitats, forming blackish patches on wet peat. *Leicolea turbinata* (Raddi) Buch is also similar, but pale green and found on calcareous substrates. It is frequent in the more southern and western regions of Europe.

339. **Gymnomitrium obtusum** (Lindb.) Pears. [× 7] Small, erect, sparingly branched plants in dense, low, greyish to whitish tufts; shoots cylindrical or club-shaped. Leaves in two rows, very dense and closely overlapping, oval and shallowly bifid with two rounded lobes and very narrow sinus; margins colourless and minutely crenulate. Frequent to locally common on rocks in the mountains. *G. concinnatum* (Lightf.) Corda has more acute leaf lobes, without hyaline margins, and wider sinuses. It is common in the alpine zone.

341. **Gymnomitrium coralloides** Nees [× 7] Similar to the preceeding species but the whitish, club-shaped shoots are somewhat compressed and tinged with grey or black. Leaves so dense as to be almost indistinguishable, hyaline and soon rather eroded, scarcely bilobed but notched at apex. Found on rocks above *c.* 2,000 m altitude in northern Europe. Very rare in Britain.

340. **Diplophyllum taxifolium** (Wahl.) Dum. [× 7] Very similar to small forms of *D. albicans* (below) but lacking the pale vitta or false nerve in the leaf lobes. Grows on moist rock ledges in the mountains, above 600 m altitude. Occasional in Europe, rare in Britain.

342. **Diplophyllum albicans** (L.) Dum. [× 8] Plants erect or ascending, sometimes forked, often in large patches; shoots up to 5 cm long, 3 mm wide, dull green or brown. Leaves bi-lobed, both lobes elongate, the smaller lobe folded back over the larger one; larger lobe about twice as long as the smaller, lanceolate, toothed near the blunt or obtuse apex, spreading at right angles to stem; smaller lobe similar but forwardly directed; both lobes with a conspicuous, colourless median band (vitta) resembling a midrib. Gemmae often present on tips of younger leaves. Very common and widely distributed on acid soils and damp,siliceous rocks in woodlands, moorlands and mountains.

172

336 △   337 △

338 △   339 △   ▽ 341   340 △   ▽ 342

343. *Scapania subalpina* (Nees) Dum. [×9] Plants ascending, up to 5 cm tall, occasionally more, 4 mm wide, leafy above but stems more or less denuded and dark below, sparingly branched. Leaves conduplicate bilobed, the upper lobe almost as large as the lower, erect, widely crossing the stem, margin slightly dentate; lower lobe rounded, decurrent, recurved and toothed. Upper leaves often with whitish or purplish gemmae. Grows in whitish or reddish tufts on wet, siliceous rocks and shingle in mountainous regions; rare in the lowlands.

347, 348. *Scapania nemorosa* (L.) Dum. [×7] Shoots erect, up to 10 cm tall, 4 mm wide. Leaves conduplicate bilobed, the upper lobe very much smaller than the lower; upper lobe ovate with broadly pointed apex, erect and appressed to stem; under lobe 2–3 times larger, broadly oval, rounded, slightly decurrent; both lobes strongly toothed. Rust-coloured gemmae nearly always present at shoot apices. Grows in green or olive tufts on acid humus; lowland and subalpine. *S. gracilis* (Lindb.) Kaal. differs in having both lobes rounded; the upper lobe reflexed. It occurs in olive or brownish tufts in similar habitats. Frequent in the west, rare or absent elsewhere. Common in western Britain.

349. *Scapania undulata* (L.) Dum. [×7] Plants prostrate or ascending, 2–8 cm long, up to 5 mm wide, typically dark reddish-purple to almost black but sometimes green. Leaves conduplicate bilobed, the lower lobe about twice as large as the upper. Upper lobe rounded, often untoothed; under lobe broadly oval, usually strongly toothed (green, immersed forms often entire). Gemmae sometimes present on upper leaves. Grows on wet rocks in and by streams, waterfalls and mires. Common and widely distributed, especially in hilly regions. (See also p. 268).

344. *Calypogeia fissa* (L.) Raddi [×22] Plants delicate, pale, creeping, whitish green to bluish-green, similar to *C. muellerana* (below) but narrower with less overlapping leaves. Leaves ovate or rounded-triangular, narrowed to apices which are shallowly but distinctly bilobed. Amphigastria twice as wide as stem, $\frac{2}{3}$ divided into two lobes, each lobe with a broad tooth at the side. Stems often drawn out and ascending towards apex, with reduced leaves and producing terminal heads of gemmae. Common and widely distributed on damp, shaded soil in woodlands and among mosses on moors.

345. *Calypogeia muellerana* (Schiffn.) K. Müll. [×16] Whitish to pale, bluish green, creeping plants, 2–4 cm long, 2–3 mm wide. Leaves incubously shingled, broadly oval, the apex rounded and entire or minutely notched. Amphigastria large, three times as wide as stem, orbicular and $\frac{1}{3}$–$\frac{1}{2}$ divided into two lobes, or more or less orbicular and undivided (var. *neesiana*). Gemmae commonly produced at shoot apices. On acid humus, rotting wood and damp soil. Common, especially in lowland areas. *C. trichomanis* (L.) Corda is practically identical superficially but deep blue-green. Frequent on wet peat and acid humus in mountainous areas.

346. *Cephaloziella divaricata* (Sm.) Schiffn. [×16] Plants exceedingly small, irregularly branched; shoots up to 1 cm long. Leaves bilobed, very small, not much wider than stems, divided into two, divergent, acute lobes. Amphigastria very small except on fruiting branches. Gemmae commonly present at shoot apices, yellow-green to reddish brown. Grows in low mats or reddish brown to blackish or dark green patches on dry soils and exposed rocks. Locally frequent and widely distributed.

343 △   344 △

345 △   346 △   ▽ 348   347 △   ▽ 349

350.   *Porella platyphylla* (L.) Pfeiff. [× 7] Plants green to olive, regularly bipinnately branched, more or less horizontal. Leaves conduplicate bilobed, the upper lobe several times larger than the underlobe; upper lobe convex oval rotund; lower lobe about ½ as large as amphigastria, oblong-oval, not decurrent. Amphigastria rounded-quadrate, with strongly recurved margins, broadly decurrent. Grows in lax tufts on rocks, walls and tree-bases. Frequent and widely distributed.

351.   *Porella   arboris-vitae* (With.) Grolle (syn. *P. laevigata* (Schrad.) Lindb.) [× 6] Plants similar to the preceding species but upper lobes of leaves usually ending in more or less acute or mucronate points. Under lobes almost as large as amphigastria. Amphigastria narrower, nearly flat and with dentate margins. Plants have a peppery taste. Frequent in montane and western Europe.

352.   *Odontoschisma sphagni* (Dicks.) Dum. [× 3] Plants elongate, creeping, sparingly branched, up to 7 cm long, typically brown, with leafless, downward-growing flagallar shoots from the underside of stems. Leaves rotundate, ascending. Amphigastria absent or vestigial near shoot apex. Commonly lacking gemmae. Grows on wet peat in bogs and acid moors. Frequent; lowland to subalpine. *O. denudatum* (Nees) Dum. is much smaller, reddish brown, with abundant gemmae at the shoot apices. Common on dry peat and rotting stumps.

353.   *Lejeunea cavifolia* (Ehrh.) Lindb. [× 13] Plants small, pale green or yellowish, irregularly or more or less pinnately branched; shoots 1–2 cm long, 1–2 mm wide. Leaves incubous, bi-lobed but the underlobe minute and inrolled to form a water-sac; upper lobe rotund and slightly convex. Amphigastria 2–4 times as large as underlobes, rotund, ⅓ divided into two broadly pointed lobes. Grows on shaded trees and rocks, often associated with Radula and Metzgeria. Common and widely distributed; lowland to low alpine. *L. ulicina* (Tayl.) Gott. is much smaller, with well spaced, tiny leaves that consist mainly of the water-sacs; upper lobes small. Common on bark of trees in woodlands.

354.   *Frullania tamarisci* (L.) Dum. [× 22] Plants bipinnately branched, prostrate or ascending, reddish brown to dark purple. Leaves bilobed, the upper lobe rotund, very convex with downwardly curved, bluntly pointed tips, with a median, often broken line of dark cells; under lobe very small, in the form of a minutely stalked, helmet-shaped but elongated water-sac. Amphigastria twice as wide as stem, shallowly bilobed and with narrowly recurved margins. Common and widely distributed on trees, rocks and stony ground in exposed or lightly shaded situations.

355.   *Frullania dilatata* (L.) Dum. [× 7] Plants always prostrate, dull green to reddish-brown, flat patches; shoots more or less pinnately branched. Similar to the preceeding species but leaves lacking the median line and under lobes wider, shortly helmet-shaped. Grows mainly on trees, occasionally on rocks; common.

356.   *Radula complanata* (L.) Dum. [× 7] Plants green or yellowish, irregularly or pinnately branched, 2–3 cm long, in flat patches. Leaves conduplicate bilobed; upper lobe much larger than lower, rotund; underlobe about ¼ as large and more or less quadrate. Amphigastria lacking. Perianths frequent, flat. Discoid gemmae commonly produced from the margins of younger leaves. Common and widely distributed on trees and rocks in damp, shaded places.

350 △   351 △

352 △   353 △   ▽ 355   354 △   ▽ 356

357. Beard-lichens on a tree in the mountains of the Black Forest (Germany). Because of the spread of air pollution and, to a much lesser extent, reduced humidity, many beard-lichens have suffered marked reductions in their distributions. Fortunately in the mountainous areas of central Europe, especially where the altitude exceeds 1,000 m, and in oceanic parts of western Europe, there still occur trees thick with festoons of *Usnea* (**389–394**), *Bryoria* (**383–387**), *Alectoria sarmentosa* (**382**), *Evernia divaricata* (**397**), and *Ramalina farinacea* (**545**) hanging from the branches. At lower altitudes may be found the hanging strap-shaped thalli of *Ramalina* (e.g. **541**) and *Evernia prunastri* (**395**), together with foliose species of *Parmelia* (**409–433**), *Xanthoria parietina* (**602**), and *Physcia* s. lat. (**610–621**), these last even occurring on street trees. Similar communities are widespread in the British Isles.

358. Lichen heath on the Rondane plateau (Norway). In Scandinavia on the Fjellen the vegetation is completely dominated by lichens. A thick yellowish lichen heath carpets the mountains. In the photograph are *Cladonia stellaris* (**472**), *Alectoria ochroleuca* (**381**), *Cetraria nivalis* (**407**), and *C. cucullata* (**404**), all especially abundant. A similar lichen heath occurs at *c* 1,000 m (3,000–3,250 ft) on windswept slopes in the Cairngorm Mountains in Scotland.

359. Map lichens on boulders of primitive rocks in the Alps in the Silvretta-Gruppe (Austria/Switzerland borders). The rocks are thickly covered with different crustaceous lichens, of which yellow *Rhizocarpon* species (**459**) are conspicuous. Also present are numerous *Umbilicaria* species (**523–536**). These lichen communities are common on rocks in highland Britain.

360. Maritime lichens. Coastal rocks are especially covered with lichens. *Ramalina siliquosa* (**540**) is particularly frequent, seen here with various crustaceous species. Also frequent on maritime rocks are *Anaptychia fusca* (**608**) and in certain localities *Roccella* species (**644–645**) and the crustaceous *Verrucaria maura* which forms a black zone just below high-tide level. Above this zone, not submerged by sea-water, *Xanthoria parietina* (**602**) is frequent. A fine zonation of maritime lichens occurs on coastal rocks in the western parts of the British Isles.

361. Variegated earth lichens. A characteristic group of species on chalky ground in warm sunny localities; especially common in southern Europe. In the photograph are *Fulgensia fulgens* (**603**), *Psora decipiens* (**458**), *Toninia caeruleonigricans* (**463**) and *Cladonia convoluta* (**503**). Another lichen which occurs frequently in this habitat is *Squamarina cartilaginea* (**446**). This community occurs in 12 places, chiefly on rabbit-grazed chalk grassland in warm coastal localities in southern England, Wales, and Ireland, and in the Suffolk Breckland; here it is at the northern limit of its range.

357 △

358 △ ▽ 360   359 △ ▽ 361

Calicium (362, 365) The genus gives its name to the order Caliciales (362–370). The fruiting bodies of these coniocarpic lichens decompose when ripe to a powder of spores and remains of the paraphyses; this is called a mazaedium. Many species are called 'pin lichens' because the fruiting body consists of a stalk and capitulum (head) and is therefore pin-like in appearance (362, 364–366). The thallus of *Calicium* is either a thin crust or is immersed in the substrate (chiefly wood and bark). The fruiting heads, which are almost always stalked, are small and therefore easily overlooked. There are a number of species. Microscopic characters are used to separate the species from those in related genera; the spores are ellipsoid and one-septate.

362.   Calicium viride Pers. [× 7] Thallus yellow-green, granular; somewhat variable in form and colour. Dark fruiting bodies 2–6 mm tall. Widespread on the bark and wood of old trees throughout Britain and Europe.

365.   Calicium adspersum Pers. [× 13] Thallus greyish-white, forming scaly granules on wood and bark. Dark fruiting bodies to 2 mm tall, yellowish-green with golden yellow pruina. Dispersed over central and northern Europe (including Britain), but rather scarce.

Chaenotheca Thallus forming a crust on bark and wood. Fruiting bodies stalked. There are a number of species. Differs from *Calicium* in having simple, round, brown spores.

364.   Chaenotheca chrysocephala (Turner ex Ach.) Th. Fr. [× 7] Thallus crustaceous, yellowish or greenish, often forming a thick covering on bark and wood. Fruiting bodies dark, *c* 1 mm tall, with yellow pruina. Found chiefly on conifers in mountain woods. In Britain the most common species of *Chaenotheca* is *C. ferruginea* (Turner ex Sm.) Mig.; it has a thallus of grey granules and rust-coloured soredia are frequently present. It grows chiefly on the north and east sides of old oak trunks.

Coniocybe The thallus forms a thin crust on bark, wood, earth, and stone, or is immersed in the substrate. The fruiting bodies usually have long stalks and brightly coloured heads. Spores round and simple.

366.   Coniocybe furfuracea (L.) Ach. [× 17] The yellowish to yellow-green thallus forms a powdery coating. The fruiting bodies have thin stalks 2–4 mm long with dark heads covered with a bright pruina. The species is widely dispersed on soil etc. in crevices.

Sphaerophorus (363, 367–8) A shrubby lichen, often swardy and brittle. Fruiting heads globose, produced on swollen branches. Grows chiefly on acid soils, mossy rocks, and tree bases. Arctic-alpine and oceanic. There are three species in Europe, all illustrated here. Can be confused with *Stereocaulon* (509–22).

363.   Sphaerophorus globosus (Huds.) Vainio [× 2.5] Lichen with distinct main stems and lateral branches, both of which are rounded, the branches having whitish tips. Fruiting heads frequent, globose, at the tips. Medulla turns mauve with the application of iodine. Grows in swards on acid substrates, especially mossy rocks, heaths, and tree boles. Widely distributed, but frequent only in oceanic areas. In Britain common in the north and west (i.e. highland zone).

367.   Sphaerophorus melanocarpus (Swartz) DC. [× 2.5] Lichen with distinct main stems and lateral branches, both of which are distinctly flattened. Fruiting heads formed on the sides and tips of the branches. Common in oceanic districts on rocks and old trees.

368.   Sphaerophorus fragilis (L.) Pers. [× 2.5] Lichen without a main stem, composed entirely of forked rounded branches. Without whitish tips. Grows on acid rocks. An arctic-alpine oceanic species. In Britain common on mountain rocks at higher altitudes.

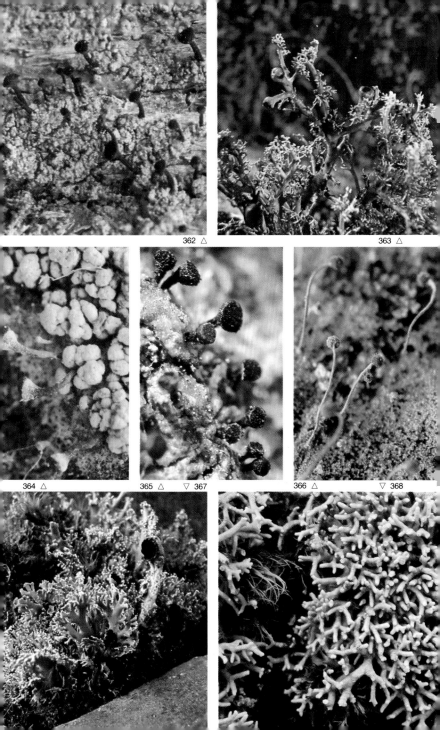

362 △

363 △

364 △

365 △ ▽ 367

366 △ ▽ 368

Tholurna Differs markedly from related genera in its small fruticose appearance. There is only one species:

369. *Tholurna dissimilis* Norm. [× 10] Thallus of small, coralloid, scaly lobes. Apothecia powdery and crumbling, on truncated, thick stalks. Rare on spruce branches at the timber-line in Scandinavia. Absent from the British Isles.

Cyphelium The crumbling fruiting bodies are sessile (i.e. without stalks) in contrast to other coniocarpous lichens. There are about 15 species, most of them scarce. They grow on wood and rock.

370. *Cyphelium tigillare* (Ach.) Ach. [× 13] Fruiting bodies in yellowish-green to dark green, or – as shown here – pale green, thallus warts, one per wart. It grows chiefly near the timber-line, on dead conifers and fence posts and rails. *C. inquinans* (Sm.) Trevisan differs in having a grey thallus with crumbling apothecia which cause black spore stains on the fingers; it is common on gate posts and rails in parts of lowland Europe, including Britain, especially in the eastern counties.

Collema (371–374) Together with *Leptogium* the genus *Collema* constitutes the jelly lichens. The numerous species are dark in colour, being brownish-black or greenish-black. The lobes of the thallus contain blue-green algae (*Nostoc*) and the thallus has a pulpy appearance when damp. When dry the thallus becomes cartilaginous and hard. Apothecia often reddish-brown. Frequent on bark, calcareous soils and rocks. Some of the species closely resemble those of *Leptogium*, which differs in having a cortex.

371. *Collema polycarpon* Hoffm. [× 3] Thallus ridged, with numerous small apothecia. Widely distributed on calcareous stone; frequent in places.

372. *Collema furfuraceum* (Arnold) Du Rietz [× 3] Thallus lobes in compact, closely-adhering rosettes on the bark of old broad-leaved trees. The centre of the thallus has minute, compact, cylindrical or coralloid isidia. Widely dispersed in oceanic areas where it is frequent, but almost absent from central Europe.

373. *Collema cristatum* (L.) Weber [× 7] Thallus lobes narrow and grooved. Grows on calcareous rocks; frequent throughout Europe.

374. *Collema nigrescens* (Huds.) DC. [× 2] Thallus of large lobes, often somewhat yellow-brown in places. Mostly thick with compact red-brown apothecia. Grows on mossy broad-leaved trees, seldom on rock. Dispersed throughout Europe, rather local, but frequent in oceanic districts.

Leptogium (375–7) The thallus resembles in structure and form the genus *Collema* (q.v.). It differs in having a cortex. The thallus is dark or grey, and sometimes felt-like or hairy. The species are liable to be confused with those of *Collema*.

375. *Leptogium hildenbrandii* (Garov.) Nyl. [× 5.5] Thallus sturdy, greyish-brown with a distinctly folded upper side and a felt-like hairy underside. Grows on the bark of broad-leaved trees in western and southern Europe. In Britain rare in the north. A characteristic species which should not be confused with others.

369 △   370 △

371 △   372 △   ▽ 374   373 △   ▽ 375

376. Leptogium burgessii (L.) Mont. [×6] Thallus grey-brown or bluish, composed of crenulate lobes. Apothecia large and brown, the margins with crenulate lobules. A characteristic species which can scarcely be mistaken. Grows on mossy trees in extreme oceanic areas of western Europe, including Britain.

377. Leptogium saturninum (Dickson) Nyl. [×2.5] Thallus lobes broad and rounded, with a greyish-black upper side and lighter hairy underside. Cortex with minute isidia. On bark of old trees and on acid stone. Widely dispersed in moist parts of Europe; in Britain local in western districts.

Coelocaulon (378–9) Thallus fruticose, richly branched, with a cartilaginous (hard and glossy) cortex. Terricolous.

378. Coelocaulon muricatum (Ach.) Laundon [×2] Plant densely branched and spiny with more or less rounded delicate branches. Found on sandy soils and stony heaths from sea-level to high mountains, widely dispersed. In Britain rather local. The photograph shows it forming cushions around young plants of mountain-houseleek (*Sempervivum montanum*). Often difficult to distinguish from *C. aculeatum.*

379. Coelocaulon aculeatum (Schreber) Link [×2] Closely resembles *C. muricatum* but coarser, with pitted, uneven, flattened branches, and often with distinct pseudocyphellae within some of the pits. Forms cushions or irregular thalli on poor sandy soils, especially on heaths. Very common, but not always easy to distinguish from *C. muricatum.*

Cornicularia Thallus fruticose, erect, sparsely branched, with a cartilaginous cortex. Saxicolous.

380. Cornicularia normoerica (Gunn.) Du Rietz [×2.5] This small fruticose lichen grows on stone. The thallus is sparsely branched, flattened, and almost always with apical apothecia. Easily identified. Occurs in middle and high mountains, especially widespread in atlantic districts, and frequent in parts of Britain.

Alectoria (381–2) A small genus of greenish-yellow (fuscous black in one) pendant to erect lichens, distinguished from *Usnea* by the absence of a whitish central thallus strand, and from *Bryoria* by the thallus colour and spores. In *Alectoria* the spores are large and brown when mature, and there are 2–4 per ascus; in *Bryoria* the spores are smaller, remaining colourless, and there are eight per ascus. The species are local in Britain.

381. Alectoria ochroleuca (Hoffm.) Massal. (with trailing azalea, *Loiseleuria procumbens*) [×0.7] This fruticose species of spiny yellow-green forked branches forms thick cushions on soil. The large, urceolate, brown apothecia, shown in the photograph, are rare. The lichen grows on windy heaths on high mountains, especially in Scandinavia, where it is very frequent and covers large areas. In Britain confined to the Cairngorm Mountains, where it is very rare. It resembles *Coelocaulon* in form, but differs markedly in colour. *A. nigricans* (Ach.) Nyl. differs in its dark colour, the branches being black above but usually light brown towards the base. It grows on the ground amongst arctic-alpine vegetation and is local in highland Britain.

376 △

377 △

378 △   ▽ 380 379 △   ▽ 381

382. Alectoria sarmentosa (Ach.) Ach. subsp. *sarmentosa* [×3] (with *Hypogymnia physodes*, **438**) Thallus filamentous, up to 30 cm long, forming festoons from spruce trees. With scattered light spots (pseudocyphellae) which are not granular (resembles *Ramalina thrausta* (Ach.) Nyl., which differs in having small granular soralia). A lichen of dense boreal conifer forests. In Britain very rare, occurring only on rocks in the north. Liable to confusion with *Evernia divaricata* (**397**) and species of *Usnea* (**388–394**), the latter having a whitish central strand. *A. sarmentosa* subsp. *vexillifera* (Nyl.) D. Hawksw. differs in being prostrate with flattened main stems; it grows on the ground in arctic-alpine localities, including the Scottish highlands.

Bryoria (**383–385**, **387**, **VI H**) This large genus has been recently separated from *Alectoria*. It differs in having a brown to olivaceous thallus and quite different spores. Common in northern parts of Britain and Europe.

383. Bryoria capillaris (Ach.) Brodo & D. Hawksw. [×2] Thallus pale grey, smooth, fine, pendent. Widespread in conifer woods, but not frequent. Rare in the Scottish highlands.

384. Bryoria chalybeiformis (L.) Brodo & D. Hawksw. [×0.7] (with *Umbilicaria hirsuta* **531**) Thallus very dark brown with stout stems in short festoons on rocks and soil. Widespread in mountains, especially on rocks influenced by bird droppings. In Britain scattered throughout upland areas of the highland zone.

385. Bryoria fremontii (Tuck.) Brodo & D. Hawksw. [×7] Thallus forms brown festoons on bark and wood. Delimited yellow soralia are often present on the branches, these rendering it distinct from related species. Found in Scandinavia and Germany; absent from the British Isles.

387. Bryoria fuscescens (Gyelnik) Brodo & D. Hawksw. (Syn. *Alectoria jubata* auct.) [×3] Thallus forms dark brown pendent festoons with a pale base and a mixture of fissural and tuberculate light-coloured soralia which are P + red. The most common species of *Bryoria* in lowland northern Europe, including Britain. There are a number of closely related species.

Bryoria furcellata (Fr.) Brodo & D. Hawksw. (Syn. *Alectoria nidulifera* Norrl.) [×25] Thallus forms small bushy brown growths, the branches with fissured white soralia from which isidia develop. The soredial isidia distinguish this lichen from related species. Widespread in the wooded districts of Scandinavia, but scarce in the Alps. Rare in the Scottish highlands. (See also **VI H**, p. 22)

Usnea Beard-moss (**386**, **388–394**) Most species hang in festoons from bark, wood, or stone, and are greenish-grey in colour. Only a few are erect. They are much branched, and short lateral branches from the main stems are frequent. In some the side branches are grooved where they are attached to the main stem. Isidia or tubercles often occur on the cortex. Distinguished from *Alectoria*, *Bryoria*, and *Evernia divaricata* (**397**) by the tough whitish central strand. Widespread in wooded areas, and abundant where there is high humidity, particularly in mountain forests.

386. Usnea filipendula Stirton [×2] Thallus forms festoons up to 25 cm long on trees. The bases of the main branches are often warted. These main branches have numerous short side-branches and isidia set at right-angles. Widespread and frequent in mountain woods; locally common in Scotland.

388. Usnea cavernosa Tuck. (with *Hypogymnia physodes*, **438**) [×3] Festoons about 30 cm long, very delicate. Thallus sparsely branched, without short, widespread side-branches or isidia. Conspicuous cavities occur in the thicker branches (see photograph). In high mountain woods. Apparently extinct in the British Isles.

382 △   383 △

384 △   385 △   ▽ 387   386 △   ▽ 388

389.   *Usnea longissima* Ach. [×0.7] Thallus in single, almost unbranched, filaments from tree branches, and not in thick festoons. Branches up to several metres long, with side branches at right-angles. Cortex brittle. Found in old spruce forests, scarce. Absent from Britain.

390.   *Usnea florida* (L.) Weber [×2] Thallus bushy, sub-erect or drooping, on wood and bark. Main branches with papillae, but isidia and soredia absent. Large, dish-shaped apothecia are always present. Widely dispersed, and in south-west England quite frequent. *U. subfloridana* Stirton is closely related, but has abundant soredial isidia, and apothecia are scarce; this is the most common species of *Usnea* in England and the neighbouring parts of lowland Europe.

391.   *Usnea ceratina* Ach. [×4] This species has very rigid branches with large whitish papillae, breaking open to form soralia. Branches up to 15 cm long, frequently angular bowed. On the side branches small apothecia (much enlarged in the photograph) are occasionally developed. Grows on trees; widely distributed in Europe; frequent in southern Britain.

392.   *Usnea hirta* (L.) Weber [×2.5] Thallus forming small festoons. With many peg-like isidia. Widely dispersed on conifers and the wood of fences. Frequent in parts of Scotland. Difficult to distinguish from other species of *Usnea.*

393.   *Usnea articulata* (L.) Hoffm. [×1.5] Older branches segmented and very swollen (see photograph), appearing like a different species from the rest of the plant. Grows on trees, seldom also on rock or soil, in western Europe to north-west Germany. Nowhere abundant, but occasional in parts of south-west England.

394.   *Usnea rubicunda* Stirton [×2] The main branches are red or reddish-brown, thick, with papillae and soredial isidia. Easily identified by its colour. Grows on trees in western Europe, where it is frequent in places, including southern England.

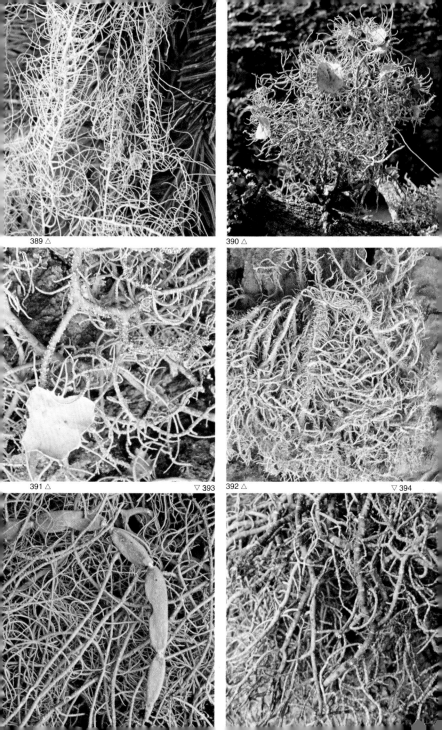

389 △

390 △

391 △ ▽ 393

392 △ ▽ 394

Evernia (**395**, **397**) There are about six species in the genus but only the two illustrated here are frequent in Europe. The thallus is strap-shaped and forms loose hanging festoons on bark and wood, rarely on rock.

395.   *Evernia prunastri* (L.) Ach. **Oak moss** [×1.5] Thallus strap-shaped, forked like antlers, hanging downwards from its base. Upper surface greenish-grey, underside greyish-white. Margin usually soredidate, and apothecia rare. Variable in appearance, the thallus becoming stunted under unfavourable conditions. Abundant on trees, rare on rocks. Confusion is possible with *Pseudevernia* (**396**), but this lichen has a grey upper surface and a black underside. *Ramalina* (**539**–**543**; **545**) differs in having both surfaces green in colour.

397.   *Evernia divaricata* (L.) Ach. [×1.5] Thallus forming long contorted strands, the cortex broken into segments. Hangs in festoons from bark and twigs. Thallus soft. Apothecia rare. Uncommon but widely dispersed in mountain woods. Absent from the British Isles. Can be mistaken for a species of *Usnea*.

Pseudevernia Distinguished from *Evernia* by the thallus richly branching in a single plane. The genus has only a single species:

396.   *Pseudevernia furfuracea* (L.) Zopf **Tree moss** [×0.3] Branches strap-shaped, forked like antlers, hanging from bark, wood, and rock. The grey upper surface is often thickly isidiate. The underside of the older branches is black, thus distinguishing it from *Evernia* (whitish) and *Ramalina* (greenish). Apothecia scarce; large with olive-brown discs. The lichen is stunted when growing in unfavourable conditions. Widespread; especially frequent on conifers in mountain woods. In Britain common in the north but rare in the south.

Dactylina This genus occurs in the Arctic and in the higher regions of the Alps. The thick radial branches form clumps on earth.

398.   *Dactylina arctica* (Hook.) Nyl. (with *Cetraria nivalis*, **407**) [×2] Branches of radial structure, very swollen, divided like fingers. Confined to the Arctic, and absent from the British Isles.

Letharia Distinguished by its citron yellow thallus, whitish medulla and richly branched form. In Europe there is only one species:

400.   *Letharia vulpina* (L.) Hue **Wolf's moss** [×0.7] In form resembles *Evernia*, *Ramalina*, and *Usnea*, but differs in the strong yellow colour. Sorediate. Apothecia scarce; large and brown (see photograph). Found at high elevations on mountains, chiefly on the bark and wood of larch. Absent from the British Isles.

Cetraria (**399**, **401**–**408**, **411**) A genus not uniform in appearance. Some species are fruticose, erect, with ± grooved stems, and grow on the ground. Other species are foliose, resembling *Parmelia* species but with upturned margins, and grow on bark, wood, and rock. It is likely that the genus will soon be divided into two separate groups.

399.   *Cetraria islandica* (L.) Ach. **Iceland moss** (with cowberry, *Vaccinium vitis-idaea*) [×1.5] Branches greenish-grey to dark brown, ± tubular, the margin with tiny spiny fibrils. The exterior (thallus underside) has whitish pseudocyphellae. Apothecia scarce, in short, wide branches (see photograph). Forms loose or thick cushions. Widely dispersed on heaths, moors, and in acid woodlands, where it is often frequent. In Britain locally frequent in the north but absent from the south. Liable to confusion with *C. delisei* (**401**).

401.   *Cetraria delisei* (Bory ex Schaerer) Nyl. [×1.5] Forms cushions resembling *C. islandica*. Thallus however richly forked, ending in fine branches. Fibrillae absent and pseudocyphellae scarce. Apothecia (see photograph) frequent. Grows on high ground in Scandinavia and in the Arctic, where it is widespread and abundant. Rare in the Scottish highlands.

190

395 △   396 △

397 △   398 △   ▽ 400   399 △   ▽ 401

402. *Cetraria chlorophylla* (Willd.) Vainio (with *Hypogymnia physodes*, **438**) [×2.5] Thallus forming rosettes, greenish-brown, foliose, the margins upturned. Underside glossy, whitish-brown, becoming paler towards the centre. Sorediate to isidiate along the margins of the lobes. Widespread on trees and wood (sometimes also on walls) in northern wooded districts, but scarce in the Alps. In Britain frequent in northern districts. Easily confused with *Platismatia glauca* (**436**) which differs in having the underside becoming darker towards the centre.

403. *Cetraria juniperina* (L.) Ach. (on juniper, *Juniperus communis*) [×2] Thallus light yellow, thickly formed over the substrate. Apothecia large and brown, usually present. Medulla yellow, visible through breaks in the cortex. Widely dispersed in northern parts of Europe, chiefly on juniper; almost absent from central Europe. Apparently extinct in Britain. *C. tilesii* Ach. is similar, with a yellow thallus and medulla but usually sterile; it grows on earth on exposed alpine mountains and on the Baltic islands. Absent from Britain. *C. pinastri* (below) also has a yellow medulla but has marginal soredia.

404. *Cetraria cucullata* (Bellardi) Ach. [×2] Thallus whitish-yellow in thick, up-right cushions on earth. Edges of lobes incurved. Surface smooth and medulla whitish. Decayed base of thallus red. Apothecia rare, brown (see photograph). Widely dispersed on heaths at high altitudes, where it can dominate the vegetation and form 'lichen heaths' (**358**). Apparently extinct in Britain. Can be confused with *C. nivalis* (below), which differs in having the thallus not rolled inwards at the margins.

405. *Cetraria sepincola* (Ehrh.) Ach. (with *C. pinastri*, **406**) [×5.5] Grows in small brown cushions on slender twigs. Thallus of small lobes with apical disc-shaped glossy brown apothecia. On twigs, especially of birch and alder. Widespread, but very scattered and often scarce. In Britain confined to the highland zone, where it is locally frequent in a few places.

406. *Cetraria pinastri* (Scop.) Gray [×5.5] The yellow thallus, with lemon yellow soralia at the margins and yellow medulla, make this lichen easy to identify. It is widely dispersed and often frequent on conifers, especially at the base of trees. In Britain confined to the north where it is rare. Can only be confused with *C. juniperina* (see above).

407. *Cetraria nivalis* (L.) Ach. [×0.7] Thallus lobes light yellowish with a pitted network, but not rolled inwards at the margin. Apothecia yellowish (see **398**, at top of photograph in the background). Forming thick cushions on the ground at high altitudes on mountains, widely dispersed. One of the dominant plants on lichen heaths in Scandinavia (**358**). Locally abundant at 1,000 m in the Cairngorm Mountains of Scotland, but almost absent elsewhere in Britain. Can be confused with *C. cucullata* (see above) and *C. tilesii* (see above).

408. *Cetraria laureri* Krempelh. [×2] Upper surface of the curled lobes yellowish-green, underside whitish-brown. Grows loosely on the bark of conifers in alpine mountains. Absent from the British Isles.

402 △   403 △

404 △   405 △ ▽ 407   406 △ ▽ 408

411.   Cetraria hepatizon (Ach.) Vainio [×2.5] Forms small brown rosettes on stone. The lobes are slightly concave with papillose pycnidia at the margins. Widespread and frequent on mountain rocks. Can be confused with the brown species of *Parmelia* (**428–433**).

Parmelia (Syn. *Hypotrachyna, Melanelia, Neofuscelia, Parmelina, Parmotrema, Pseudoparmelia, Punctelia, Xanthoparmelia*) (**409–10, 412–33**) A large genus of foliose lichens, most with rhizinae on the undersides. Apothecia with a thalline (lecanorine) margin and simple spores. Various groups of species have been separated from *Parmelia* in attempts to create smaller natural units. Recently the sections of the genus have unfortunately been regarded by some authors as separate genera, despite the paucity of characters which separate them.

409.   Parmelia caperata (L.) Ach. [×0.7] Lobes broad and vigorous, greenish-yellow, with a wrinkled upper side and granular soredia. Underside without rhizinae in the marginal zone. Frequently dominant on mature tree boles in the warm districts of southern and central Europe, but absent from northern Scandinavia; less common on wood and acid rocks. In Britain common in the south, but becoming scarce further north. The large yellowish thallus of this lichen is unmistakable.

410.   Parmelia crinita Ach. [×5.5] Lobes grey with numerous isidia. Characteristic black rhizinae occur on the underside, at the margin, and also on the upper surface as cilia between the isidia (**VI E**, p. 23). Occurs on mossy trees and rocks in oceanic areas, and also in parts of central Europe. In Britain frequent in western districts, rare elsewhere.

412.   Parmelia taractica Krempelh. (Syn.   *P. stenophylla* (Ach.) Heugel) [× 1.5] Lobes greenish-yellow, the underside with abundant rhizinae extending to the margin. Thallus vigorous, often somewhat glossy, without soredia or isidia. Widespread; especially common in areas with a continental climate. Absent from the British Isles. Variable, and at times difficult to separate from *P. conspersa* (see below).

413.   Parmelia mougeotii Schaerer ex D. Dietr. [×4] Thallus lobes small, narrow, flat, closely appressed on stone. Lobe-ends mostly not overlapping. Upper side greenish-yellow, with small, whitish, maculiform soralia. Found throughout central Europe, but most common in cool oceanic districts. In Britain frequent on boulders in the north. Can be confused with *Parmelia incurva* (**419**) which differs in having convex overlapping lobes.

414.   Parmelia perlata (Huds.) Ach. [× 1.5] Lobes large, grey, underside dark and the margins with rhizinae. Upper side without pseudocyphellae (the distinction from *Cetrelia olivetorum*, **435**). Capitiform soralia on the margins of the lobes. Common on trees and rocks in oceanic regions, but only scattered in central Europe. In Britain common in the south and west.

415.   Parmelia conspersa (Ach.) Ach. [×0.7] Lobes greenish-yellow, thick, lying one over the other, forming rosettes closely appressed on stone. Upper surface with numerous cylindrical to coralloid isidia and usually many bowl-shaped brown apothecia. Widely dispersed and frequent on siliceous stone. In Britain common in the highland zone. Can be confused with *P. stenophylla* (see above) and *P. centrifuga* (**417**).

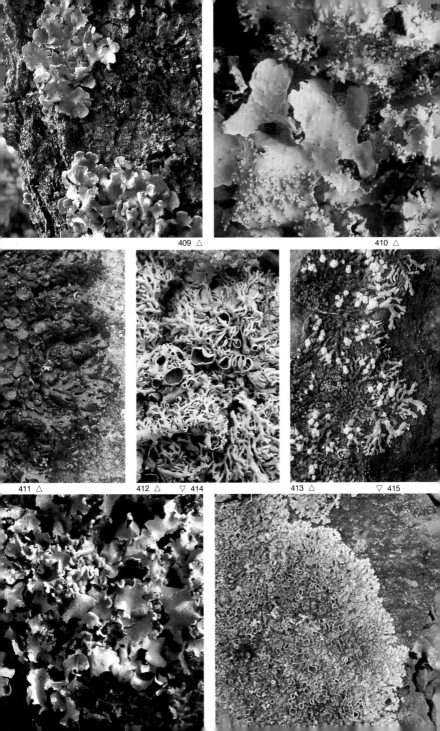

409 △   410 △

411 △   412 △   ▽ 414   413 △   ▽ 415

416.   Parmelia acetabulum (Necker) Duby [× 1] Thallus olive-green (grey-green to brownish-green) when dry, strongly dark green when damp. Nearly always with large, brown, bowl-shaped apothecia with pale margins, distorted when old. Well-separated from other foliose lichens in form and colour. Widespread throughout Europe on bark in nitrogenous situations, especially in landscaped parks and on avenues of trees. In Britain almost confined to the lowland zone, where it is rather scarce.

417.   Parmelia centrifuga (L.) Ach. [×0.2] The thallus has pale green lobes and brownish bowl-shaped apothecia, therefore resembling *P. conspersa* (**415**). Neverthe-less, the lobes are narrow and without isidia. The thallus grows in concentric circles, growing outwards whilst the centre decays; new colonies often form in the old lost centres. Occurs on acid stone in boreal regions; absent from the British Isles.

418.   Parmelia omphalodes (L.) Ach. [×2.5] This lichen forms cushions of narrow lobes. The upper surface is greyish-brown to dark brown with a metallic gloss which is covered with a whitish reticulum of pseudocyphellae. The species is distinguished by these pseudocyphellae never developing soredia or isidia, as happens in other *Parmelia* species with a conspicuous reticulate surface. Widespread on acid rocks in northern and upland Europe. In Britain common in the highland zone, but absent from the lowlands.

419.   Parmelia incurva (Pers.) Fr. [×2.5] Thallus of rather small, thick, greenish-grey, convex, contorted lobes which are closely arranged, bearing whitish globose soralia. Grows on acid rocks. A boreal species, becoming increasingly common, and advancing further south in England by colonising walls.

420.   Parmelia laevigata (Sm.) Ach. [×2.5] Thallus large, whitish-grey, with con-spicuous hemispherical soralia at the lobe-ends. The lobe-axils are broad and U-shaped. Medulla KC+ orange. Occurs on trees and rocks in upland oceanic areas of western Europe, extending to the Alps. In Britain common only in parts of the west. Can be confused with *Cetrelia* (**435**), as well as other species of *Parmelia*.

421.   Parmelia taylorensis M. Mitchell [× 1.5] Thallus grey, the upper surface crumb-ling in places to show the dark lower cortex. Lobe-axils broad and U-shaped. Apothecia usually present. Medulla C+ orange. Occurs on rocks and trees in oceanic districts, and in the north-east Alps. In Britain confined to the west, where it is rather local.

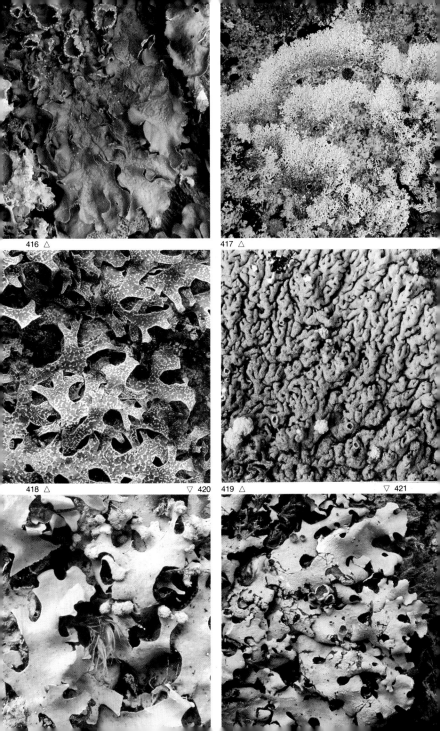

416 △

417 △

418 △   ▽ 420

419 △   ▽ 421

422. *Parmelia tiliacea* (Hoffm.) Ach. [× 1.5] Thallus whitish-grey, large (often over 10 cm diameter), with short, rounded lobes. The inner lobes have cylindrical isidia but are without pseudocyphellae. Widespread on roadside and avenue trees and on rocks. Rather uncommon in eastern Britain.

423. *Parmelia saxatilis* (L.) Ach. [× 2] Thallus bluish-grey to grey, in rosettes on stone or bark. Surface with a network of small, whitish pseudocyphellae on which are formed numerous cylindrical to coralloid isidia. Apothecia occasionally present, bowl-shaped, brown. Widespread and especially common at higher altitudes and latitudes. Common on bark and acid stone throughout the British Isles. Can be confused with two other species of *Parmelia* with a network: *P. sulcata* (below) having soredia and no isidia, and *P. omphalodes* (**418**) having neither soredia nor isidia.

424. *Parmelia quercina* (Willd.) Vainio (Syn. *P. carporrhizans* Taylor) [× 2] Thallus smooth, usually with apothecia, and without isidia, soredia, or pseudocyphellae. Axils between the lobes rounded-sinuate. Loosely attached to tree bark. Mediterranean species extending to Bayern. In Britain confined to a few places in the extreme south of England.

425. *Parmelia sulcata* Taylor [× 2] Thallus bluish-grey to grey, with a network of whitish lines towards the margins, and rimiform soredia on the older central areas. Widespread throughout Europe and common on bark and acid stone. One of the most common species of *Parmelia* in the British Isles.

426. *Parmelia borreri* (Sm.) Turner [× 2.5] Lobes vigorous and broad. Upper surface grey to greyish-brown with rounded whitish pseudocyphellae which develop into maculiform soralia, C + orange. Underside quite dark. Widespread on bark in south and west Europe, but scarce in central Europe. In Britain scarce in the south. Can be confused with *P. sulcata* (above) which has elongated soralia and is C − , and *P. subrudecta* (below) which has a light brownish underside.

427. *Parmelia subrudecta* Nyl. [× 4] Thallus whitish-grey, bluish-grey, or brownish-grey. Upper side with spots forming whitish pseudocyphellae and later maculiform soralia, which are C + red. Underside (in top left of photograph) light brownish. Widespread and often frequent. In Britain common in the lowland zone, scarce elsewhere. Liable to confusion with *P. borreri* (above), which has a dark underside and a different chemistry.

422 △

423 △

424 △   ▽ 426

425 △   ▽ 427

428. *Parmelia exasperatula* Nyl. (with *Hypogymnia physodes*, **438**, on mountain pine, *Pinus mugo*) [× 4] Thallus olive green to brown, with claviform isidia. Widespread on isolated trees and shrubs. Occurs throughout the British Isles but everywhere rare.

429. *Parmelia glabra* (Schaerer) Nyl. [× 2] Thallus brown, with fine hairs on the younger lobes (use lens!). Widespread in the mountains of south-central Europe. Absent from the British Isles.

430. *Parmelia septentrionalis* (Lynge) Ahti [× 3] Thallus brown, always with numerous apothecia, which are crowded and erect. Upper surface glossy, smooth, seldom with pseudocyphellae. Grows on bark, especially willow, alder, and birch. *P. olivacea* (L.) Ach. is very similar, with a mat, finely tumid upper surface with pseudocyphellae, and dispersed, erect apothecia with crenate margins. Both species are widespread and frequent in boreal woodlands, but rare in central Europe. In Britain *P. septentrionalis* occurs only in the Scottish highlands, where it is scarce; *P. olivacea* has yet to be confirmed from the British Isles.

431. *Parmelia pulla* Ach. [× 3] Thallus brown, usually with a characteristic bronze-coloured gloss. On sunny siliceous rocks. Widespread and often frequent throughout Europe. In Britain frequent only in the extreme west, mostly on maritime rocks.

432. *Parmelia exasperata* de Not. [× 2.5] Thallus brown. Margins of apothecia prominent, with warty isidia which act as breathing pores. Found on trees throughout Europe, but absent from arctic-alpine regions. In the British Isles found chiefly in the highland zone.

433. *Parmelia subaurifera* Nyl. [× 4] Thallus brown. Surface with isidia and also yellowish-white punctiform soralia, by which the species is identified. Widespread on the small branches of trees. *P. glabratula* (Lamy) Nyl. is similar but without soralia; it grows on both bark (subsp. *glabratula*) and acid rock (subsp. *fuliginosa* (Fr. ex Duby) Laundon). The medulla of both species is C + red. Both are common throughout the British Isles.

Pseudephebe A fruticose genus but with the dark thallus rosette-forming and closely adpressed. There are two species, one being absent from Britain.

434. *Pseudephebe pubescens* (L.) M. Choisy (Syn. *Alectoria pubescens* (L.) R.H. Howe) [× 2] Thallus filamentous, the branches often nodulose, growing in thick black swards on acid rocks (quartz in the photograph). Widespread on mountains in boreal regions. In Britain frequent on boulders and outcrops above 600 m, but almost absent at lower levels; occurs chiefly in the Scottish highlands, Cheviots, Cumbria, and north Wales.

428 △

429 △

430 △

431 △ ▽ 433

432 △ ▽ 434

Cetrelia Differs from *Cetraria* in having submarginal, as opposed to marginal, apothecia, and from *Platismatia* in having large ellipsoid spores. In Europe there is one species comprising several chemical strains.

435.   Cetrelia olivetorum (Nyl.) Culb. & C. Culb. [×2] Thallus composed of loose lobes with marginal soralia. Upper surface with whitish punctiform pseudocyphellae. Underside black. Grows on bark and acid stone in oceanic parts of Europe, but becoming scarce in south Scandinavia. In Britain found in the west, where it is rare. Can be confused with *Parmelia perlata* (**414**).

Platismatia Closely related to *Cetrelia*, but differing in having small subspherical spores. In Europe there are two species, one of which is common:

436.   Platismatia glauca (L.) Culb. & C. Culb. [×2.5] Lobes large, upturned, grey to grey-green, the margins often lacerated, and with soredia and/or isidia. Underside black, becoming darker towards the centre. Forms loose thalli on bark, especially tree branches, and on acid stone walls. Widespread and frequent throughout much of Europe. Common throughout the British Isles, especially in upland areas. Can be confused with *Cetraria chlorophylla* (**402**), which differs in having the underside becoming lighter towards the centre.

Hypogymnia (**437**–**40**) Thallus grey to greyish-brown with a black underside. Differs from *Parmelia* in the absence of rhizinae. Most species have hollow lobes, which give them a characteristic inflated or puffed up appearance.

437.   Hypogymnia bitteriana (Zahlbr.) Räsänen [×2.5] Lobes grey, swollen. Margin of the thallus also grey and not brownish. Inner areas of the thallus surface thickly covered with soredia. Widespread but infrequent on bark; very rare in Britain.

438.   Hypogymnia physodes (L.) Nyl. [×2.5] Thallus of rather small inflated lobes with typical labriform soralia. The black edge of the lower cortex is often visible at the sides of the lobes of the thallus. Polymorphic. Widespread and abundant on bark, wood, and stone. This is often the only macrolichen to occur around polluted towns. One of the most common lichens in the British Isles.

439.   Hypogymnia tubulosa (Schaerer) Havaas [×2] Thallus grey, resembling *H. physodes* (above), with small inflated lobes. The ends of the lobes however have capitiform soralia. Widespread, especially on tree branches, but rather local. Common throughout the British Isles. Can be confused with *H. physodes*, which differs in having lip-shaped as opposed to globular soralia.

440.   Hypogymnia intestiniformis (Vill.) Räsänen [×2.5] Lobes not as convex as in the other species of *Hypogymnia*. Forms thick rosettes on boulders. Apothecia, with shining brown discs, always present. Soredia and isidia absent. Widespread on rocks in mountain areas. Rare in the Scottish highlands.

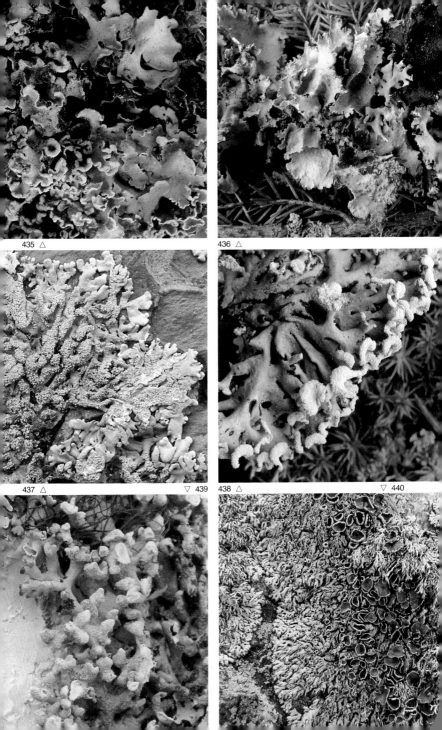

435 △

436 △

437 △   ▽ 439

438 △   ▽ 440

Parmeliopsis (**441**, **443**) The three species resemble small rosettes of *Parmelia*, differing in their narrower and more appressed lobes. They grow chiefly on conifer wood and bark in the boreal and montane parts of Europe.

441.   *Parmeliopsis ambigua* (Wulfen) Nyl. [×2.5] Thallus yellow-green, nearly blending in colour with the maculiform soralia which have farinose soredia. The bowl-shaped brown apothecia (see photograph) are quite rare. Occurs throughout the British Isles, most commonly in the north.

443.   *Parmeliopsis hyperopta* (Ach.) Arnold (with *Cetraria pinastri*, **406**) [×3] Thallus very similar in form to *P. ambigua*, but differing markedly in its ash-grey colour. Soralia always present. *P. aleurites* (Ach.) Nyl. is also this colour, but differs in having isidia instead of soredia. The small overlapping lobes form comparatively thick cushions. Both occur throughout the British Isles, but are abundant only in the Scottish highlands.

Menegazzia Resembles *Hypogymnia* but has holes through the cortex. In Europe there is only one species:

442.   *Menegazzia terebrata* (Hoffm.) Massal. [×3.5] Thallus greyish-green in large rosettes, with large holes scattered over the surface. Maniciform soralia are always present (the photograph also shows dispersed soredia scattered over the thallus). Widespread but scarce in areas of high rainfall in central and northern Europe. In Britain scarce in the west. Easily identified by the holes and distinctive soralia.

Solenopsora A squamulose genus of predominantly Mediterranean distribution.

445.   *Solenopsora candicans* (Dickson) Steiner [×2.5] Thallus crustaceous but with lobes at the margin. Apothecia with thalline margins always present. Both thallus and apothecia have a white pruina. Occurs in central and western Europe on warm calcareous stone, less commonly on chalky soil. In Britain locally abundant especially in the south-west. Resembles *Diploicia canescens* but has marginate apothecia and no soredia.

Squamarina The species resemble lobed taxa of the genus *Lecanora*, but differ in being large, thick, and cretaceous.

446.   *Squamarina cartilaginae* (With.) P. James (Syn. *S. crassa* Poelt) [×3] Thallus of greenish squamules, large at the margin and overlapping towards the centre. Apothecia yellowish-brown, the thalline margin becoming excluded. Frequent in the warmer parts of Europe on earth and rock, especially chalk and limestone. In Britain now confined chiefly to western calcareous areas, where it is quite local.

Rhizoplaca A small genus of squamulose species of greenish colour.

447.   *Rhizoplaca chrysoleuca* (Sm.) Zopf (Syn. *Lecanora rubina* (Hoffm.) Ach.) (left side of photograph); ***R. melanophthalma*** (DC.) Leuck. & Poelt (right side of photograph) [×2] The thalli of both species have thick connate squamules. Often the thalli grow only from the centre. Apothecia with light reddish (in *R. chrysoleuca*) or greenish (in *R. melanophthalma*) discs. Widespread on mountain boulders used as bird-perching stones. Both are absent from the British Isles.

Lecanora (**444**; **448–52**) A large genus of variable crustaceous lichens. The sessile apothecia have a thalline (i.e. thallus-coloured) margin and the spores are simple.

444.   *Lecanora conizaeoides* Nyl. ex Crombie **Pollution lichen** [×3] Thallus green, granular sorediate, P + red. Apothecia yellowish. On bark, wood, and acid stone. Abundant where the air is polluted; absent elsewhere. Widespread in industrial and densely populated parts of Europe. Abundant in England, but becoming quite rare in northern Scotland and Ireland. Unknown in Europe before 1860.

441 △   442 △

443 △   444 △   ▽ 446   445 △   ▽ 447

448.   *Lecanora muralis* (Schreber) Rabenh. [×2.5] Thallus greenish-grey, the margin with small lobes. Always fertile, with crowded brownish discs in the centre of the thallus. Very variable. Nitrophilous. Widespread and occasional on rock outcrops, but becoming increasingly abundant on buildings and pavements in towns.

449.   *Lecanora epibryon* (Ach.) Ach. [×6] The thick white granular thallus and white-margined apothecia are characteristic. Widespread on moss and plant remains on calcareous earth in arctic-alpine areas. In Britain rare in the north.

450.   *Lecanora chlarotera* Nyl. (with *Graphis scripta*, **635**) [×5] Thallus thin and light grey, with light brownish-red apothecia. Widespread and common on smooth bark.

451.   *Lecanora badia* (Pers.) Ach. [×4] Thallus forming a dark brown, thick, shining crust; apothecia also dark brown. Found on acid rock, especially widespread in southern Europe. In Britain frequent on rocks and walls in the highland zone.

452.   *Lecanora atra* (Huds.) Ach. [×4] Thallus grey, areolate; the apothecia with black discs. Widespread and common on siliceous rocks from high mountains to the seacoast; apparently nitrophilous.

Haematomma Differs from *Lecanora* in the septate spores and reddish discs.

454.   *Haematomma ventosum* (L.) Massal. [×2] Thallus greenish-yellow (var. *ventosum*) or grey (var. *subfestivum* (Nyl. ex Crombie) Zahlbr.). Areolate, with striking blood-red apothecia. Widespread and often frequent on acid mountain rocks, especially above the timber-line. In Britain common on exposed mountain rocks.

Lecidea This very large genus has recently been divided into a number of smaller, more natural, units. In contrast to *Lecanora* (above), the margins of the apothecia are the same colour as the disc and are therefore not thalline. The species are crustaceous and many are common. Unfortunately space allows only one to be included here:

455.   *Lecidea vernalis* (L.) Ach. [×8] Thallus forms a thin crust over mosses on the ground etc., arising from which are yellowish to light brown globular apothecia. Widespread on heaths. In Britain rare in the north.

453.   *Rhizocarpon umbilicatum* (Ramond) Flagey [×2.5] Described on p. 208.

456.   *Toninia rosulata* (Anzi) H. Olivier [×2.5] Described on p. 208.

206

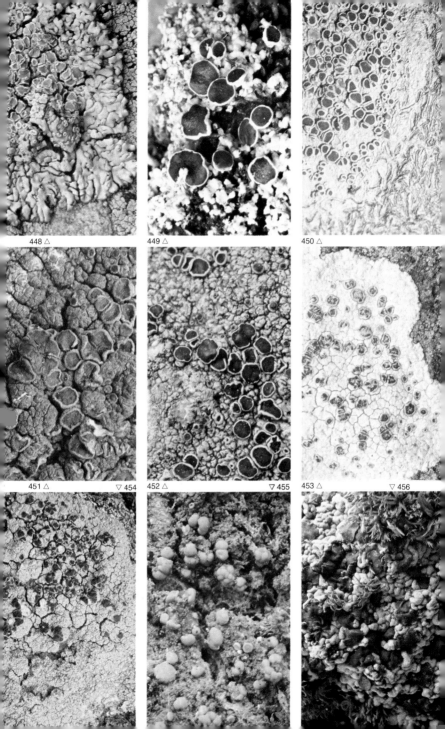

448 △   449 △   450 △

451 △   ▽ 454   452 △   ▽ 455   453 △   ▽ 456

Aspicilia Distinguished from *Lecanora* by the sunken apothecia, larger spores, and shape of the paraphyses.

457.   *Aspicilia caesiocinerea* (Nyl. ex Malbr.) Arnold [×0.1] The thallus is dark grey and areolate, often with a zonate margin, K −. Apothecia black. A nitrophilous species, widespread on flints and acid rock outcrops throughout lowland areas of Europe, including Britain.

Psora Squamules rounded, pink to brown, usually crowded. Grows on earth.

458.   *Psora decipiens* (Hedw.) Hoffm. [×8] Thallus squamulose. Apothecia black, convex, amongst the reddish thalline squamules which have whitish margins. Frequent and widespread especially in southern Europe, where it is a characteristic species of chalky soils.

Rhizocarpon (**453, 459–61**) Crustaceous lichens on acid rocks (except *R. umbilicatum* **453** which occurs on limestone). Most have angular yellow or grey areolae, the black prothallus visible in the cracks. Apothecia plane, black, with coloured septate to muriform spores.

453.   *Rhizocarpon umbilicatum* (Ramond) Flagey [×2.5] (photograph on p. 207) Apothecia immersed in the thick chalky thallus, as in *Aspicilia*. Widespread and frequent on pure limestones in mountains and on the Baltic islands. Local in the British Isles, chiefly in the west.

459.   *Rhizocarpon geographicum* (L.) DC. **Map lichen** [×5.5] The greenish-yellow thallus is conspicuous on siliceous boulders. Black apothecia occur between the areolae of the thallus. The black prothallus (on right of photograph) is conspicuous. Widespread in mountain areas. In Britain abundant in the highland zone, but scarce in the lowlands. Easily recognised by its form and colour.

460.   *Rhizocarpon oederi* (Weber) Körber [×6] The thallus has a characteristic rusty-red colour. Widespread but scarce; grows chiefly on rocks rich in heavy metals. In Britain local in upland areas.

461.   *Rhizocarpon lecanorinum* Anders [×6] Resembles *R. geographicum*, but with apothecia at least partly within the areolae and not between them. Widespread. In Britain scarce in upland localities.

Hypocenomyce Thallus of shell-like squamules on wood and bark.

462.   *Hypocenomyce scalaris* (Ach. ex Liljeblad) M. Choisy (Syn. *Lecidea scalaris* (Ach. ex Liljeblad) Ach.) [×7] Thallus of greenish, shell-like, overlapping squamules with sorediate margins, C + red. Apothecia black (see photograph), scarce. Widespread; especially common on conifer bark, dead trees, and wooden posts. Easily identified.

Toninia (**456, 463**) Crustaceous lichens with a squamulose or warted thallus. The spores are fusiform, 1–3 septate.

456.   *Toninia rosulata* (Anzi) H. Olivier [×2.5] (photograph on p. 207) Thallus squamules light in colour. Apothecia black with a blackish margin. Grows on calcareous stone. Widespread in the Alps. Absent from Britain. Liable to be confused with species of *Lecidea*.

463.   *Toninia caeruleonigricans* (Lightf.) Th. Fr. [×3] The thallus forms greyish- · brown inflated squamules, at times quite dispersed. Apothecia black, situated between the squamules. Thallus and apothecia usually with a blue-grey pruina. Widespread on dry calcareous earth. In Britain widespread but local.

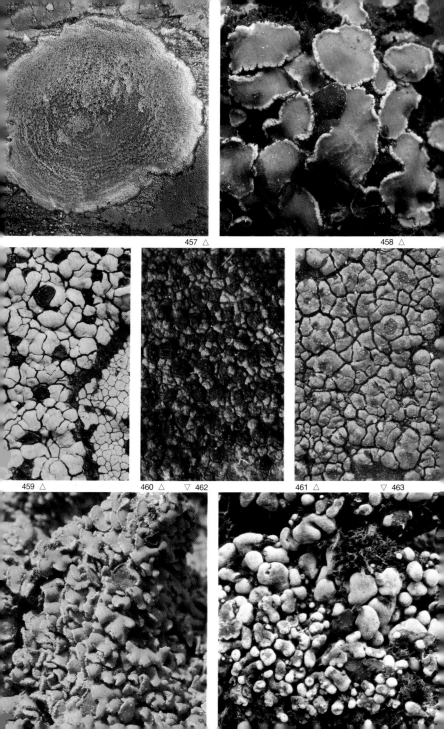

457 △　　　　　　　　　458 △

459 △　　　　460 △　　▽ 462　　　461 △　　　▽ 463

Candelaria Thallus foliose, yellow, without parietin. There is one species in Europe:

464. Candelaria concolor (Dickson) Stein [×3] Thallus pure yellow, of small lacerated lobes, with sorediate margins. Apothecia rare. Widespread on bark, scarce on stone. In Britain declining and now scarce. Differs from *Xanthoria* in being K−.

Candelariella (**465–6**) Yellow crustaceous lichens which are K−.

465. Candelariella aurella (Hoffm.) Zahlbr. [×7] Thallus mostly immersed in the substrate but with numerous yellow apothecia on the surface. A dark prothallus is sometimes present. Widespread and frequent on calcareous stone. Abundant in towns but often quite scarce in natural habitats.

466. Candelariella coralliza (Nyl.) Magnusson [×5.5] Thallus of spherical granules forming small cushions on the tops of acid boulders used as bird perches. An ornithocoprophilous species. Frequent in northern and central Europe. Local in Britain. *C. vitellina* (Hoffm.) Müll. Arg. is similar, but has flat subsquamulose granules; it is abundant on acid and calcareous rocks, walls, and wooden fences.

Baeomyces (**467–8**) Thallus crustaceous or almost squamulose. Often sorediate. Apothecia of stalked hymenial discs.

467. Baeomyces rufus (Huds.) Rebent. [×4] Thallus granular, green, often minutely squamulose at the margin. Frequently sorediate. Hymenial discs brown. Common and widespread on acid stone and loamy soil. *B. placophyllus* Ach. is similar, but has large squamules at the margin of the thallus; in Britain it is restricted to mountain areas.

468. Baeomyces roseus Pers. [×4] Thallus whitish to light pink, with characteristic rounded granules scattered on the surface. Hymenial discs pink. Widespread on sandy ground and heaths. Often sterile.

Icmadophila A genus of two species. Thallus crustaceous. Hymenial discs on very short stalks.

469. Icmadophila ericetorum (L.) Zahlbr. [×2] Thallus greyish-green to whitish. Apothecia flesh-coloured, with very short stalks. Grows on very acid peat and stumps of conifers. In Britain common only in Scotland. Can be confused with *Baeomyces* (above).

Cladonia (**470–504, 507**) A genus of numerous species, remarkably variable in appearance. There is a squamulose or crustaceous primary thallus from which arise the hollow poedetia to form shrubby branches or cups. The podetia are essentially part of the apothecial tissue, and the hymenial discs which they possess are either brown, red, or (rarely) yellow. In some species the basal thallus disappears to leave only the podetia, whilst in others the squamules predominate, and podetia are scarce. The species are variable, and not easy to identify. The colour test with P (see pp. 27–8) is useful for identification, but this chemical must be used with caution.

470. Cladonia amaurocraea (Flörke) Schaerer [×2] Primary thallus quickly disappearing. Podetia branched, inflated, smooth, corticate, with narrow cups or inflexed ends. P−. Belongs, with the following species, to sect. *Unciales*. Found on the ground and between stones in mountain areas. Apparently extinct in Britain.

471. Cladonia uncialis (L.) Weber [×2] Primary thallus quickly disappearing. Podetia strongly divergently branched, inflated, smooth, corticate, with holes in the axils of the branches (**VII C** p. 24). Hedgehog-shaped. P−. Widespread on acid soils and over rocks.

464 △

465 △

466 △

467 △   ▽ 469   ▽ 470   468 △   ▽ 471

472. *Cladonia stellaris* (Opiz) Pouzar & Vezda (Syn. *C. alpestris* (L.) Rabenh.) (with blue heath, *Phyllodoce caerulea*) [×0.2] Belongs, together with species **473–6** & **478**, to subgen. *Cladina*. Podetia without a main central stem, and branching into (3-) 4 (-5) short stubby tips (when young) at the apices which point in all directions. The rounded tops are characteristic. P−. Grows in thick cushions on high mountains and is dominant over parts of Scandinavia, below, on, and above the timber-line. Apparently extinct in Britain.

473. *Cladonia rangiferina* (L.) Weber (on right side of photograph) and *C. arbuscula* (Wallr.) Rabenh. (on left side of photograph) [× 1.5] See below.

474. *Cladonia rangiferina* (L.) Weber **Reindeer moss** [×3] Podetia grey, with robust stems which curve over in one direction. Ends of podetia characteristically smooth and silky, branching into four tips. P + red. Forms thick cushions on the ground. Dispersed in the mountain and arctic parts of Europe. Locally frequent in the Scottish highlands, extending south to northern England, Wales, and Ireland, where it is rare.

475. *Cladonia arbuscula* (Wallr.) Rabenh. [×3] Podetia yellowish-grey, with robust stems which curve over in one direction. Ends of podetia characteristically knobbly, branching into 3–4 tips. P + red. Forms thick cushions on the ground over much of Europe. In Britain common. *C. mitis* Sandst. is similar, but has stubby tips and is P −; it is very rare in the British Isles.

476. *Cladonia ciliata* Stirton var. *ciliata* [×4] Podetia grey, with slender stems which curve over in one direction. Identified by the branches which divide into two tips. P + red. Occurs in the more oceanic parts of western Europe, always at low altitudes. Frequent in Britain. Var. *tenuis* (Flörke) Ahti differs only in its yellow-grey colour and chemistry (it contains usnic acid).

477. *Cladonia rangiformis* Hoffm. [× 1.5] This species resembles the reindeer lichens but differs in having the podetia erect at the apices and in retaining small squamules beneath the podetia. Grey, the branches dividing into two tips. P − or P + red. Widespread on dry heaths and in chalk grassland. Can be confused with *C. furcata* (**490**) which is much less vigorously branched.

478. *Cladonia portentosa* (Dufour) Coem. (Syn. *C. impexa* Harm.) [× 1.5] Podetia yellowish-grey with rather slender stems which curve in all directions. Branches divide into three tips. P −. Forms thick cushions on the ground and is the most common 'reindeer lichen' in lowland suboceanic parts of Europe, including the British Isles.

472 △

473 △

474 △

475 △ ▽ 477

476 △ ▽ 478

479.   *Cladonia macilenta* Hoffm. [×2] The following species (to **487**) have red hymenial discs and belong to sect. *Cocciferae*. In *C. macilenta* the basal squamules and podetia are greyish-green. The podetia are thickly covered with farinose soredia, and have blunt tips. P + orange, K + yellow. Widespread; especially common on conifer stumps. In Britain common in the east. *C. polydactyla* (Flörke) Sprengel differs in having narrow proliferating cups; it is a common species in the west of Britain.

480.   *Cladonia digitata* (L.) Hoffm. [×2.5] Basal squamules conspicuously large (*c* 1 cm diameter) with upturned margins with white farinose soredia on the undersides. Podetia antler- or irregularly cup-shaped, sorediate above. Hymenial discs large and red, but scarce. Squamules P + orange, K + yellow. Widespread and frequent on rotting wood and, less commonly, sandy soils.

481.   *Cladonia floerkeana* (Fr.) Flörke (with *C. gracilis*, **494**) [× 7] Recognised by its grey, erect podetia, 1–2 cm tall, with a granular sorediate surface becoming decorticate, terminating in conspicuous red hymenial discs. P – . Widespread on the peaty soils of acid heaths; common in Britain.

482.   *Cladonia pleurota* (Flörke) Schaerer [× 4] Thallus grey-green to yellow-green. Podetia forming broad cups with red hymenial discs at the margins. Surface in places sorediate (granular to powdery). P – . Widely distributed on acid soils. Rare in Britain.

483.   *Cladonia deformis* (L.) Hoffm. [×0.7] The primary thallus forms small yellowish-green to grey squamules from which arise slender cups; these are corticate below and farinosely sorediate above. Hymenial discs and pycnidia red. P – . Widespread in mountain woods. In Britain rare in the Scottish highlands.

484.   *Cladonia coccifera* (L.) Willd. [× 4] Identical with *C. pleurota* (**482**) except for the absence of soredia. Instead the surface of the podetia is warted-areolate. P – . Widespread on acid soils. Common throughout the British Isles.

485.   *Cladonia sulphurina* (Michaux) Fr. (Syn. *C. gonecha* (Ach.) Asah.) [× 1] Podetia inflated, the cortex with long cracks. Yellowish farinose soredia are always present and often red hymenial discs too. P – . Widespread on earth and rotten wood in boreal mountain regions. In Britain occurs chiefly on moorland in the north. Some forms resemble *C. deformis*, but these are distinguished by the presence of squamatic acid.

486.   *Cladonia bacillaris* auct. [× 1.5] Podetia antler-shaped, up to 5 cm tall, grey, with farinose soredia. Hymenial discs red, sometimes absent. P – . Widespread on peat and rotting wood. Scarce in Britain.

479 △   480 △   481 △

482 △   ▽ 484 ▽ 485   483 △   ▽ 486

487. *Cladonia bellidiflora* (Ach.) Schaerer [×3] A handsome species with thick podetia, 2–10 cm tall, covered with yellowish-green to greyish-green squamules, and usually terminating in prominent red hymenial discs. P —. Grows amongst mosses, stones, and peat in the mountains of central and northern Europe. In Britain common in parts of the Scottish highlands, but scarce further south.

488. *Cladonia botrytes* (Hagen) Willd. [×7] Belongs to a small group of species with brownish-yellow hymenial discs (sect. *Ochroleucae*). Podetia short, verrucose-areolate, umbellate-branched, and always producing hymenial discs. P —. Widespread on decaying wood in boreal conifer forests. In Britain confined to the Scottish highlands, where it is rare.

489, 492. *Cladonia crispata* (Ach.) Flotow [×3 and ×2] The following species of *Cladonia* all have brown hymenial discs. *C. crispata* has podetia with a glossy, smooth, brownish cortex and denticulate cups. P —. In Europe there are two geographical varieties: var. *crispata* (shown here) with prominent cups, and var. *cetrariiformis* (Delise ex Duby) Vainio with very narrow cups or without cups at all. The species is widespread, with var. *crispata* in continental Europe and var. *cetrariiformis* in oceanic regions, including Britain.

490. *Cladonia furcata* (Huds.) Schrader [×2] Podetia narrow, with a smooth brownish cortex, divergent branching, and no cups. P + red. Quite variable. Some forms have numerous squamules on the podetia (see photograph), whilst others have none. Widespread; characteristic of grass-heaths. Can be confused with *C. rangiformis* (**477**), which is more richly branched, the branches diverging at wider angles.

491. *Cladonia turgida* Ehrh. ex Hoffm. [×2] Primary thallus with very large lobes (up to 2.5 cm long). Podetia inflated, with perforated axils. P + red. Found on sand and heaths in boreal regions. Apparently extinct in Britain.

493. *Cladonia caespiticia* (Pers.) Flörke [×7] Primary thallus forms a thick sward of small squamules, amongst which the tiny short-stalked hymenial discs are hardly visible. P + red. Widespread on acid soil, mossy tree boles, etc., but seldom frequent.

487 △   488 △

489 △   490 △   ▽ 492   491 △   ▽ 493

494. *Cladonia gracilis* (L.) Willd. subsp. ***gracilis*** [× 4] Podetia with a smooth cortex and without perforations in the axils. The podetia are always erect and simple or very sparsely branched, and are either pointed or carry slender cups. P + red. Common on heaths etc., especially in oceanic parts of Europe (including Britain); the subsp. *turbinata* (Ach.) Ahti is frequent in continental regions.

495. *Cladonia subcervicornis* (Vainio) Kernst [×2] Primary thallus-dominant, of large elongated upturned squamules, which are dark grey at the base of the undersides. These squamules form thick cushions. The podetia are frequently absent, but when present they are short and form irregular cups which are often brownish and cracked. P + red. Confined to acid substrates, especially blanket bogs and rock crevices, in the oceanic parts of Europe. In the British Isles confined to the highland zone.

496. *Cladonia strepsilis* (Ach.) Vainio [×2] Primary thallus dominant, of thick semi-erect squamules, crowded into dense cushions. Podetia of irregular cups; often absent. The plant is easily identified by its C + deep green medulla. P + yellow. Grows on both sandy acid heaths and wet peat bogs. Widespread but uncommon in Britain and Europe.

497. *Cladonia cervicornis* subsp. ***verticillata*** (Hoffm.) Ahti [×2] Podetia of several cups, one above the other, each arising from the centre of the one below. Cortex almost smooth. Primary thallus poorly developed. In *C. cervicornis* (Ach.) Flotow subsp. *cervicornis* the primary thallus of erect squamules, the ends of which are turned over to expose the whitish (often blue-tinged) undersides, predominates, and the podetia generally consist only of single cups. P + red. Subsp. *cervicornis* predominates in oceanic western Europe and is frequent throughout Britain, whilst subsp. *verticillata* is widespread in northern Europe, and is now rather scarce in the British Isles.

498. *Cladonia pyxidata* (L.) Hoffm. subsp. ***pyxidata*** **Cup-moss** [×2.5] Podetia with large, broad cups, the inner and outer surfaces of which are warted-areolate but not sorediate. Hymenial discs are produced from the margins of the cups. Primary thallus of upturned scattered squamules. P + red. Widespread and frequent on acid mineral soils and amongst mosses. Subsp. *pocillum* (Ach.) E. Dahl is a calcicolous race; it has a primary thallus of horizontal squamules forming thick greenish-brown rosettes; it is widespread on chalky soils and over mosses on limestone.

499. *Cladonia chlorophaea* (Flörke ex Sommerf.) Sprengel [×2.5] Very similar to *C. pyxidata* in possessing broad cups on short stalks, but with granular soredia in the cups and on the outsides. P − or P + red (there are several chemotypes). Widespread and common on acid substrates.

500. *Cladonia fimbriata* (L.) Fr. [×2] This species has graceful podetia with typically long slender stalks and short narrow cups. The cups are covered with farinose soredia. A widespread and common species on humus and wood, occurring in a wide variety of habitats.

494 △   495 △

496 △   497 △   ▽ 499   498 △   ▽ 500

501.   *Cladonia ochrochlora* Flörke [×2.5] Podetia usually with narrow proliferating cups, sometimes carrying light brown apothecia. The upper parts of the podetia are covered with farinose soredia, whilst the lower parts are corticate. P + red. Occasional, chiefly on acid peat, widespread.

502.   *Cladonia foliacea* (Huds.) Willd. [×3] Distinguished by the primary thallus, which consists of prominent erect squamules, the ends of which are turned over to expose the yellowish-white undersides. The margins of the squamules sometimes have blackish fibrils (use lens). Podetia of smooth cups, often absent. P + red. Grows on bare, especially basic, soils without humus; widespread in oceanic regions. In Britain locally common at the coast but rather scarce inland.

503.   *Cladonia convoluta* (Lam.) Cout. [×0.7] This lichen resembles *C. foliacea*, differing in having much larger strap-shaped basal squamules, sometimes with light fibrils (use lens) from the margins. P + red. Widespread on chalky soils in middle and southern Europe. In Britain confined to the south, where it is scarce.

504.   *Cladonia coniocraea* auct. [× 4] Podetia mostly simple, tapering to a point, the surface covered with farinose soredia; squamules are often present towards the base. P + red. Widespread and common at the base of trees and on rotting wood.

507.   *Cladonia squamosa* (Scop.) Hoffm. [×2.5] Podetia covered with small squamules which peel away from the surface in a characteristic manner. Very variable. P − or (rarely) P + orange. Frequent throughout Britain and Europe on acid soils.

***Pilophorus* (505–6)** A genus with a granular primary thallus (which can disappear when the lichen becomes old) and pseudopodetia carrying deep black apothecia which are immarginate and globular when mature.

505.   *Pilophorus strumaticus* Nyl. ex Crombie [× 10] Pseudopodetia up to 2 mm tall, without soredia. Black apothecia always present. Grows on mountain rocks in the oceanic parts of the British Isles and Scandinavia, where it is rather scarce. Resembles *P. cereolus* (Ach.) Th. Fr., which differs in being sorediate and often sterile; it has a continental distribution and is absent from Britain.

506.   *Pilophorus robustus* Th. Fr. [× 4] The pseudopodetia are up to 25 mm (rarely 50 mm) tall and umbellate-branched above. Grows on rocks on high mountains in Scandinavia, where it is scarce. Absent from Britain.

Pycnothelia Primary thallus crustaceous, with podetia which are papilliform. Formerly included in *Cladonia*. The genus has one species.

508.   *Pycnothelia papillaria* (Ehrh.) Dufour [× 5] Primary thallus of globular convex granules. Podetia forming warted, inflated, brittle stalks, which are often irregularly branched. Hymenial discs scarce, occurring on the ends of the podetia. Widespread on peat, but often poorly developed. Local in Britain, chiefly in the north.

501 △ 502 △ 503 △

504 △ 505 △ ▽ 507 506 △ ▽ 508

Stereocaulon (**509–22**) The genus is well-differentiated by the granular, usually quickly transient, primary horizontal thallus from which is developed the richly branched, erect, fruticose thallus (pseudopodetium). This is covered with granular or scaly outgrowths (phyllocladia). Most species form grey to greyish-brown cushions. Dark cephalodia and dark brown apothecia are often present. Widespread on earth and rock, several species being associated with habitats rich in heavy metals. The genus is easily recognised (it might be confused with *Sphaerophorus* (p. 180)), but the species are very difficult to determine, and all are liable to confusion.

509, 511. ***Stereocaulon alpinum*** Laurer (**509** with net-leaved willow, *Salix reticulata*) [×2 and ×3.5] Primary thallus usually disappearing. On earth between stones, loosely attached. Cephalodia not apparent. Phyllocladia forming warts at first, later convex scales with crenulate margins. Widespread in arctic-alpine areas, often in compact masses. In Britain very rare in the Scottish highlands.

510. ***Stereocaulon tomentosum*** Fr. [×10] Branches thick and tomentose with squamulose phyllocladia. Apothecia small, lateral. Loosely colonising stones and earth. Widely distributed, but scarce, on heaths. In Britain rare in the Scottish highlands.

512. ***Stereocaulon pileatum*** Ach. [×4] Primary thallus persistent, warty-granular, not sorediate. Pseudopodetia forming short stalks with apical spherical soralia. Widespread on siliceous rocks, but everywhere scarce. *S. nanodes* Tuck. is similar, but the soralia are developed on one side of erect scales. In Britain both species are scarce on rocks in the highland zone, but they have been colonising acid walls in lowland towns and cities since 1950; *S. pileatum* is more frequent than *S. nanodes.*

513. ***Stereocaulon depressum*** (Frey) Lamb [×13] Forms low compact cushions on rocks. Pseudopodetia fragile, tomentose-hirsute, with whitish phyllocladia. Rare in Scandinavia. Absent from the British Isles.

514, 515. ***Stereocaulon vesuvianum*** Pers. [×2.5 and ×13] The lichen forms a compact thallus on acid rocks. Most phyllocladia (**515**) have a dark spot in the centre, a characteristic of this species. Variable, with several forms and varieties. Widespread throughout the whole of Europe. This is the most common species of *Stereocaulon* in the British Isles.

509 △   510 △

511 △   512 △   ▽ 514   513 △   ▽ 515

516,518. *Stereocaulon paschale* (L.) Hoffm. [× 1 and × 13] Pseudopodetia loose on earth. Stalks light in colour, with groups of cylindrical phyllocladia. The numerous cephalodia are small and blackish, with irregular surfaces. Widespread in boreal regions, being abundant in Scandinavia, but rare or absent in central Europe. In Britain very rare in the Scottish highlands.

517, 520. *Stereocaulon dactylophyllum* Flörke [× 4] Pseudopodetia compact on stones. Stalks not tomentose. Phyllocladia digital-squamulose to cylindrical-coralloid. Apothecia large, apical. Grows on siliceous rocks in woods up to the timber-line. Distributed throughout much of Europe. In Britain locally frequent in the highland zone. Forms with digital phyllocladia are relatively easily identified.

519, 521. *Stereocaulon evolutum* Graewe [× 1.5 and × 6] The primary thallus soon disappears. The pseudopodetia are dorsiventral, with the squamulose phyllocladia confined to one side. Grows on stone in flat cushions. Found chiefly in atlantic regions and Scandinavia, but becoming scarce in central Europe. Locally frequent in highland Britain.

522. *Stereocaulon botryosum* Ach. [× 2.5] Pseudopodetia with irregular granular-warty phyllocladia, well-developed on the upper parts of the stalks. Resembles a cauliflower with its umbellate appearance. Forms cushions on acid rocks. Occurs in the higher altitudes of the Alps and on the mountains of Scandinavia, as well as in the arctic. Apparently absent from the British Isles.

516 △   517 △

518 △   519 △   ▽ 521   520 △   ▽ 522

Umbilicaria **Rock-tripe (523–36, 538)** Foliose lichens attached to the substrate at a single more or less central point (umbilicus) on the underside. The fruiting bodies are apothecia with open discs, in contrast to *Dermatocarpon* which has perithecia. The surface of the apothecia takes different forms. The species are common on acid rocks in arctic-alpine areas. In Britain the genus is almost confined to the highland zone (i.e. west and north of a line from the rivers Exe (Devon) to the Tees (Cleveland)).

523. *Umbilicaria cylindrica* (L.) Delise ex Duby (with *Rhizocarpon geographicum*, **459**) [× 7] Thallus grey, composed of one or several lobes, with dark cilia at the margins. Underside with few or no rhizinae. Apothecia almost always present, spirally ridged, and often almost stalked. Widespread and often common on mountain rocks, including those in the British Isles.

524. *Umbilicaria torrefacta* (Lightf.) Schrader [× 2.5] The margins of the lobes are perforated like a sieve. Upper surface brown, mostly with angular star-shaped apothecia. Underside with radial lamellae. Common on mountains in central and northern Europe, including those in the British Isles.

525. *Umbilicaria decussata* (Vill.) Zahlbr. [× 2] Upper surface areolate, with strong, light, ribbed reticulations, especially towards the centre. The middle of the underside is sooty black, without rhizinae. An ornithocoprophilous species on the mountains in central and northern Europe. Absent from the British Isles. Liable to be confused with *U. proboscidea* (**535**).

526. *Umbilicaria deusta* (L.) Baumg. [× 1.5] Thallus of small lobes which are dark brown when dry, and greenish-brown when damp. The upper side has many tiny, warty isidia (use lens), a characteristic feature which distinguishes it from other species. Widespread on mountain boulders, but quite local in Britain.

527. *Umbilicaria vellea* (L.) Ach. [× 0.7] The thallus forms large lobes (5–15 cm across), the underside covered with rhizinae. Upper surface whitish-grey, farinose, finely cracked, reddish or brownish in places. Apothecia scarce. Widespread, but scarce, on high mountains. Absent from the British Isles.

528. *Umbilicaria rigida* (Du Rietz) Frey [× 0.7] Upper surface thickly cracked areolate, whilst the underside is finely cracked. The centre of the underside is light in colour, becoming dark towards the margins. Apothecia smooth. On boulders on mountains in Scandinavia. Absent from the British Isles.

529. *Umbilicaria spodochroa* (Ehrh. ex Hoffm.) DC. [× 1] Lobes large, up to 15 cm across. Upper surface whitish or light to chocolate brown, smooth and glossy. Apothecia umbilicate, often in pits in the thallus. Underside with numerous rhizinae. Occurs in the Atlantic and Baltic regions, but is absent from central Europe. In Britain very rare in the Scottish highlands.

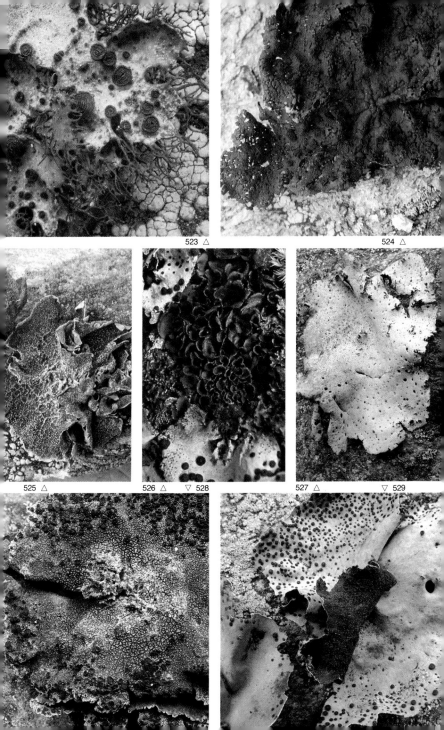

523 △   524 △

525 △   526 △   ▽ 528   527 △   ▽ 529

530.   *Umbilicaria polyphylla* (L.) Baumg. [×2] Lobes small, lacerated at the margins. Upper side dark brown; underside sooty black, without rhizinae. Grows on acid rock outcrops from the lowlands to the mountains; locally common in the British Isles.

531.   *Umbilicaria hirsuta* (Swartz ex Westr.) Hoffm. (with polypody, *Polypodium vulgare*, **96**) [×0.7] Upper side grey, often somewhat cracked, sorediate towards the margin. Underside light brown, with numerous rhizinae. Mostly sterile. A nitrophilous species on acid rocks, but absent from high elevations. In Britain found only in north Wales, where it is rare. Liable to be confused with *U. crustulosa* (**533**) and *U. grisea* (**534**).

532.   *Umbilicaria havaasii* Llano [× 1] Thallus areolate, dark grey to brown, but clayey whitish-grey above the umbilicus, often lacerated towards the margin. Underside light in the centre, becoming pruinose grey or sooty towards the margin. Grows in western Scandinavia. Absent from the British Isles.

533.   *Umbilicaria crustulosa* (Ach.) Frey [× 1.5] Thallus grey, the surface often almost powdery. Apothecia numerous, often in cavities on the surface. Underside light in colour, with rhizinae. Widespread on most European mountains. In Britain confined to the Lake District, where it is rare. Can be confused with *U. hirsuta* (**531**) and *U. grisea* (**534**).

534.   *Umbilicaria grisea* Hoffm. [× 1.5] Lobes grey, the margins often dissolved into soredia. Underside dark, coarsely verrucose, without rhizinae. Mainly distributed in the Atlantic and Baltic regions of western central Europe. In Britain known only from the Channel Islands. Can be confused with *U. hirsuta* (**531**) and *U. crustulosa* (**533**).

535.   *Umbilicaria proboscidea* (L.) Schrader [×0.7] Upper surface with whitish-grey reticulate ribs over the umbilicus. Underside uniformly grey pruinose, with scattered appressed rhizinae. Apothecia numerous, sessile. Frequent on north European mountains, becoming less common further south. In Britain frequent in the north. Can be confused with *U. decussata* (**525**).

536.   *Umbilicaria hyperborea* (Ach.) Hoffm. [× 1.5] Thallus copper-brown, with numerous humps and corresponding recesses on the underside. Lower surface light or dark brown, without rhizinae. Distributed in the European mountains. In Britain confined to the Scottish highlands, where it is rare. Can be confused with *Lasallia pustulata* (**537**), but this species has large pustules.

530 △

531 △

532 △ 533 △ ▽ 535 534 △ ▽ 536

538.   *Umbilicaria polyrrhiza* (L.) Fr. [× 1.5] Thallus glossy brown, smooth. Underside covered with cylindrical, forked, dark rhizinae, which often project from the margin. Usually sterile. Apothecia with folded surface. Occurs in north-west Europe. Locally frequent in highland Britain.

Lasallia The thallus resembles *Umbilicaria*, but is pustulate as opposed to plane or ridged. There are 1–2 large spores per ascus, in comparison with eight small to medium spores in *Umbilicaria*.

537.   *Lasallia   pustulata* (L.)   Mérat   (Syn.   *Umbilicaria   pustulata*   (L.) Hoffm.) [×2.5] Thallus brownish-grey, thick, pruinose, covered with large oval pustules. Upper side with blackish coralloid isidia, seldom fertile. Underside without rhizinae, but with recesses corresponding to the pustules above. Often dominant on warm, illuminated, inclined outcrops of acid rock, where it forms a spectacular dark covering. Throughout much of Europe, but absent from north Scandinavia. In Britain local, chiefly in the west.

Ramalina (539–43, 45) Thallus greenish and corticate, strap-shaped, uniform on both sides. The thallus can be erect or pendulous from its attachment disc. Can be confused with *Evernia prunastri* (**395**), which differs in having a whitish underside.

539.   *Ramalina polymorpha* (Ach.) Ach. [× 1.5] Thallus composed of broad, almost unbranched, clusters of strap-shaped lobes. Oval or irregular soralia occur on the surface or at the margins of the lobes, which also have pseudocyphellae forming lattice, pits, or perforations. Occurs on bird-frequented boulders, especially in the coastal regions of Scandinavia. In Britain it is very local, found only in a few places in Scotland, Wales, and Northumberland. (See also **542** below.)

540.   *Ramalina siliquosa* (Huds.) A. L. Sm. **Sea ivory** [×2] Thallus of narrow ligaments, often with terminal or marginal apothecia. Erect or pendulous, usually greenish-grey to the base. Cortex uneven, pitted, frequently with numerous tubercles containing pale pycnidia. Very variable. Widespread and often abundant on coastal rocks (**360**), but scarce inland. Resembles *R. cuspidata* (Ach.) Nyl., which has black pycnidia and smooth main branches, which are frequently blackened at the base. *R. cuspidata* is abundant on hard, acid rocks on the coasts of Britain and western France, but is rare elsewhere.

541.   *Ramalina fastigiata* (Pers.) Ach. [×2.5] Thallus of short, vigorous ligaments, forming thick cushions, almost always with large, terminal apothecia. The thick tufts on tree bark are very characteristic. Widespread, but not always frequent. In Britain common in unpolluted localities, especially near the coast.

542.   *Ramalina polymorpha* (Ach.) Ach. (Syn. *R. capitata* (Ach.) Nyl. ex Crombie) (with *Rhizoplaca chrysoleuca*, **447**) [× 7] Small tufted plants with delimited soralia and without pseudocyphellae, formerly called *R. capitata*, are now considered to be forms of *R. polymorpha* (**539**).

230

537 △

538 △

539 △

▽ 541

540 △

▽ 542

543. *Ramalina fraxinea* (L.) Ach. (with *Parmelia acetabulum*, **416**) [×0.7] Thallus mostly of broad, long lobes, with very small side-lobes and large apothecia. The cortex often has tiny white pseudocyphellae. Widespread on bark, locally frequent. In Britain occurs chiefly in unpolluted lowland sites. Typical plants are easily identified, but forms with narrow lobes can be confused with other species.

545. *Ramalina farinacea* (L.) Ach. [×2] Thallus lobes narrow, diminishing in width, with delimited soralia on the margins. The similar *R. pollinaria* (Westr.) Ach. possesses in addition laminal and apical undelimited soralia, and usually has broader lobes. *R. farinacea* is widespread and common on bark, whereas *R. pollinaria* is more local, occurring on both trees and acid rocks.

Pannaria (**544**, **547**) Thallus foliose to almost crustaceous. The bluish-grey colouring of the thallus and soralia, as well as the red-brown colour of the apothecia, is characteristic. Differs from *Parmeliella* in having a thalline margin to the apothecium.

544. *Pannaria rubiginosa* (Ach.) Bory [× 1.5] Thallus of grey rosettes, the outside with foliose lobes, whilst the interior is composed of imbricate squamules. Apothecia reddish-brown. Occurs on mossy bark and stone in oceanic regions. In Britain locally frequent in the west.

547. *Pannaria pezizoides* (Weber) Trevisan [× 7] Thallus grey, composed entirely of small squamules. Reddish-brown apothecia with crenate margins are almost always present. Amongst mosses on rocks, trees, and soils. Frequent in atlantic and mountainous regions.

546. *Parmeliella testacea* P. Jørg. [× 3] See description on p. 234.

Acarospora (**548–50**) Thallus crustaceous, of prominent areolae. The embedded apothecia have many minute spores per ascus. All species grow on rocks.

548. *Acarospora smaragdula* (Wahlenb. ex Ach.) Massal. [× 7] Thallus of yellowish to rust-red areolae, the cortex C− and the medulla K + yellow to red. Widespread, but scarce, on rocks and slag rich in heavy metals. There are several closely related species.

549. *Acarospora chlorophana* (Wahlenb. ex Ach.) Massal. [× 7] Thallus bright greenish-yellow with marginal lobes. Apothecia becoming convex and immarginate. Grows on overhangs and cliffs on high mountains. Absent from the British Isles. Easily recognised.

550. *Acarospora oxytona* (Ach.) Massal. [× 7] Differs from *A. chlorophana* in having apothecia which remain flat with persistent margins. A mountain species which is absent from the British Isles.

232

543 △   544 △

545 △   ▽ 548   546 △   ▽ 549   547 △   ▽ 550

Parmeliella (**546**, **551**–**2**) The greyish thallus is either foliose or squamulose, with a cottony prothallus. Closely related to *Pannaria*, differing in having no thalline margin to the apothecium.

546. ***Parmeliella testacea*** P. Jørg. [× 3] (photograph on p. 233) Thallus with marginal lobes and bluish-grey soralia; usually sterile. Grows on mossy bark in mediterranean-atlantic regions. Local in the British Isles.

551. ***Parmeliella pumbea*** (Lightf.) Vainio [× 1.5] Thallus forms bluish-grey rosettes with a characteristic radiating structure; prothallus bluish-black. Upper surface rather warty, with red-brown apothecia. Frequent on bark and mossy rocks in oceanic regions, including western Britain. Easily recognised.

552. ***Parmeliella atlantica*** Degel. [× 2] Closely resembles *P. plumbea*, differing in having spherical to branched isidia, and in usually being sterile. It has the same ecology and distribution as *P. plumbea*, but is less common.

Psoroma Thallus squamulose. Apothecia with thalline margins. In Europe there is only one species.

553. ***Psoroma hypnorum*** (Vahl) Gray [× 2.5] Thallus of ochre yellow to greenish squamules. Apothecia large, reddish-brown, with raised crenate margins. Grows on moist acid soils, mosses, and plant remains in mountainous areas, especially above the timber-line. In Britain locally frequent, chiefly in the highland zone.

Lichina (**554**–**5**) Small shrubby black lichens, forming a thick sward on maritime rocks. The fruiting bodies occur in the swollen ends of the branches.

554. ***Lichina pygmaea*** (Lightf.) Agardh (with barnacle, *Balanus*) [× 6] Branches flattened. West European coasts. In Britain it has the same distribution as *L. confinis*.

555. ***Lichina confinis*** (Müll.) Agardh [× 13] Branches rounded. On most European coasts. In the British Isles occurs on maritime rocks, chiefly in the west, where it is common just above high-tide level.

Nephroma (**556**–**60**, **564**) Lobes corticate on both surfaces, growing loosely over the substrate. Underside often tomentose. Apothecia are produced on the underside near the margins of the lobes. These fertile lobes are often more or less erect, so that the apothecia are visible.

556. ***Nephroma arcticum*** (L.) Torss. [× 0.7] Thallus very large. Upper surface yellow-green, sometimes with cephalodia. Underside light at the margins, but becoming black in the centre. Apothecia rare, brown, very large. Grows on the ground in the arctic. In Britain found only in the Scottish highlands, where it is very rare.

557. ***Nephroma expallidum*** (Nyl.) Nyl. [× 0.7] Thallus curly, the lobes ascending at the margins, brownish when dry but light green when wet. Usually sterile. Grows in mossy heaths. Widespread in Scandinavia, but scarce in the Alps; absent from the British Isles. Easily confused with *Peltigera* (**566**–**79**) which, however, has a non-corticate underside.

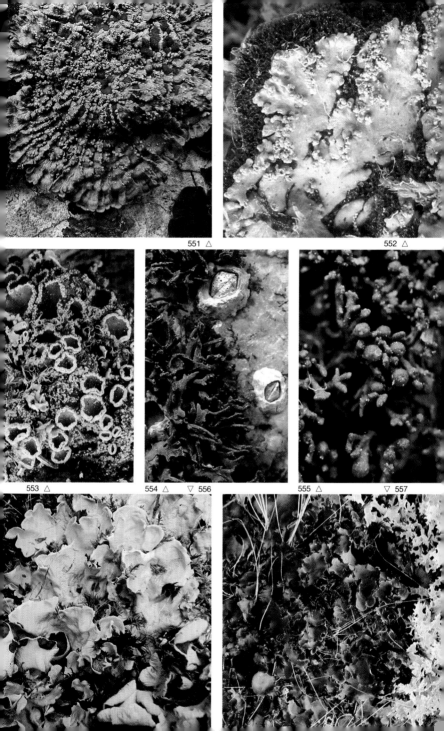

551 △   552 △

553 △   554 △   ▽ 556   555 △   ▽ 557

558.   *Nephroma laevigatum* Ach. [×3] Thallus grey, the underside only weakly hairy. Medulla usually light yellowish (break thallus, observe with lens). Apothecia almost always present on the undersurface of the overturned lobes. Found on mossy bark and stone in oceanic regions. Frequent in such situations in the British Isles.

559.   *Nephroma parile* (Ach.) Ach. [×3] Underside usually tomentose (i.e. with a felt-like covering of hairs). Upper side with bluish-grey soredia, especially developed at the margin. Found on rocks and bark in boreal and mountain areas. Locally frequent in highland Britain.

560.   *Nephroma resupinatum* (L.) Ach. [×5] Underside strongly hairy, with large, often scattered, papillae. Apothecia usually present. Widespread on rocks and bark in boreal and mountain areas. Very rare in the Scottish highlands. Easily recognised by the presence of papillae.

564.   *Nephroma bellum* (Sprengel) Tuck. [×2.5] Thallus grey, the underside often wrinkled. Medulla white (break thallus, observe with lens). Rather scarce on rocks and bark in boreal and mountain areas. Absent from the British Isles.

Solorina (561–3, 565) Foliose lichens, with large, brownish, often pitcher-shaped apothecia sunk in the surface. The algae are green, but blue-green algae in cephalodia are also usually present.

561.   *Solorina octospora* (Arnold) Arnold [×1.5] Thallus large, brownish-green, somewhat warty. Apothecia brown, pitcher-shaped. Distinguished from *S. saccata* by the presence of eight spores in the ascus. Grows on moss and calcareous soil on high mountains. Absent from the British Isles.

562.   *Solorina spongiosa* (Sm.) Anzi [×4] Thallus bright green, taking the form of a collar around the large, brown, pitcher-shaped apothecia. The rest of the thallus is bluish-black, squamulose (with blue-green algae). The asci contain four spores. *S. bispora* Nyl. is rather similar, but has one or two spores per ascus. Both species occur in calcareous earth on mountains, but are rather local. Both are scarce in highland Britain.

563.   *Solorina saccata* (L.) Ach. [×1.5] Thallus green, shell-shaped, with brown, pitcher-shaped apothecia. Spores four per ascus. Often frequent in calcareous regions of Britain and Europe, both at low altitudes and on mountains.

565.   *Solorina crocea* (L.) Ach. [×2] Upper surface grey-green, and underside brick-red. Apothecia large and brown, usually present. Occurs on the ground in calcareous regions, growing mostly at the timber-line. In Britain confined to the Scottish highlands, where it is locally abundant above 900 m (3,000 ft). Easily identified by the reddish underside.

558 △   559 △   560 △

561 △   562 △   ▽ 564   563 △   ▽ 565

Peltigera (566–79) Thallus of large, loose lobes, corticate only on the upper surface. The underside is often tomentose, with a network of veins and rhizinae (**VII B,** p. 24). The apothecia are often formed on narrow, erect, revolute thalline stalks formed on the margin of the thallus.

566.   *Peltigera aphthosa* (L.) Willd. [×0.2] Thallus very large, greyish-green when dry and bright green when damp. Upper surface with dark warts (cephalodia). Underside tomentose, almost without veins. Apothecia brown, on narrow, erect stalks (see right at rear of photograph). The underside of the apothecium is uniformly corticate. Frequent on soil in boreal and alpine regions. Now rather scarce in the British Isles. *P. leucophlebia* (Nyl.) Gyelnik is similar, differing in the presence of distinct pale or dark veins on the underside, and with only a single small piece of warty cortex on the underside of the apothecium. Locally frequent in highland Britain.

567, 568.   *Peltigera membranacea* (Ach.) Nyl. [×0.7] Thallus large, grey, shell-shaped, decumbent (**568**) or ascending (**567**). Upper side with greyish-white tomentum (at lobe margins, use lens). Underside with a reticulum of thick veins and separate, slender squarrose rhizinae (see **VII B**, p. 24). Apothecia on narrow, ascending stalks (**567**). Widespread and common. Confused with *P. canina* (L.) Willd. Dog lichen, which differs in having united rhizinae (at least at the base); it is local on sandy soils.

569.   *Peltigera lepidophora* (Nyl. ex Vainio) Bitter [×3] Lobes small, shell-shaped. Upper side with peltate isidia. Grows amongst higher plants and therefore often overlooked. In Britain found only in the Scottish highlands, where it is very rare. The species is easily recognised by its isidia.

570.   *Peltigera horizontalis* (Huds.) Baumg. [×2.5] Upper surface glabrous and glossy. Underside with flat, spreading, uniting, brownish veins. Apothecia on slender stalks, clearly horizontal. Widespread and frequent on earth, tree stumps, and stone. In Britain local; chiefly found in old forests. Easily recognised by the horizontal arrangement of the apothecia; sterile specimens are easily confused with *P. polydactyla* (**578**).

571.   *Peltigera malacea* (Ach.) Funck [×0.7] Lobes large, thick, with fine, erect hairs near the margins; grey-green when dry, dark green when damp. Underside tomentose and without veins. Widespread but scarce on acid soils in boreal and mountain regions. Very rare in Britain. Easily recognised.

572.   *Peltigera collina* (Ach.) Schrader [×2.5] Lobe margins with farinose to granular soredia. Infrequent throughout Europe on mossy bark and stone. In the British Isles scarce in old forests, chiefly in highland Britain. Identified by the presence of soredia.

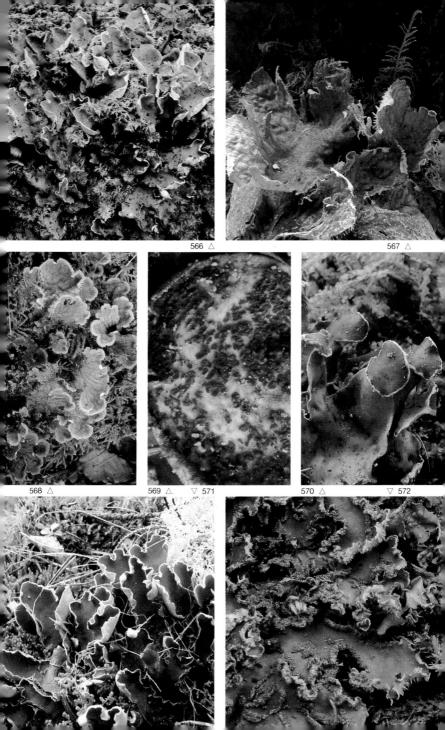

566 △

567 △

568 △

569 △   ▽ 571

570 △   ▽ 572

573. *Peltigera praetextata* (Flörke ex Sommerf.) Zopf [×5] Very similar to *P. membranacea* (**567, 568**), but thallus margins and cracks thickly covered with crowded,flattened isidia. Widespread in Europe, and common in Britain. Easily identified by the isidia, but can be confused with *P. lepidophora* (**569**).

574, 575. *Peltigera spuria* (Ach.) DC. [×2 and ×1.5] This lichen changes its appearance as it develops. The young plants are shell-shaped with circular soralia (**575**). Later the soralia disappear and apothecia develop on thalline stalks (**574**). Plants are small, under 2 cm across. The upper side is grey, with appressed hairs. The underside has persistently pale veins. Widespread but infrequent. In Britain fairly common.

576. *Peltigera rufescens* (Weis) Humb. [×2] Similar to *P. canina*, but the sterile lobes have upturned margins and are under 1 cm broad. Upper surface frequently white pruinose. Veins soon darkening towards thallus centre on the underside, and rhizinae richly branched and confluent. Widespread on dry basic soils; common in Britain.

577. *Peltigera scabrosa* Th. Fr. [×7] Underside with dark veins. Upper side rough. The photograph shows a young apothecium breaking through the cortex. Scarce in arctic-alpine habitats. In Britain known only from the Orkneys.

578. *Peltigera polydactyla* (Necker) Hoffm. [×1.5] Upper surface glabrous and glossy. Underside with spreading, uniting veins. Thallus large, the margins frequently curled. Apothecia saddle-shaped on narrow, erect stalks. Widespread on earth, stone, and tree stumps. Distinguished from *P. horizontalis* (**570**) by the vertical apothecia, and from *P. hymenina* (Ach.) Delise ex Duby by the brown (as opposed to ochraceous) veins. In Britain *P. polydactyla* is local in the north, but *P. hymenina* is widespread and common.

579. *Peltigera venosa* (L.) Hoffm. [×2] Thallus small, shell-shaped, dark green when dry and bright green when damp. Apothecia almost always present, marginate and flat. Underside with dark veins. Infrequent on acid wood-soil in northern Europe and mountainous areas. In Britain chiefly in the highland zone; locally frequent on calcareous rocks in Scotland, but scarce elsewhere.

Lobaria (**580–84**) The species of the genus are very large and compact, with both surfaces corticate and the undersides often hairy. Several species have glabrous patches within their tomentum on the under surface.

580. *Lobaria linita* (Ach.) Rabenh. [×0.7] Thallus grey-green when dry, bright green when damp. Upper side coarsely reticulate. Occurs on earth and moss between boulders. Scarce in mountains above the timber-line. Absent from the British Isles.

573 △   574 △   575 △

576 △   577 △   ▽ 579   578 △   ▽ 580

581. *Lobaria pulmonaria* (L.) Hoffm. **Tree lungwort** [×0.7] Similar to *L. linita* (**580**), but with granular soredia on the ridges of the reticulate surface (**VI G**, p. 22). Underside tomentose, with convex glabrous patches (see top right of photograph). Upper side grey-green when dry, light green when damp. Apothecia scarce, brown, but often blackened by a parasite. Found on bark and rocks throughout most of Europe, but frequent only in oceanic regions. In Britain locally frequent in the west, elsewhere almost confined to the medieval wood-pasture of royal forests and parks. Unmistakable.

582. *Lobaria scrobiculata* (Scop.) DC. [×0.7] Thallus yellow-green when dry, but blue-grey when damp. Upper surface with an irregular reticulum bearing blue-grey soredia. Usually sterile. On stone and bark in cool, moist regions, chiefly in oceanic areas; rather scarce. In Britain locally frequent in some western areas.

583. *Lobaria amplissima* (Scop.) Forss. [×0.3] Thallus grey to greyish-brown. Upper side with thick clumps of small, fruticose, branched, dark cephalodia. Apothecia brown, dish-shaped, scarce. On rocks and bark in areas of high rainfall; frequent only in oceanic districts. In Britain locally frequent only in parts of western Scotland. Resembles *Parmelia* spp., but readily distinguished by the cephalodia.

584. *Lobaria laetevirens* (Lightf.) Zahlbr. [×0.7] Thallus greyish-brown when dry but light green when damp, the surface often wrinkled. Apothecia dish-shaped, abundant. On trees and rocks in western oceanic areas. In Britain locally frequent in the west. Easily confused with *Parmelia* spp.

Sticta (**585–88**) Large-lobed lichens, corticate on both surfaces. The underside is tomentose, with regular perforated holes (cyphellae, **VI B**, p. 22). The closely related genus *Pseudocyphellaria* has irregular holes (pseudocyphellae).

585. *Sticta canariensis* Bory ex Delise [×0.3] The large thallus has forked branching, and is greyish-green when dry, and light green when damp. It contains green algae. Scarce in south-west Europe. In Britain confined to western districts, where it is scarce. The lichen fungus of *S. canariensis* also combines with a blue-green alga to form the lichen called '*S. dufourii* Delise', and single specimens of both morphotypes are occasionally found.

586. *Sticta sylvatica* (Huds.) Ach. [×3] Thallus brownish, divided, with a light reticulum and small isidia. Underside grey-brown, but lighter at the margins, with whitish cyphellae hidden in the tomentum. Occurs in moist mountainous areas, especially in western Europe and south-west Scandinavia, but usually infrequent. In Britain occasional on mossy trees and rocks in the west. Easily recognised, though very similar to *S. fuliginosa* (**587**).

581 △

582 △

583 △   ▽ 585

584 △   ▽ 586

587.   Sticta fuliginosa (Dickson) Ach. [×2] Very similar to *S. sylvatica* (**586**), but differing in the rounded, almost undivided, lobes. The distribution too is similar, but it is generally less frequent.

588.   Sticta limbata (Sm.) Ach. [×5] Thallus greyish-yellow, the margins with greyish-blue soredia. In western Europe and west Scandinavia. Occurs on mossy trees and rocks in Britain, where it is locally frequent in the west.

Pseudocyphellaria (**589–90**) The genus resembles *Sticta*, but differs in the presence of irregularly formed pseudocyphellae on the underside.

589.   Pseudocyphellaria crocata (L.) Vainio [×2.5] Lobes brown with a whitish medulla (break thallus, observe with lens). Golden yellow soralia occur on the upper side and yellow pseudocyphellae are developed on the underside. Rare on mossy trees and rocks in western parts of Norway and the British Isles. Unmistakable.

590.   Pseudocyphellaria intricata (Delise) Vainio (Syn. *P. thouarsii* (Delise) Degel.) [×2.5] The species resembles *P. crocata* in form, differing in the presence of whitish pseudocyphellae and bluish-grey soralia. Scarce on earth, bark, and rocks in west Norway, the British Isles, and north-west France. Easily identified.

Teloschistes (**591–2**) A small genus of fruticose yellow to orange lichens, K + violet-red. In some species the thallus is often grey.

591.   Teloschistes flavicans (Swartz) Norman [×4] Branches rounded or slightly angular, richly branched in loose fruticose tufts, yellow or orange. Usually sterile. Small soredia are developed in breaks in the cortex. Found on twigs and rocks, chiefly in south-west Europe. In Britain now confined to the south-west, where it is rare.

592.   Teloschistes chrysophthalmus (L.) Th. Fr. (on Blackthorn, *Prunus spinosa*) [×4] Thallus small and fruticose, with flattened yellow to orange to grey branches. Apothecia almost always present, with orange coloured discs and greyish cilia at the margins. Scarce on tree branches in western Europe. In Britain confined to southern England, Ireland, and the Channel Islands, where it is now very rare. This lichen cannot be confused.

587 △

588 △

589 △   ▽ 591

590 △   ▽ 592

Caloplaca (593–601) All species are crustaceous, but some have lobed margins (e.g. **594**, **598**). The thallus is usually yellow, orange, or red, but some are grey (e.g. **597**). The apothecia are almost always yellowish or reddish, seldom brown. The yellow to orange parts of the lichen react K + violet-red. In most species the spores are polarilocular (i.e. of two lumina connected by a canal). There are many species, several still awaiting critical study.

593. *Caloplaca citrina* (Hoffm.) Th. Fr. [× 7] Thallus citron yellow, dissolved into soredia. Lobed margin absent. Apothecia plane, sessile. Widespread and common on nitrogenous calcareous substrates throughout Britain and most of Europe; also grows on the ground, on bark, and on wood.

594. *Caloplaca biatorina* (Massal.) Steiner [× 4] Thallus orange-red to red, in regular rosettes with marginal lobes. The apothecia are peltate. Scarce on acid rocks in the Alps. Absent from the British Isles.

595. *Caloplaca cerina* (Ehrh. ex Hedw.) Th. Fr. [× 7] Thallus forms either a thin whitish-grey crust or a bluish-black prothallus. Apothecia yellow-orange, more or less peltate, often with crenate or flexuose margins. Frequent throughout most of Britain and Europe on the bark of a wide variety of trees; occurs also on wood and rarely on mossy rocks.

596. *Caloplaca saxicola* (Hoffm.) Nordin [× 7] Thallus very variable, in small rosettes of crowded apothecia surrounded by short, pruinose, orange (rarely yellowish or reddish) lobes. A nitrophilous species which is frequent throughout much of Britain and Europe on both calcareous and acid rocks and walls.

597. *Caloplaca viridirufa* (Ach.) Zahlbr. (Syn. *C. aractina* (Fr.) Häyrén; *C. fuscoatra* (Bayrh.) Zahlbr.) [× 7] An example of a dark-coloured *Caloplaca*, only the reddish fruiting bodies indicating its true position. Thallus areolate, without marginal lobes. Widespread, but scarce, on acid rocks. In Britain rare in the north.

598. *Caloplaca thallincola* (Wedd.) Du Rietz [× 6] Thallus forming regular, orange-yellow rosettes, with very elongated marginal lobes with almost parallel furrows between them. The lichen grows on both acid and calcareous maritime rocks, just above the spray or upper littoral zone where *Verrucaria maura* is dominant. *C. heppiana* (Müll. Arg.) Zahlbr. is very similar, but the lobes are pruinose and less elongated, without prominent furrows; in Britain it is common inland on calcareous stone.

599. *Caloplaca cirrochroa* (Ach.) Th. Fr. [× 7] The thallus grows in small, lobed rosettes and also as small, flat, elongated, digitiform, scattered lobes. On some of the lobes are small, citron yellow, delimited, farinose, soralia. Widespread on mountain limestone. In Britain scattered in the west.

600. *Caloplaca marina* (Wedd.) Zahlbr. [× 7] The thallus is reddish-orange, becoming yellow in shade. Apothecia are always very numerous, and marginal lobes are present but inconspicuous. The lichen often forms a lower supralittoral zone on the coastal acid and calcareous rocks of the Atlantic Ocean, and the North and Baltic Seas, above the black upper littoral zone dominated by *Verrucaria maura*.

601. *Caloplaca insularis* Poelt [× 7] A parasitic lichen growing on an *Aspicilia* species. The thallus is poorly developed, but the orange-brown apothecia form conspicuous groups on the whitish thallus of the host. Confined to the Alps. Absent from the British Isles.

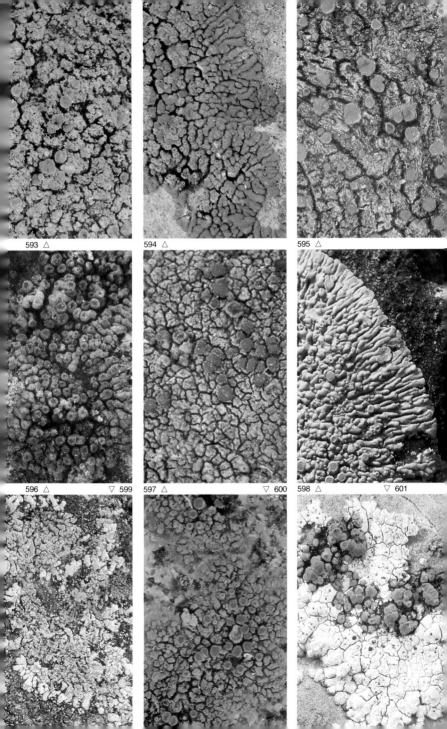

593 △   594 △   595 △

596 △   ▽ 599   597 △   ▽ 600   598 △   ▽ 601

Xanthoria (602, 604–5) Thallus yellow or orange to red, of very small to large lobes or almost shrubby, K + violet-red. Liable to be confused with lobed species of *Caloplaca*, from which it differs in possessing a lower cortex, and *Fulgensia*, from which it differs in having polarilocular spores. Nitrophilous.

602.   *Xanthoria parietina* (L.) Th. Fr. [× 2.5] Thallus large, yellow-orange, of flat, broad lobes 1–7 mm across. Many apothecia, from young to mature, are usually present. Common on bark, wood, and stone throughout Britain and Europe, occurring from sea-level to high altitudes.

604.   *Xanthoria fallax* (Hepp) Arnold [× 7] Thallus of small, appressed lobes, with elevating, sorediate margins. Relatively large apothecia are rarely present. Widespread on bark, especially at the base of old trees, but nowhere abundant. Rare on rocks.

605.   *Xanthoria elegans* (Link) Th. Fr. [× 7] Small thallus of narrow, convex, closely adhering lobes, usually with scattered to crowded apothecia. Very variable in colour, ranging from yellow to red. Occurs on acid and calcareous mountain rocks, and is now spreading in the lowlands by colonising artificial substrates (e.g. asbestos-cement roofs).

Fulgensia (603, 606) Crustaceous, squamulose, or lobed, yellow to brownish-orange, K + violet-red. Underside compact. On chalk-rich substrates. Distinguished from *Caloplaca* and *Xanthoria* by having simple spores.

603.   *Fulgensia fulgens* (Swartz) Elenkin [× 5] Thallus of distinct lobes, whitish-yellow to yellow-orange. Apothecia frequent, orange coloured. Grows on chalky soils in submediterranean regions, occurring as far north as the Baltic islands. In Britain confined to a few southern localities chiefly in rabbit-grazed chalk grassland.

606.   *Fulgensia bracteata* (Hoffm.) Räsänen [× 4] Thallus of small, yellow to orange-brown squamules, at best forming lobes only at the margin. Numerous, crowded, orange apothecia are usually present. Widespread on gypsum and chalky soils in arctic-temperate regions. In Britain occurs on a single limestone outcrop in the Scottish highlands.

Anaptychia (607–8) Thallus foliose to fruticose, with a fibrous cortex. The spores are brown and one-septate.

607.   *Anaptychia ciliaris* (L.) Körber [× 1.5] Thallus almost strap-shaped, in thick, rosette-forming cushions. The branching is almost fruticose. Mouse-grey to light brown, with long thallus-coloured cilia at the margins. Apothecia are frequent; these are brownish-black, usually grey pruinose. Nitrophilous; widespread on bark, scarce on stone. Formerly common, but now rather scarce. In Britain occurs only in the east and south, especially in parks and on roadside trees.

608.   *Anaptychia fusca* (Huds.) Vainio [× 3] Thallus of brown appressed lobes without cilia. Frequent on coastal rocks bordering the Atlantic Ocean and the North and Baltic Seas. In Britain also occurs inland on prehistoric stone monuments and near-by trees.

602 △   603 △

604 △   605 △   ▽ 607   606 △   ▽ 608

Heterodermia (**609**, **617**) Thallus foliose to weakly fruticose, light grey. Fibrillae are often present. The spores are thick-walled with a smooth surface, in comparison with *Anaptychia* which has thin-walled sculptured spores.

609. *Heterodermia leucomelos* (L.) Poelt [× 10] Thallus slender, whitish-grey, with conspicuous black fibrillae. In loose, almost shrubby, cushions. Underside not corticate. Occurs on earth and stone in south-west Europe, including southern England and Ireland.

617. *Heterodermia speciosa* (Wulfen) Trevisan [× 2.5] (photograph on p. 253) Thallus light grey, pinnate, in irregular rosettes. Soredia and inconspicuous light fibrillae are situated at the margins. Apothecia scarce. Rare on mossy trees in mountain woods. Absent from the British Isles.

Physcia (Syn. *Phaeophyscia*) (**610**–**16**) Thallus grey or greyish-brown, often pruinose, and rather small. The dark brown to blue-black, often pruinose, discs of the apothecia are characteristic. Spores brown, one-septate. The species are nitrophilous. Can be confused with *Physconia* (p. 252) and *Hyperphysica* (p. 252).

610. *Physcia aipolia* (Ehrh. ex Humb.) Fürnrohr [× 4] Thallus grey, in rosettes, with inconspicuous whitish speckles over the surface (use lens). Apothecia almost always present, black, often grey pruinose. Widespread on the bark of deciduous trees. Common in the British Isles. Distinguished by the characteristic whitish speckled appearance of the cortex.

611. *Physcia stellaris* (L.) Nyl. [× 7] Similar to the former species, but without whitish speckles. Widespread on deciduous trees. Rather scarce in Britain, chiefly in the north.

612. *Physcia orbicularis* (Necker) Poetsch [× 6] Lobes loosely appressed, greyish-green to brownish-green. Surface with delimited soralia. Widespread and common throughout Britain and Europe, on bark, stone, and mosses. Similar to *P. caesia* (**615**), but differing in the darker colour when damp.

613. *Physcia adscendens* (Fr.) H. Olivier [× 3] Thallus forming swards, the lobes small and whitish, with light- to dark-coloured fibrillae at the margins. The lobe-ends are arched and helmet-shaped, containing soredia. Widespread and common on bark and stone throughout Britain and Europe. *P. tenella* (Scop.) DC [× 10] (**VI F** p. 22) is very similar but with labriform soralia, and no helmets formed at the lobe-ends. Distribution as in *P. adscendens.*

614. *Physcia semipinnata* (Gmelin) Moberg (Syn. *P. leptalea* DC.) [× 3] Thallus forming small rosettes, the lobes narrow, and the upper surface often lightly speckled. Light to dark fibrillae occur at the margins. Apothecia usually present, the discs blackish, often pruinose. Frequent on trees in atlantic and mediterranean districts. In Britain local, being confined to unpolluted areas. The species is recognised by the presence of fibrillae and apothecia, and the absence of soredia.

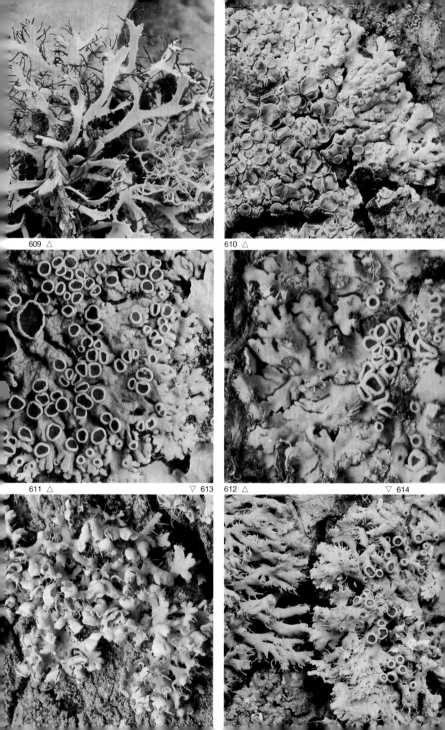

609 △

610 △

611 △   ▽ 613

612 △   ▽ 614

615.   *Physcia caesia* (Hoffm.) Fürnrohr [× 3] Thallus whitish-grey to blue-grey, of convex lobes with whitish speckles and conspicuous, delimited, light grey, convex soralia, with a tinge of blue. Widespread and common on calcareous stone throughout Britain and Europe.

616.   *Physcia sciastra* (Ach.) Du Rietz [× 6] Lobes narrow, richly branched, arranged in thick, dark brownish rosettes. Dark isidia are developed on the lobes, which occasionally simulate soredia where they are broken off. Widespread on wood, stone, and mosses. In Britain rare, chiefly on acid lakeside boulders in the north. Easily identified.

617.   *Heterodermia speciosa* (Wulfen) Trevisan [× 2.5] Described on p. 250.

***Physconia* (618–20)** Separated from *Physcia* by the character of the spores and the pruinose thallus.

618.   *Physconia grisea* (Lam.) Poelt [× 7] Thallus pruinose, with soredia developed at the margins at first, later often becoming diffuse. Underside light in colour, with simple or forked, light rhizinae. Widespread on bark and stone, extending to southern Sweden. Common in Britain.

619.   *Physconia muscigena* (Ach.) Poelt [× 5] Lobes strongly divided, pruinose, the underside with black, squarrose rhizinae. Widespread and often frequent on soil and moss, especially over chalk. In Britain very rare and confined to the Scottish highlands.

620.   *Physconia pulverulacea* Moberg [× 2] Thallus vigorous, brownish-grey, usually pruinose. Apothecia usually present, the dark discs pruinose. Variable. Widespread and frequent, chiefly on bark, extending to central Scandinavia. Common in Britain in less polluted areas.

***Hyperphyscia* (Syn. *Physciopsis*)** Distinguished from related genera by lack of developed rhizinae and the filiform conidia.

621.   *Hyperphyscia adglutinata* (Flörke) Mayrhofer & Poelt [× 10] Thallus thin and delicate, inconspicuous, in tiny, compact, adnate rosettes. The centre of the thallus is almost crustaceous, whilst the lobes bear small, round, greenish-white, delimited soralia. Frequent in western and southern Europe. Local in the British Isles.

615 △

616 △

617 △

618 △ ▽ 620

619 △ ▽ 621

Diploicia Thallus orbicular, with prominent lobes at the circumference. Apothecia black, without thalline margins, with brown, one-septate spores.

622. *Diploicia canescens* (Dickson) Massal. (Syn. *Buellia canescens* (Dickson) de Not.) [× 7] Thallus grey, forming rosettes, lobed at the margin, with whitish-grey farinose soralia. Common in atlantic regions of Europe, including the British Isles, on stone, wood, and bark, especially in somewhat shaded habitats.

Buellia Thallus crustaceous. Apothecia black, without thalline margins, with brown, one-septate spores. There are many species.

623. *Buellia subdisciformis* (Leighton) Vainio [× 7] Thallus grey, often areolate, K + yellow to red, often intersected by the black lines of the prothallus. On maritime rocks in atlantic regions. Locally frequent on sunny shores in the British Isles.

Dimelaena Distinguished from *Diploicia* by the apothecia having a thalline margin.

624. *Dimelaena oreina* (Ach.) Norman [× 3] Thallus light greenish-yellow, of angular areolae, with marginal lobes. Apothecia innate in the areolae. Grows on mountain rocks, often abundant. Absent from the British Isles. Easily identified.

Ochrolechia (**625–7**) Thallus crustaceous, often thick and irregular, warty. The thick thalline margins to large apothecia, with yellowish or flesh-coloured discs, are characteristic.

625. *Ochrolechia frigida* (Swartz) Lynge [× 3] Thallus greyish-white, at first forming a thin crust over mosses, later becoming coral-like and spiny, C + orange. Apothecia large, with rose-brownish, unpruinose discs. Grows on the ground over decaying plants, especially on mountains. Common in northern Europe, but absent from southern Germany and the Alps. In Britain common over 600 m (*c.* 2,000 ft).

626. *Ochrolechia parella* (L.) Massal. **Perelle** [× 5] Thallus grey, warty-areolate, C−. Apothecia crowded, thus becoming angular distorted, white pruinose. Occurs on acid stone, rarely on bark. Scarce in central Europe, but abundant in atlantic regions. Common in the British Isles.

627. *Ochrolechia tartarea* (L.) Massal. **Cudbear lichen** [× 3] Thallus thick and sometimes globular-papillate, C + orange. Apothecia large, with flesh-coloured, unpruinose discs. Locally frequent in oceanic regions, scarce elsewhere. Locally common on acid rocks and tree bases in highland Britain.

Pertusaria (**628–9**) Polymorphic crustaceous lichens, either with immersed apothecia in large warts or with delimited white soralia. There are many species, some difficult to identify.

628. *Pertusaria amara* (Ach.) Nyl. [× 3] Thallus greyish, with white soralia of bitter taste, KC + violet. Common on bark throughout Britain and Europe.

629. *Pertusaria pertusa* (Weigel) Tuck. [× 7] Thallus wrinkled, grey. Apothecia immersed in warts, with only a narrow ostiole visible; there are one to several apothecia in each wart. Common on the bark of deciduous trees throughout Britain and Europe.

Dimerella Thallus green, undifferentiated, without a cortex. Apothecia yellow-orange. Easily recognised.

630. *Dimerella lutea* (Dickson) Trevisan [× 7] Apothecia orange-yellow, 1–2 mm across. Frequent on bark and mosses in the tropics. Scarce in central Europe. In Britain local on mosses on both trees and rocks.

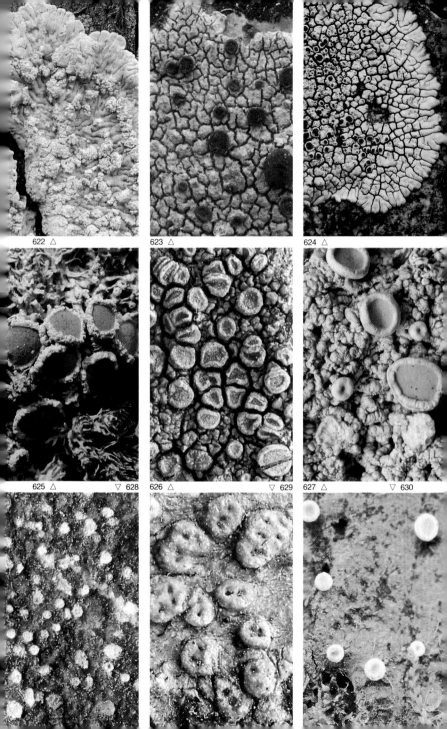

622 △   623 △   624 △

625 △   ▽ 628   626 △   ▽ 629   627 △   ▽ 630

Thelotrema Apothecia with thalline margins, immersed in verrucae. Spores septate.

631.   *Thelotrema lepadinum* (Ach.) Ach. [× 10] Thallus crustaceous, grey to yellowish-white. Apothecia with a characteristic double margin, the inner noticeably sunken and irregular. Found chiefly on old trees, extending to Scandinavia. Local in Britain, where it is mainly a relict of medieval wood-pasture (i.e. in royal forests and chases used for hunting, in ancient parks, and on commons).

Gyalecta Thallus not corticate. Apothecia pitcher-shaped, marginate, with yellowish to reddish discs. Spores septate.

632.   *Gyalecta jenensis* (Batsch) Zahlbr. [× 7] Apothecia margins grooved. Discs orange. Grows on calcareous stone throughout much of Britain and Europe.

Petractis Apothecia conical. Spores fusiform, septate.

633.   *Petractis clausa* (Hoffm.) Krempelh. [× 15] Apothecia whitish, cone-shaped, the pore partly covered by a build-up of thalline tissue which is often radially cracked. Thallus otherwise almost immersed in calcareous rock. Scarce from the Mediterranean to Scandinavia, but frequent in Britain.

Placopsis Crustaceous, with lobes at the margin. Apothecia with thalline margins. Cephalodia present.

634.   *Placopsis gelida* (L.) Lindsay [× 2] Thallus forming greyish-white, adnate rosettes. Usually sterile, often with soralia. Conspicuous pink cephalodia form clumps on the surface. Grows on siliceous rocks in north-west Europe. Locally frequent on mountain rocks in the British Isles. Easily recognised.

Graphis Letter lichen (635–6) Thallus forming a thin crust with innate apothecia forming black lines (lirellae) with raised margins. Spores colourless, multiseptate.

635.   *Graphis scripta* (L.) Ach. [× 6] Apothecia narrow-elongate, with entire margins. Frequent on smooth, shaded bark throughout temperate Europe. Common in Britain in unpolluted regions.

636.   *Graphis elegans* (Borrer ex Sm.) Ach. [× 13] Thallus wrinkled. Apothecia elongate, with longitudinally furrowed margins. Common on smooth, shaded bark in oceanic parts of Europe, including Britain.

Phaeographis Lirellae flat, innate. Spores brown, mulitseptate.

Phaeographis dendritica (Ach.) Müll. Arg. (**VI C** on p. 22) [× 13] Apothecia black, branched, immersed in the whitish grey thallus. On smooth-barked deciduous trees in western parts of Europe. Frequent in parts of the British Isles, especially the south-west.

Diploschistes (637–8) Apothecia pitcher-shaped, immersed. Spores muriform, becoming brown.

637.   *Diploschistes scruposus* (Schreber) Norman [× 7] Thallus grey, thick, and areolate, C + orange. Apothecia pitcher-shaped, immersed in the thallus. Found on acid rocks throughout much of Europe. Frequent in Britain.

638.   *Diploschistes muscorum* (Scop.) R. Sant. (Syn. *D. bryophilus* (Ach.) Zahlbr.) [× 7] Resembles the preceeding species, differing in the thinner thallus. A hemiparasite of mosses and lichens (especially *Cladonia pyxidata* subsp. *pocillum*) on chalky soils and calcareous rocks. Locally frequent in Britain.

Pyrenula Thallus crustaceous, with pseudothecia. Spores brown, septate.

639.   *Pyrenula nitida* (Weigel) Ach. [× 3] Thallus olive-coloured, thin, with prominent, black, convex pseudothecia. On smooth, shaded bark. Widespread in central Europe, reaching mid-Scandinavia. Rare in Britain, where it is largely replaced by *P. macrospora* (Degel.) Coppins & P. James.

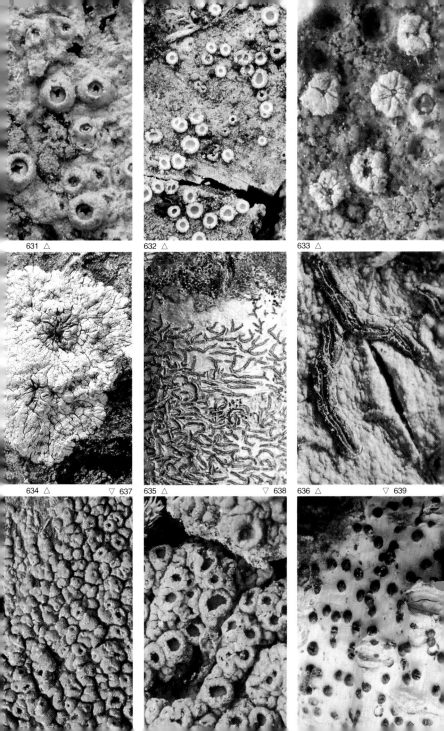

631 △   632 △   633 △

634 △   ▽ 637   635 △   ▽ 638   636 △   ▽ 639

Dermatocarpon (**640**, **642**–**3**) The species form small foliose lobes attached centrally from the underside by means of an umbilicus. Resembles *Umbilicaria* (pp. 226–30), but possesses pseudothecia immersed in the thallus, visible only as dark ostioles. The species grow on rock.

640. ***Dermatocarpon intestiniforme*** (Körber) Hasse [×1.5] Thallus many-lobed, grey pruinose, with inrolled margins. Differs from *D. miniatum* (**643**) in having spores 7–9 μm broad. An arctic-alpine species on calcareous rocks. Rare in Britain.

642. ***Dermatocarpon rivulorum*** (Arnold) Dalla Torre & Sarnth. [×1.5] Umbilicate lobes up to 4 cm across. On siliceous rocks irrigated with water in arctic-alpine habitats above the timber-line. Very rare in the Scottish highlands.

643. ***Dermatocarpon miniatum*** (L.) Mann [×2] Similar to *D. intestiniforme* (**640**), but with narrow spores, 5–6 μm across. Widespread on calcareous rocks in both Britain and Europe.

Catapyrenium Differs from *Dermatocarpon* in having a small squamulose thallus with rhizinae. The species grow on soil and, less commonly, on bark.

641. ***Catapyrenium lachneum*** (Ach.) R. Sant. (Syn. *Dermatocarpon rufescens* (Ach.) Th. Fr.) [×7] Thallus of red-brown squamules, with sunken pseudothecia. Grows on chalky soils. Scarce in Britain.

Roccella **Orchil lichen** (**644**–**5**) Fruticose maritime lichens, grey-brown to violet. The lobes are strap-shaped, resembling *Ramalina*, from which it may be distinguished by the colour.

644. ***Roccella phycopsis*** (Ach.) Ach. [×2] Lobes rounded, in thick clusters from a yellowish attachment disc. Sorediate and usually sterile. Cortex C+ orange; soredia C−. Grows on Atlantic cliffs extending to southern England and Wales, where it is rare.

645. ***Roccella fuciformis*** (L.) DC. [×0.7] Lobes flat, in large pendulous clusters from an unpigmented attachment disc. Sorediate and usually sterile. Cortex C−; soredia C+ orange. Grows on atlantic cliffs extending to south-west England and south Wales, where it is rare.

Opegrapha Crustaceous, with rounded or elongated fruiting bodies. The lirelliform fruiting bodies are smaller, shorter, and sessile in comparison with *Graphis* (**635**–**6**). There are many species.

646. ***Opegrapha atra*** Pers. [×13] Thallus whitish with crowded fruiting bodies. Spores tri-septate. Common in Britain and Europe on smooth illuminated bark in unpolluted regions.

Arthonia Crustaceous. Fruiting bodies irregular to elongate, innate. Spores septate.

647. ***Arthonia tumidula*** (Ach.) Ach. (Syn. *A. cinnabarina* (DC.) Wallr.) [×7] Fruiting bodies irregularly stellate, cinnabar-red, immersed in the light-coloured thallus. Widespread on bark in southern lowland Europe, extending north to the Baltic. In Britain frequent in the west.

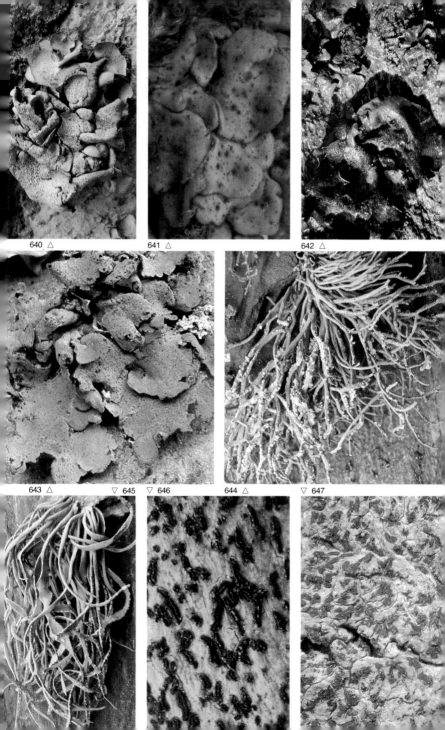

640 △   641 △   642 △

643 △   ▽ 645   ▽ 646   644 △   ▽ 647

Normandina Thallus squamulose, non-corticate. Fruiting bodies unknown, all reports referring to a parasymbiont.

648. *Normandina pulchella* (Borrer) Nyl. [× 7] Squamules 1–2 mm across, grey-green, shell-shaped, with raised, often sorediose, margins. Sterile. On mosses and hepatics, especially *Frullania* (**355**) in oceanic regions. In Britain frequently found on mossy tree boles and rocks, chiefly in the west. Easily recognised.

Lecanactis Thallus crustaceous. Fruiting bodies with dark discs, often pruinose. Spores fusiform, tri- to septi-septate. Several species.

649. *Lecanactis abietina* (Ach.) Körber [× 7] Thallus smooth, with conspicuous whitish-yellow pruinose fruiting bodies. Pruinose pycnidia are usually present, the tips C + orange. Occasional on old acid bark in north-west Europe, including Britain.

Acrocordia Crustaceous lichens with pseudothecia containing uni-septate spores uniseriate in cylindrical asci.

650. *Acrocordia gemmata* (Ach.) Massal. [× 6] Thallus white, with black immergent pseudothecia 1 mm broad. Widespread, but rather scarce, on deciduous trees. In Britain frequent, especially in the south.

Arthopyrenia Crustaceous lichens with pseudothecia containing uni- to cinque-septate spores massed in ovate asci.

651. *Arthopyrenia halodytes* (Nyl.) Arnold [× 3] Thallus immersed, with only the black pseudothecia visible as tiny spots. On littoral calcareous rocks and, especially, shells of sea animals (on limpet, *Patella*, in the photograph). Widespread on sea coasts, including those of the British Isles.

Siphula Thallus fruticose, of erect solid branches. Sterile.

652. *Siphula ceratites* (Wahlenb.) Fr. [× 2.5] Thallus of white, erect branches with a compact medulla. Forming thick swards on the ground. A rare arctic species, in Europe confined to north Norway and north-west Scotland.

Thamnolia Thallus fruticose, of rounded, hollow, prostrate branches. Sterile.

653. *Thamnolia vermicularis* (Swartz) Schaerer (with *Cetraria nivalis*, **407**) [× 1.5] Thallus of white, worm-like, pointed branches, creeping or forming thick cushions. Occurs on mountains above the timber-line and also on Öland and Gotland, especially on chalky soils. In Britain locally common at high altitudes on some mountains.

Coriscium Thallus of greenish, rounded squamules. The fungus partner is a basidiomycete, *Omphalina*, which forms small mushroom fruiting bodies.

654. *Coriscium viride* (Ach.) Vainio [× 5] Thallus of shell-shaped squamules, to 5 mm across, with raised whitish margins. Frequent on peat banks in Britain and Europe, especially on mountains. The fungus partner in the association is *Omphalina hudsoniana* (Jennings) H. Bigelow.

Geosiphon This plant is now considered to be a phycomycete with blue-green alga, *Nostoc*, as a symbiont. In contrast to all other lichens the algae are enclosed within the fungal vesicles.

655. *Geosiphon pyriforme* (Kütz.) F. Wettst. (with *Anthoceros*, **286**) [× 17] Forms small, black, glossy vesicles on clay soils. Scarce, growing with the hepatic-related hornwort *Anthoceros*. Not recorded in Britain.

648 △   649 △   650 △

651 △   ▽ 653   ▽ 654   652 △   ▽ 655

Additional Mosses and Liverworts

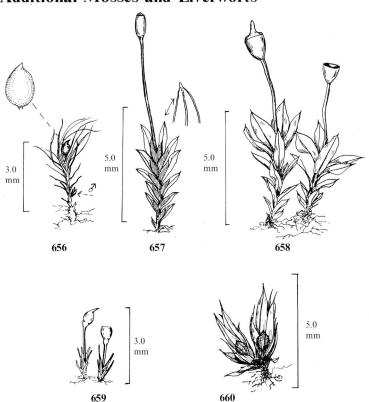

656

657

658

659

660

656. ***Pleuridium acuminatum*** Lindb. Small plants in low, green or yellowish tufts 3–10 mm tall. Leaves long and very narrow, the uppermost being the longest. Capsules small, ovoid, lacking lid or peristome, stalkless and immersed among the leaves. Frequent on bare soil in fields and gardens, being most conspicuous in winter and early spring when the capsules mature.

657. ***Fissidens bryoides*** *See p. 120*

658. ***Pottia truncata*** (Hedw.) Fürnr. Small, green plants forming low tufts or patches up to 2 mm tall. Leaves lanceolate with shortly excurrent midribs. Capsules are erect, shortly cylindrical or top-shaped, with wide mouths but devoid of peristome teeth, borne on slender setae 2–5 mm long. Found on bare soil in fields and gardens; common except in the far north or at high altitudes.

659. ***Selegeria calcarea*** (Hedw.) BSG One of a genus of exceedingly small mosses in which the shoots are usually less than 2 mm tall, with a few narrow, more or less linear leaves. The small, usually erect capsules are produced abundantly in spring on short,

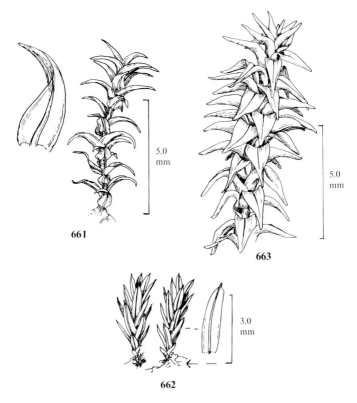

661

663

662

erect setae 1–2 mm tall. Frequent on calcareous rocks, crevices and underhangs of limestone cliffs and fragments of chalk or limestone in woodlands. Widely distributed throughout Europe and the British Isles.

660. *Phascum cuspidatum* Hedw. Low, almost stemless, small plants in low green tufts 2–6 mm tall. Leaves lanceolate, the uppermost larger, with midribs running into, or beyond the tips. Capsules ovoid, borne on exceedingly short setae and immersed among the perichaetial leaves, lacking lids or peristomes (i.e. cleistocarpons). Common on bare soil in fields and gardens but inconspicuous except during winter and early spring.

661. *Barbula fallax* See p. 122

662. *Barbula unguiculata* See p. 122

663. *Dicranella palustris* (Dicks.). Warb. Small to quite large plants; shoots erect, typically 20–100 mm tall, forming rather soft, pale green to yellowish tufts. Leaves more or less broadly lanceolate but bent sharply back at about the middle with the upper parts standing out at right angles from the stems (squarrose). Midrib thin, ending below the rather blunt leaf-tips. It is frequent in very wet places by streams, springs and in mires, except in agricultural or urban regions.

263

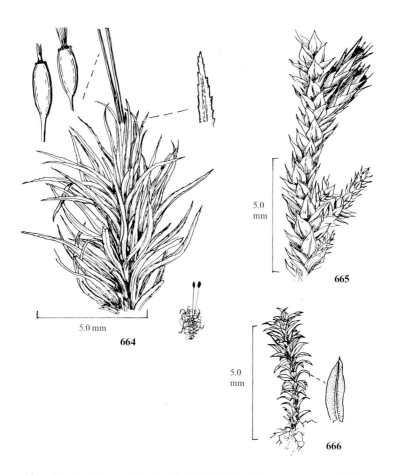

664. ***Ptychomitrium polyphyllum*** (Sw.) B.S.G. Plants forming compact, dull green or brownish cushions 10–50 mm tall, blackish within. Leaves densely arranged, long and narrow, tapering to fine, denticulate tips, strongly curled when dry. Setae often produced two to three at a time from a single perichaetium, 4–8 mm tall; capsules oval-cylindrical, erect, with beaked lids. Common over most of Britain and Europe on lime-free rocks and walls; rare to absent in southern and lowland Britain.

665. ***Cryphaea heteromalla*** (Hedw.) Mohr Leafy shoots ascending, irregularly pinnately branched, up to 6 cm long, dull or yellowish green, usually with several fertile branches along one side. Leaves dense, ovate, shortly acute, widely spreading when moist, erect and appressed to the stems when dry. Midrib ending well below leaf tip. Perichaetial leaves much larger than ordinary leaves and with midribs projecting into long bristles, enfolding the ellipsoid capsules which have only very short setae. Common and widespread in Britain and Europe except in the north, on the bark of deciduous trees and shrubs (especially Elder).

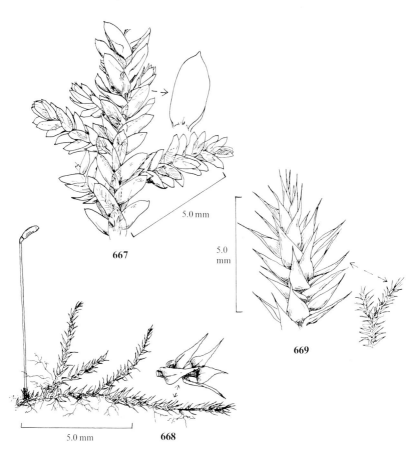

667

5.0 mm

5.0 mm

5.0 mm

669

668

666. ***Zygodon viridissimus*** (Dicks.) R. Br. Plants small, in low, dense, deep green to bright green tufts 5–15 mm high. Leaves small, acute, lanceolate, widely spreading from the stem when moist, strongly twisted when dry. Capsules small, ovoid, smooth at first, then grooved when old and empty, on slender setae; peristome lacking. Club-shaped, brownish gemmae are often present on stems, among the leaves. Common (except in polluted areas) on rocks, trees and walls.

667. ***Neckera complanata*** See p. 142

668. ***Amblystegium serpens*** See p. 144

669. ***Campylium stellatum*** (Hedw.) Lange & C. Jens. Creeping or, usually, erect or ascending, irregularly branched plants forming yellowish to orange-brown tufts up to 8 cm tall. Leaves widely spreading from the stems, broadly oval-triangular at base then finely tapering to narrow, almost filiform tips; margins entire. Midrib lacking. Common in slightly acid to basic mires and wet meadows. *C. chrysophyllum* (Brid.) Lange is much smaller, forming yellow tufts or small patches in dry calcareous grasslands and on damp, basic rocks.

265

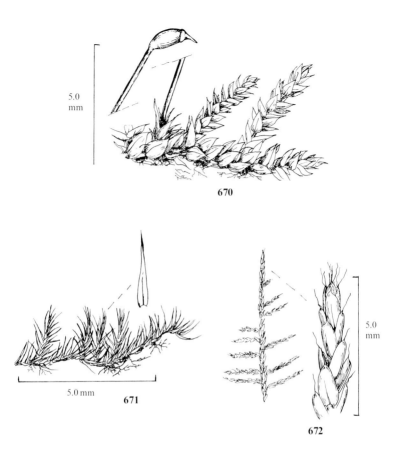

5.0
mm

670

5.0 mm

671

5.0
mm

672

670. ***Rhynchostegium confertum*** (Dicks.) B.S.G. Shoots more or less prostrate, with prostrate or ascending branches, light green, forming mats. Leaves ovate to broadly lanceolate, erect-spreading, minutely denticulate; midribs ending below the acute leaf tips. Capsule ovoid, inclined to horizontal; lids with long beaks; setae rather short (less than 20 mm) and quite smooth. Common on rocks, walls and tree bases throughout Britain and Europe. Distinguished from *Brachythecium valutinum* by the beaked capsules and smooth setae, and generally has broader leaves.

671. ***Rhynchostegiella tenella*** (Dicks.) Limpr. Small and slender, creeping plants forming low, silky green or yellowish patches. Leaves small and very narrow, linear-lanceolate and finely tapering, with thin midribs. Capsules small, horizontal, ovoid with beaked lids, borne on thin, smooth or slightly roughened setae. Common on shaded, basic or calcareous rocks, stones and walls, occasionally on old trees, throughout Britain and Europe.

672. ***Cirriphyllum piliferum*** See p. 148

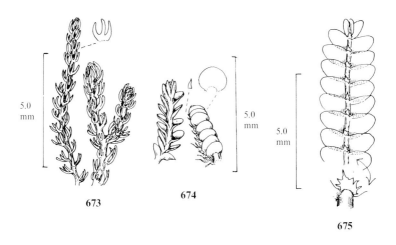

673   674

675

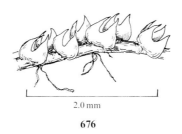

2.0 mm

676

673. *Kurzia pauciflora* (Dicks.) Grolle (*Lepidozia setacea*) *See p. 166*

674. *Nardia scalaris* (Schrad.) Gray Very similar to *Solenostoma crenulatum* (p. 170) but has minute amphigastria.

675. *Saccogyna viticulosa* (L.) Dum. Plants prostrate, shoots sparingly branched, 20–50 mm long, scattered among mosses or forming yellowish to pale brown mats. Leaves unlobed with entire margins, only slightly overlapping and arranged in opposite pairs. Amphigastria unlobed but irregularly toothed. Common in western districts of Britain and Europe but rare or absent in eastern regions; found on rock ledges in shaded situations, mainly in lime-free areas. (Distinguished from *Chilescyphus* by the more or less opposite leaves and unlobed amphigastria; from *Calypogeia* by the succubous leaf arrangement.)

676. *Cephalozia bicuspidata* *See p. 172*

267

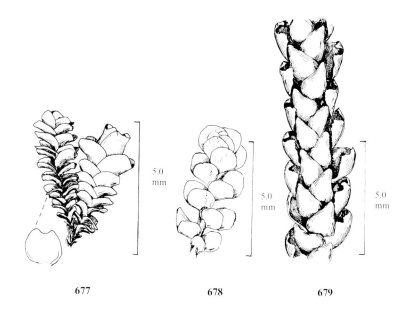

5.0 mm

5.0 mm

5.0 mm

677　　　**678**　　　**679**

677. *Marsupella emarginata* (Ehrh.) Dum. Plants sometimes prostrate but usually more or less erect, forming tufts or patches varying from brownish-green to dark blackish purple; shoots 10 50 mm long. Leaves almost transversely attached and clasping the steam, closely arranged, shallowly bilobed and widely spreading (almost squarrose). Amphigastria lacking. Fertile shoots have conspicuously larger leaves below the perianths. Widespread in Britain and Europe: common in hilly districts in wet, lime-free places, among rocks and on stony ground by streams; rare in lowland, cultivated regions.

678. *Scapania undulata* See p. 174

679. *Pleurozia purpurea* Lindb. Shoots mainly prostrate, long and sparingly branched, up to 12 cm or more long, reddish-yellow to dark purplish red or almost black. Leaves divided into two very dissimilar lobes, the upper lobe concave, toothed and shallowly cleft, the lower lobe smaller and developed into a complex water-sac which is said to act also as a trap for small organisms. Amphigastria lacking. Frequent in the west and north of Britain and Europe on wet, acid moors and bogs, commonly on *Sphagnum.*

Index of genera

Figures in *italics* refer to pages in the keys, those in **bold** are illustration numbers

271

Trichomanes *32*, 80
Trichostomum *45*
Tritomaria *39*, *40*, 168, **326**

Ulota *42*, *44*, 138, **219**
Umbilicaria 29, 30, *52*, 178, 226, 228, 230, 258, **523–36**
Usnea 23, 24, 28, *54*, 178, 186, **357**, **386**, **388–94**, **VIIA**

Verrucaria 49, 178, 246

Weisia *43*, *45*
Woodsia *33*, 82, **46–7**

Xanthoria 29, *52*, 178, 210, 248, **602**, **604–5**

Zygodon *44*, 265, **666**

Index of common names

Figures in **bold** are illustration numbers